Malcolm Boyden is a columnist f(
began his career in journalism
winning the Heart of England J(
later went on to work as sport
Daily News and then sports sub-editor on the *Daily Star*.
He also has his own radio show which has an enormous
following in the West Midlands, where he is well known
for his colloquial catchphrases. He is a double Sony award-
winning radio presenter and a successful actor, his most recent
role being the character of Lenny Cox in *Wallop Mrs Cox* at
the Birmingham Rep. He is an ardent fan of West Bromwich
Albion Football Club, and in March 2003 he became the only
British football commentator to commentate on a football
match from the pitch while the game was in progress. His
historical broadcast was unfortunately cut short when he was
sent off by the referee ten minutes from the end for 'interfering
with play'. Malcolm lives in Worcestershire with his wife
Maxine, and two sons, Elliott and Oliver, and wrote this book
in a cupboard underneath his stairs!

PERFECT

WRITTEN IN A CUPBOARD

HOUSE OF
STRATUS

This edition published in 2003 by House of Stratus, an imprint of
House of Stratus Ltd, Thirsk Industrial Park, York Road, Thirsk,
North Yorkshire, YO7 3BX, UK.

www.houseofstratus.com

Typeset by House of Stratus, printed and bound by Short Run Press Limited.

A catalogue record for this book is available from the British Library
and the Library of Congress.

ISBN 0-7551-1371-3

To Maxine

I would also like to thank, for their invaluable support and encouragement, Justin Edgar, Paul McDonald, Fiona Dye, Dave Reeves and Ian Billings. With special thanks to Helen Kirk at House of Stratus, and John Plimmer (I couldn't have done it without you both).

' 'Twas a dark and stormy night
And the rain came down in torrents.
But the captain of the ship yelled...
Horatio! Tell us a tale.
And so a tale was told
Of a man who went to sea.'

1

It began to go downhill the day Brenda Burston got tongued on the Witch's Hat. I remember the moment as if it were yesterday. A group of lower school kids (we called them 'the tiddlers') was attempting to make a house out of a pile of freshly cut grass. The council workmen had just finished mowing and the smell was delicious. I was frantically flicking through the pages of *Shoot* magazine looking for my free set of football league ladders when suddenly I saw her, in full flow; home-made yellow frock hitched up around her waist. She was carefree, lapping up every minute. I'll never forget it. I realized in an instant I was a sexual retard. The whole class had grown up before my very eyes leaving me drowning in a sea of their combined body juices. I hadn't even started to think of girls in a grown-up way. It was the most horrible sexual wake-up call you could ever imagine – to this day it makes me shudder to the core. It was the turning point, the start of my great slide…and I've been unsuccessfully trying to play catch-up ever since.

As I recall, things didn't get any better on the bus ride home. A middle-aged couple were on the seat in front of me. The bloke turned casually to his wife and said, 'Beverley, we've been married nearly eleven years – isn't it time we started discussing anal sex?' I almost dropped through the floor. I was fifteen and a half years old. It was such a severe setback that I was unable to finish off the peanut-butter

1

crackers I'd saved since lunch-time. I realized there and then that everyone was at it, and I decided it was time for me to come of age and get at it myself.

Unfortunately, twenty-two years later, I'm still playing catch-up. And I'm still haunted by that fateful day. Nothing much became of Brenda Burston, she turned out to be the local ride – but I didn't get within a sniff of her. I even missed the boat when she started flogging her knockers for two quid a feel. As luck would have it, I'd just spent my pocket money on a pint of maggots. Probably for the best. I came clean to myself about boobs just a fortnight ago while watching my *Best of It's a Knock-out* video. The Belgians had just flopped on a balloon bursting game when it finally dawned on me. 'Breasts,' I sighed with a heavy heart. 'I've never really known how to handle a pair.'

Knockers… Where do I stick them on my list of vital statistics? It's a real poser. I mean they're a big part of a woman's overall package. Maybe they belong in the 'not so vital but could come in handy when push comes to shove' department. After all my workmate, Dicky Cox, swears by them. Wouldn't dream of using anything else (mind you, he is head of forward planning). A decent set of swingers – can they be overlooked as I take a more mature last-gasp hold on the meaning of love? I don't know, sometimes the pressures of going on holiday are too much to bear.

How many words can I find to describe a good old-fashioned knocker before the traffic lights turn? More than ten, and it's going to be a vintage vacation. Less and I'm in for another serious seaside flop. Bazookas, breasts, bosoms, jugs, bojangles, swingers, dingers, dongers, melons, dollys (obvious. Named after the queen of country and western music, Mrs Parton). Red-amber. It's going to be the holiday from heaven.

For the record, Mrs Lighthouse the dinner lady sometimes called her breasts 'dingers'. Other times, depending on her mood and who was asking, she'd call them 'dongers'. She died tragically. Fell in the playground like a sack of potatoes when a stray 'clacker' hit her on the forehead, and never regained consciousness. Lovely service. The whole school performed Marvin Gaye's classic, 'Heard it Through the Grapevine'. I played the triangle. Mrs Lighthouse wasn't a big Marvin Gaye fan of course (don't think she even knew who he was), but our music teacher idolized him.

Pity she snuffed it, Mrs Lighthouse. She was always very popular in the playground. Used to turn her hand to anything. Once tried to knit a lawnmower. Not content with that, she went on to run up a complete kit for the school football team. It would have worked as well, but she dropped one when she should have been pearling two on the centre forward's shorts and he ended up playing almost half a game in his pants while strands of navy blue wool littered the opposition's penalty area. The home economics department tried to come to the rescue at half-time with an emergency crocheting kit, but it was all to no avail. The school became youth football's laughing-stock. A Stockport County of its day. The games master resigned and the new head of PE tried to steer the ship in a different direction. Being Scottish, she introduced us to the art of curling – a circular rock-shaped thing is flung towards a target while three team-mates frantically sweep the ice with brooms. Very big in the winter Olympics but it never really caught on in the West Midlands.

Still, due to the general lack of ice rinks, the school remained the undefeated British under fourteens curling champions of central England, which saved the skin of Mrs Lighthouse. Indeed, she became a bit of a martyr in many ways. I admired her tremendously. Well I would, being a dab hand at arts and crafts myself. I spent the whole of one autumn term knocking up a guard dog out of toilet roll. It turned out all right, but it didn't bark. In memory of Mrs

Lighthouse, I'll grade knockers quite highly on my list of priorities.

It's important that I get my preparation right. After all, I'm not just going on a cruise here you know. That's what I told them at the British Potato Marketing Board. 'Malcolm's having it off at last,' joked Margaret Chandler, our co-ordinator. (I call her 'Bargepole' – as in, I wouldn't touch her with one.) Face like a trod-on chip. And on top of that she calls everyone in the office her 'little scrag-end'. 'You haven't taken a decent break since that nasty business with What's-her-name, have you my little scrag-end?' shrieked Mrs Chandler as I gathered up my file on the marvels of a Maris Piper. I long to let the world in on my catchy new advertising slogan: 'Mash a Maris and I'll show you my Harris!' My mother's always said I'm a genius. She's an angel, you know.

As for Mrs Chandler, she was right on two points. That nasty business with What's-her-name put me back a good ten years. Despite my never-ending quest to put the Brenda Burston incident to one side, my sexual scoreboard reads as follows:

> Age: thirty-seven and three-quarters
> Successful sexual encounters: one

My shag-o-meter has stopped swinging. Seized up on the day Wet Wet Wet hit the top of the charts with 'Love is All Around'. I knew something was up the moment I set eyes on Marti Pellow. I could feel it in my fingers – then I felt it in my toes.

Point two: I hated travel. Couldn't stand it. I was sick at the airport when nerves got the better of me just before a package tour to Palma. Then there was the fiasco at the travel agents when I took the plunge and went to book this excursion. Who should be waiting at the counter but Denis McGowan, the very same lad who was doing the tonguing while Brenda Burston was lapping it up on the Witch's Hat.

He later threatened to put my head down the toilet and flush the chain on my first day at the County High School. I hated him, and now the bastard was trying to sell me the 'holiday of a lifetime'.

I told my mother about him at the time but she said I should take no notice of the McGowans – by all accounts they were a bad lot. She said his mother was to blame. Mrs McGowan (I think her first name was Sheila) was very big in the world of showjumping, but she turned nasty after losing a jump-off against the clock to a stablemate of Harvey Smith's in the early 1970s. They say she was never the same again.

Anyway, I finally got my revenge on McGowan, the bully turned travel agent. He was very helpful, almost too nice. He was one of those people who could never smile – it would always turn too quickly into a smirk. He asked me to sit on his right hand while we flicked through a few options. He gave me a few handy hints and tips and, quite out of character, I swindled him. Square on. Without so much as a second thought I took my business to Flopsy Wright, an independent in Tyne Street. Flopsy did me a good turn once on a day trip to Watchett in Somerset (aim for Minehead, then fork off at Quantock's Head). Beautiful spot. I've always remembered it and I like to stay loyal. I'm the only person left in this 'kick bollock and scarper' world who still abides by the old adage, 'One good turn deserves another'.

So here I am. About to weigh anchor on a cruise that is going to reshape my life. I'm going to cast off into the sunset...and cast away my 'Chirpy, chirpy, cheep, cheep' image. (Number one in 1971 for Middle of the Road.) That's me see. Middle of the Road. 'Chirpy, chirpy, cheep, cheep.' But this time I'm not here to make up the numbers. I've made up my mind. I'm out to find a wife and be tossed passionately around on the high seas. I'm 'England's last hope'. I'm Julie Andrews as she strides from the convent and over the mountains towards Captain Von

Trapp's mansion swinging her small suitcase as she sings. Is this too much to expect from an eleven-night excursion to the Mediterranean on the 'June Jewels of the Sultry South' cruise of a lifetime? *No!* Not on your sodding nelly. This is the new me. (See, I'm feeling unusually brave already.)

I mean, the brochure looked promising. The good ship *Perfect* boasts ten passenger decks and has one crew member to every two passengers. There's bound to be some un-suspecting bint on board that fancies transforming my world. And that's the deal. I'm not looking for a scrubber. There's no quick shag on the poop deck with me.

I'm feeling strangely cock-a-hoop as I tag on to the end of the meandering queue that's winding its way towards the gangplank. I can't see anything that resembles a boat from where I'm standing, but then, as always, I'm pretty near the back. Already I'm starting to pigeon-hole my fellow passengers. Elderly married couple; clean looking pair wearing matching lime-green-and-yellow-striped tank tops; daughter and mother (you can tell, they've got the same shaped nose); middle-aged bloke on his own; funny looking thing who's probably in the wrong queue; young family that doesn't look as if they've got enough money to come on board – that sort of thing. I'm also trying to work out what I've forgotten. I just hope I've remembered my pack of 'three T-shirts for two quid' from the market. I got them cheap because one of the navy blue sleeves had started to fade. Still, the woman on the stall saw me all right. I got a nice pair of flip-flops for eight pounds with a free bottle of suntan oil thrown in – best day's shopping I'd done in a long time.

The queue moves on and, true to form, my newly found and quite unexpected burst of cock-a-hoopness begins to seize up. Before long there's not an ounce of it left in my body. It's drained from my soul like water running from a bath. I'm always the same. Whenever I start to feel in control, the good Lord pulls the plug and I'm back to square one. My fumbling side has started to rear its ugly head as I near the front of the line. And no wonder. I'm about to embark upon the SS *Perfect*.

That's the name of the ship. *Perfect*. I mean, why would anyone call *anything* 'Perfect'? It's asking for trouble. As soon as one of the whingeing hordes finds a fault, the first thing they'll do is bring up the name and throw it right back in your face. Still, you've got to give it to them for having the guts. Here's to the SS *Perfect*. (I would imagine that's what you call a vessel of this size. Come to think of it, I'm not at all sure. SS, HMS, SOS – it's all the same to me. Some sailor I'm going to be, hardly likely to challenge Popeye or Sinbad for the 'King of the Seas' title. I liked Sinbad. Pulled on his magic belt and became mighty. Never worked for me. I pulled mine and stayed limp.)

I'm limpish now, and I can feel myself going from bad to worse, but I'm determined to keep my end up. After all, it's still early days. I spend the next few minutes shuffling slowly towards my fate. For a moment I mull over my 'Spud Log': a carefully engineered, yet slightly lustful blueprint for holiday romance that I prepared in the office before I set off. It's an imaginary blow-by-blow account of how I struck gold off the coast of Gibraltar, had a fumble in Florence, romanced in Rome, proposed in Propriano...and bonked myself barmy in Barcelona – off the cuff, so to speak.

It sounds good on paper, but Dicky Cox warned me that nobody ever got into a girl's knickers on paper. I feel he was right. Sadly, my plans soon begin to go haywire. It's my fault for thinking something good was about to happen – I reckon I'm often the merchant of my own doom.

Disaster One. The STS (Ship To Shore Liners Inc.) representative beckons me towards the embarkation desk. Dreaming ends, reality sets in – I heave. More disaster.

'You haven't filled in your emigration form properly.'

Never thought. 'Oh, you'll have to excuse me. I've never done this before.'

God, I'm trembling and they've only asked me to fill in a bloody form. Suddenly, I don't know whether I'm on foot or on horseback. That's me all over; I spend eighty per cent of the time in a state of nervous confusion. The slightest little setback sets me off. Worse still, some arsewipe has written 'Mr Potato Head' in the name section – my bloody nickname. Well, I have been with the Potato Marketing Board for nearly a decade. It's either Mr Potato Head or Spud. Spud to my friends, and to What's-her-name, my only proper girlfriend to date. I'm shaking through the humiliation of holding up the queue. I know they've all cruised a zillion times before and they're tutting at me in their tiny heads. Yes, you well-off stinkers, you'd better get used to having Britain's biggest stumblebum on board.

Praise the Lord. With only a slight stumble, I've successfully negotiated the lady on the embarkation desk by filling in my form in record time. It was only my nimbleness of pen that got me safely over the first major obstacle. In confidence terms, I'm damp – but I'm a long way from wet.

At last I'm on board and a gaggle of hosts in waistcoats are waiting to meet me. It's like the scene from *Mary Poppins* when she meets the waiters dressed as penguins. This is living, this is style, this is elegance by the mile. And I do love a Penguin. To my mind, it's the chocolate bar that drives the nation. Very underestimated.

'Cabin F153 sir? Certainly,' says my allotted host in a waistcoat. 'Just along the corridor to your right. Danny will help you with your bits and pieces.' ('Bits And Pieces.' A 1964 hit for the Dave Clark Five if I'm not mistaken.)

Danny helps me with my rather shabby 'Spud-U-Like' satchel. I'm afraid it's more of a bit than a piece, but I'm very fond of it. And it does house my most personal possession. A packet of banana-flavoured condoms. I brought them with me just in case. You can never be too sure, and I want to cover every eventuality. I kept them with me because I didn't want them discovered by an X-ray machine as my case went through the security scan. They'd think, Randy bastard. He's only come on board for a shag.

I'm very keen on satchels. I think they might make a comeback, although my own school satchel bit the dust in the saddest of circumstances. The silver buckle came loose so I ran it up to Mr Newbold, the village cobbler. Unfortunately he went on holiday the following day and didn't come back. Drowned. I never saw the satchel again. Come to think of it, I had a lot of death and disaster to contend with in my early years. First Mrs Lighthouse, then Denis McGowan, and finally the cobbler. It's a wonder I turned out so stable.

We've arrived. Cabin F153. Blimey. I'm so close to the water-line I'm almost submerged. It's like *20,000 Leagues Under the Sea* all over again. One good wave and I'll be kissing Captain Nemo. Looking on the bright side, it might be the only kiss I get all cruise.

It's a funny business this cruising. When you're on your own, you get the chance of a cheaper 'Friendly Foursome' cabin. Imagine that, shacking up with three strangers. *Big Brother* meets *Captain Pugwash*. Now, I've had the occasional sexual fantasy about a rollicking, frolicking threesome with the girls in our 'Potatoes for Pleasure' office, but to share a cabin with three blokes you've never met in your life? Private, timid and old fashioned – that's me. In the up-to-date stakes, I'm all behind like a cow's tail. I can still remember when Opal Fruits were 'made to make your mouth water'.

Another thing, I have no social skills. I'm a bit like Donny Osmond in that way. Put Donny in a room full of strangers and he couldn't string two words together. There's a medical term for it. In the end he went on a course to help him talk to strangers. Got himself cured at about the same time Marie had a hit with 'Paper Roses'. No, I need my cabin for the job in hand (and it'll probably end up as a job in hand rather than a full-blown affair, knowing me). So, I've got a place to myself, and I've paid the supplements.

Cabin steward Danny shows me to 'home sweet home'. I can tell by his expression that he doesn't quite know what to do with my bits and pieces. I can't help him at the moment. I'm in bits and pieces myself... But it's not a bad pad. A picture window, a row of fake antique mahogany wardrobes, shower, toilet, neat little bathroom cupboards hidden behind a pair of mirrors, a bed each side of the window and two more beds clinging to the wall. I expect the cabin steward brings them down and locks them into place for a friendly foursome, but for me they're staying put. Space galore, and the *pièce de résistance* – a rocking-chair. Another song enters my head. If I'm not mistaken it's Brian and Michael's catchy B-side to 'Matchstalk Men and Matchstalk Cats and Dogs': 'She was bonny, she was fair, and she'd got a lovely pair. I'd give half the world to see her swinging in my rocking-chair.' It went something like that any road up. Suddenly it seems, I've got 'swingers', 'dingers' and 'dongers' on the brain today. Must be Mrs Lighthouse. She's turned into my security blanket.

No sooner do I get in however, and I'm out again. The sodding skipper, Captain Fletcher, has called an emergency drill. The whole boat has to traipse up the stairs with life-jackets in hand. A right rigmarole. Flopsy Wright the travel agent never mentioned the possibility that I might sink. Already I've cleverly deduced that we're in for a choppy first couple of days. The Motion Discomfort Bags have been conveniently positioned on top of the staircase. My spirits have started to sag big time. It's quite possible I've dropped a terrible ball here. Maybe it's the good Lord punishing me for the way I diddled Denis McGowan out of his cruising information. Maybe I should've played safe and settled for a week in Dorset. Suddenly the thought of scoffing a hot dog underneath the Jubilee Clock in Weymouth sounds like a far better bet.

I leave the cabin only to be squashed against the wall by a rhinoceros of a woman, the spitting image of Hattie Jacques. It's time I stamped my authority on matters and cracked a gag. 'Look at us all. I've been up and down like a merry man's backside since I got on the sodding boat.' Hattie looks straight through me. Badly timed, badly misjudged. I admit it… I'm no Tom O'Connor.

The procession continues. I'm caught behind a herd of pensioners – old folk as far as the eye can see. It's a Darby and Joan bottleneck, and there's me, hoping to find a wife in amongst this congregation of over eighties. There's one slight silver lining on the edge of my gathering storm clouds, however. In the distance, ladies and gentlemen, will you welcome please… Wife contender number one.

She's a tomboy, pleasant enough face, shortish strawberry-brown hair. Unstyled by the looks of things (in the hair department she's more Kenneth Clarke than Nicky Clarke). A little lofty in the arse department (or is that the baggy trousers – can't tell from this angle), and she's on holiday with her mum and dad at the age of thirty-twoish. To cap it all she's wearing a sweatshirt with a picture of the ship on it: 'The *Perfect* way to get away'. Ugh… No chance. Welcome to the world of the cruise bore, and there's plenty more where she came from.

It's crawling with them in the library where the passengers on decks E, F and G have gathered (harmless bunch, not much money by the looks of things – the big knobs must be on decks B, C and D). It's like a scene out of *Waiting for God*. Pensioners galore, and they're all spouting off about previous excursions.

'Now I like the *Mermaid* myself, only we did the Black Sea in October and followed that up with Essential Norway in June – very nice,' said Hattie Jacques in the corner (husband looks like a squirrel). 'You can't go wrong with Ship To Shore although we couldn't take to the *Neptune* – too big, no atmosphere. Bunty liked the *Neptune* didn't she Clive. You know – Bunty! The thin lady. Bald as a coot. Had a nasty experience with the one-legged fellow in Jerusalem.'

Hattie Jacques is one of those women who can talk without pausing for breath. It's a remarkable performance.

' "Well," I said, "Bunty," I said, "you *never* liked the *Neptune* over the *Mermaid* – no," I said, "give me the *Mermaid* any day although I do like the *Perfect*." We were on her maiden voyage you know, Christmas in the Caribbean – lovely. Clive caught shingles on day two. Eeeeeehh, I don't know how we can laugh about it now.' Clive isn't laughing. Must be hard to raise a titter when you're married to a woman with an elephant-sized behind.

Bollocks. Now I'm in a right tangle. I can't get the velcro strap attached to the back end of my life-jacket. It's like an exercise from the bloody *Krypton Factor*.

Malcolm's Log. Day One. It's Thursday, June 19th. We're off. Setting sail from Southampton and hopefully into the sun – it's unseasonably cold and the south coast of England looks dark and grey. I'm waiting for a large scotch from room service to settle my nerves – it'll probably be the only stiff 'un I'll get all holiday. Wife contender one: Miss Cruise Bore. Shagability: two and a half. Probably never had sex in her life and looked down on me during life-jacket parade as if to say, 'Virgin. He's a ghastly Cruise Virgin.'

Quite right, love. I'm new to this lark. I'm a novice, a 'chalk jockey' (an old-fashioned phrase for being inexperienced. If a jockey didn't get many rides at the big horse-race meetings, he had his name chalked onto the runners and riders board. It saved the clerk of the course wasting unnecessary money on a painted name-plate. The regulars had their own hand-painted name-plates while the occasional riders became known as the 'chalk jockeys'). One way or another, I've been a confirmed 'chalk jockey' most of my life. I'm one of nature's professional novices. Getting the hang of this cruising business is going to be no different. I don't think I'm going to take to it. Indeed, the whole thing is starting to get on top of me. I was once sick on a mackerel fishing trip off the coast of South Wales... I don't really stand a chance. And it's getting more and more absurd. Miss Cruise Bore's mum has started to hold court now. She's proudly boasting that the resident pianist in the Ritz Bar was the same bloke she met on a cruise of the Fantastic Fiords in December.

When it comes to piano players you can stick the lot of them if you ask me – all except for the king of the keyboards, Bobby Crush. Frilly cuffs, toothy smile. Came through to strike glory under Hughie Green on *Opportunity Knocks* even though he lost on the clapometer to the yodelling cobbler with the clog-dancing dog (it was a speciality act). Good job it was our votes that counted on that programme or a genius would have stayed undiscovered for ever, buried in his own ebony and ivory graveyard, along with the magical piano who refused to play for Sparky. ('Sparky and his Magic Piano.' It was an old favourite of mine on the radio show *Junior Choice*. Often sandwiched in between 'The Runaway Train' that went down the track and she blew, and 'Puff the Magic Dragon' who frolicked in the autumn mist.) Anyway, the point is this: Bobby Crush could play. But he made the biggest mistake of his life when he turned down the chance to record 'Y Viva Espana' before Sylvia got her hands on it and turned it into an international hit.

I went through a keyboard phase myself. Organs mostly. Tried to model myself on Bobby Crush. Tried to follow in his footsteps, yet in a Wurlitzer sort of way. I pictured myself coming up through the floor at the Blackpool Tower Ballroom, frilly cuffs and toothy smile, plonking my way through, 'Oh I do like to be beside the seaside'. They'd all have said it: 'Here he is. Malcolm Williams. The Bobby Crush of the organ.' I'd have been billed as 'Williams the Wurlitzer Wizard'. Posters on the sea front – the lot.

I even went for keyboard lessons with a man who proudly named himself Colin 'Fingers' Gilbert. I once tried to use his name in vain when I was three parts pissed at the office Easter egg hunt. I remember it only too well – another painful Malcolm love experiment. Beryl Palmer from finance was bent under a bush looking for eggs when I strolled over to tell her about him. Standing almost eyeball to eyeball with her ample behind, I declared, 'I'll be Colin, if you'll be Gilbert.' She turned round and floored me with a full-blooded backhander that sent me sprawling into her bush. I swore for a time never to speak to a female again.

Anyway, despite the help of Colin 'Fingers' Gilbert, my piano career was destined to flop. After three years and seven months under the maestro, I could only manage 'Pop Goes the Weasel' on a Rolf Harris stylaphone. I can still remember it now. Find Middle C and then it's a simple case of 1324331; 132431; 1324351. Now the pop is more of a slide. And you have to get your slide right to achieve a big climax (I could never quite get the hang of it). After the slide it's a 2431 finish. Bingo.

Danny comes in with my whisky. Good blokes these cabin boys – most of them are from India, and they're all willing to help. Like it used to be in *It Ain't Half Hot Mum* – you know, Windsor Davies and Don Estelle. 'Why do You Whisper Green Grass?' (Number one in 1975.)

Danny's got the kind of warm, broad smile that sucks you in and spits you back out a happier human. He's comforting and reassuring. Just what I need. And he's got the cabin beautifully clean. Must have been on his hands and knees for the best part of four hours. I like clean and I like order, but I wouldn't complain anyway. I'm strictly non-confrontation. Rather stick a cricket stump up my backside than pick a fight with anyone.

It's starting to snow outside, and I'm beginning to perk up.

Miss Cruise Bore prospects: well, she's no sex goddess from what I could make out (mind you, I only had a backend glance followed by a side-on semi-stare). Probably wouldn't know a good shag from a bad one (might come in handy for me). Parents? Could have a bit put aside for a rainy day – although the old girl looks more King Edward than Jersey Royal. Miss Cruise Bore plus points: loyal. She's unlikely to piss off and leave once married (unless she shacks up with one of the first mates on the *Mermaid*'s Crown of the Caribbean tour). Figure irrelevant – no sign of tits underneath baggie Cruise Bore sweatshirt. I can almost sense a thumbs down from Mrs Lighthouse. She could even be a man.

Overall mark out of ten: a miserable sodding three (although she's probably upstairs in cabin E654 going at it hammer and tongs with the assistant purser. I could never judge a woman and never knew when one was judging me; it's part of my problem). Still, I've made a start. I've stuck my toe in the water. And with the Gala evening meal just around the corner, the quest has begun.

Port out, starboard home. I'm feeling Posh with a capital 'P'. The search has begun. I'm after Mrs Potato Head.

2

According to the *Nautical Newsletter*, tonight is a casual night.

It looks like I'm going to get one of these photocopied bulletins every day. Issue one: 'Welcome aboard, we hope your holiday on *Perfect* will be...absolute Perfection.' Maybe I could adapt that for my next potato ad blitz: 'Go on, peel back my perfect *pomme de terre*.' Not quite right yet, but I'll work on it – no wonder they say the British potato is in good hands.

Still, casual is an open-necked shirt and no tie which suits me just fine. I can't stand anything too tight around my neck, makes me heave, and tonight the pressure's full on, believe me. Table 69 consists of yours truly and seven strangers. It's enough to put the willies up anybody. I've worked it all out and weighed it all up. By the pudding course I could be (a) uncomfortable; (b) unfortunate; (c) unattached (see b); (d) unbalanced (see b and c); or (e) unconscious. (There's always the drink to fall back on. And goodness knows, I can put it away when I want to.)

I'll study the ship's map on my way to the Monte Carlo Restaurant, and attempt to get my bearings. And I'll remember to smile at everyone. Give them a nod and a cheery 'good evening'. Well, I mean, you never know who might come in useful should the bloody thing go down. On Deck F, I'm three parts under water as it is. I'm surprised my cabin doesn't come complete with its own periscope.

Now this is more like it! At the foot of a sweeping Dynasty-style staircase, lies the reception desk – beautifully polished in fake gold and mock ivory. Behind the reception desk, a good line-up of 'possibles' sits perched on a set of fake fox-fur topped bar stools, waiting to pander to their paying guests. They're blonde and young, but, on further investigation, they're clearly bored out of their brains. Hattie Jacques is quizzing one of them: 'How much Italian money will I need for our stop off in Rome dear?'

How I'd love to intercede with a clever, yet cutting remark which leaves Hattie high and dry while the girls on reception look on in wonderment at this smooth-talking, quick-witted stranger who's jumped straight out of the Milk Tray adverts. Something like: 'It depends how much you're going to spend you stupid, fat, trumped-up tart.' Cutting and clever? It's just not me. The Man in Black? More like the Milky Bar Kid. I say nothing and walk on by. ('Walk On By.' It was a big hit for Dionne Warwick.)

I have this funny habit of talking in song lyrics when the going gets tough. There I go again! 'When the Going Gets Tough.' Billy Ocean. Now he'd have been the man I'd have picked for my cruise advertising campaign. How could you fail? A couple of verses of 'Caribbean Queen' as the ship hit Barbados and you'd have hit the jackpot. Life on the ocean wave with the man himself. Finish up with Billy on top of a mast singing: 'Get outta my dreams, get into my cabin!' Doesn't quite come off, I know, but you've got to admit, it's *almost* brilliant. I'll work on it.

Not that a boat like this needs an advertising campaign, anyway. Eight bars, a four-deck atrium, the Hippodrome Theatre, Paradise Ballroom, the Golden Penny One-armed Bandit Room, and the 1950s Happy Days Diner for the more casual eating experience. There's Alexander's Bar – posh one this. Up-market nibbles in small vase-like containers. I recall that Margaret Chandler back at work had come across these on one of her many holiday epics. 'It's because men don't always wash their hands after they've had a wee, my little scrag-end,' she told me. Down the corridor is the Champion's Bar. I'll stop off here and have another drop of scotch for Dutch courage. There's a mural of Wimbledon's Centre Court on the far wall. Bjorn Borg is lifting aloft the men's singles title. You can almost hear the roar of the crowd and taste the strawberries and cream. There's a sportsman for you. Bjorn Borg, the unflappable Swede.

I'm sure Swedes might one day take over the world. And there's me in the potato trade. I've picked the wrong team yet again.

So far, so good. In fact, I'm amazed. It all seems to sparkle. They must spend a fortune on Windowlene and Mr Sheen, and as for the cleaners, you can't move for one of them doing the Shake n' Vac and putting the freshness back. The roomy corridors are flanked on the one side by huge picture windows making sure there's sea as far as the eye can see. In the Champion's Bar, they've gone slightly over the top with the fake antique mahogany furniture. Sideboards this time, bolted onto the floor in case we have a bit of rough.

That reminds me, Dicky Cox back home often treats himself to a bit of rough. He goes out with an ugly woman once every six months. A routine he sticks to religiously. He says it helps to keep his feet on the floor. I remember him telling me in confidence that he once dated a woman who was so ugly she used to have her make-up on the National Health Service!

I sit down. Well, to be truthful, I'm perched ungainly on one end of a fake leather chaise lounge playing nervously with my fingers. But I'm not alone for long. You can't sit down on these boats without someone begging to take down your order. A young Asian girl this time, tray poised in palm, ready for action (is it true that after one night in Bangkok, the world's your oyster?). Better news still, you don't pay money on board. Just flash your cruise card and the world *is* your oyster. No questions asked.

Potatoes were once used as currency, you know. During the Alaskan gold rush in 1897 they were literally worth their weight in gold. Miners traded their gemstones for spuds to stock up on vitamin C.

They once billed me as the 'Golden Boy of the British Potato' during my early days in the press office of the marketing board. I won an award for my 'Little Willie likes a Wilja' campaign. But then it all went wrong. I gambled everything in an over-ambitious plot to get the Duke of York (yes, Prince flipping Andrew) to suck on his...Duke of York. Great plan. It had everything. A humble breed of potato meets senior royalty – head on. They loved it at the presentation stage. Then his bloody wife hit the headlines just two days later for sucking on some bald bloke's big toe. I was finished. Before you could say 'Sarah Ferguson', Margaret Chandler was moved in. In potato terms, I was smashed. (You remember: 'For mash, get smash.' Those sodding robots. The real potato's darkest hour.) The bosses decided I wasn't 'up to scratch'. They thought I'd gone to pot. But I soon bounced back.

Within days I took revenge on the slimy Mrs Chandler. Unbeknown to anyone I made a sneaky phone call to the local branch of 'Dial-a-dog-wash'. It was sheer pandemonium in the office when the man turned up in his converted transit van asking to give a bitch called Margaret a special flea rinse. It was my most treacherous moment, and I never told a soul.

It's not treachery I'm after on the high seas, though. And I'm not going to be clumsy this time. I'm taking a sip at the Last Chance Saloon. It's my sort of arrangement with God. I'm no great believer, but I've figured that if I make him aware that this is my last chance of romance, he might take pity on me and produce a fair maiden ready and willing to be bowled over. All I've got to do is convince the good Lord that I'm really serious.

I mean, let's face it. I'm a decent enough bloke. Never broken the law. Very caring too. I never used to throw my bus tickets away until they were in 'families' of at least five, sometimes seven. That way they could look after each other and comfort each other in the waste-paper bin. I'd never chuck one away on its own. At school they thought I was bonkers. But it made sense to me.

Decent, caring and honest...yet I still lead a miserable, sex-starved, romance-ravaged life. And that's not fair. I'm prepared to recognize God if he's prepared to give me a break on the woman front. So I've told him fair and square. That's the deal. If I don't pull this time, I'm pulling out altogether. And I'm sure the Lord wouldn't want to see me unhappy for the rest of my natural-born days.

I down the dregs of a Bells' and glance once more at the tennis picture. It's time for the Swedes to move aside. It's the era of the potato. I'm off to find my wife on table 69.

According to the map, it's supposed to be a pleasant route from bar to nosh but I'm buggered if I can get the hang of it at this early stage of my cruising career. I've always been hopeless at navigation. I'm like the old woman in the song 'My Old Man Said Follow the Van'. I've lost my way and don't know where to roam. I'm going all round the houses like a dustman's cart. At this rate, I'll end up in the boiler room and I'm blowed if I'm going to spend eleven nights stoking some seaman's boiler.

Ah, at last. Here it is. Table bloody 69, Monte Carlo Restaurant. I've finally arrived. It says in the brochure: 'Mealtimes in the Monte are always an event.' It looks as if they're going to be. The place gleams! Shimmering fake gold lanterns that have been polished until they sparkle stand proudly in the centre of row upon row of striking white tablecloths (they must spend a fortune on Persil). This isn't a dining-room. It's a food auditorium.

'Hello! I'm June and this is Tom – are you *Sound of Music* or *Oklahoma*, because I'm telling you now young man, I'm Julie Andrews through and through.'

Blast, I forgot, this is a Magic of the Musicals themed special. There are talks on the shows and even the odd performance in the Hippodrome Theatre.

'I'm *Les Misérables*. Thank you for asking.'

I'm trying to be as polite as possible, but I'm not very good with new people until I'm absolutely cocksure they adore me. Only then do I come into my own. But this is the new me. I'm going to throw caution to the wind and thrust myself head-long into the spotlight. Dazzled by the glamour of the Monte Carlo Restaurant, I've decided to make myself table 69's leading man. I'm going to make them like me with an early strike. I'm going to dive head first into a gag:

'Besides June, I wouldn't want the wind sweeping up my plains. You know, *Oklahoma*, where the wind comes sweeping... Well anyway.'

'I'm Alfred and this is my partner Andy,' says a small, yet perfectly groomed gentleman.

Knockers, knickers, knackers, clackers (old playground phrase that's always stuck with me – sums up Mrs Lighthouse rather nicely). I've barged in with another ill-timed gag. You can't talk about wind sweeping up your plains in front of a pair of bummers and hope to get away with it. I've boobed big time.

You wouldn't put Andy and Alfred together as partners, you know. As well as resembling a leprechaun, Alfred's got to be knocking fifty while Andy's a big strapping blonde bloke. Handsome lad though I say it myself. Alf's probably his sugar daddy and Andy's just on board for the ride.

Now I'm not against anybody who chooses to lick the stamp on the other side, or drive the other bus. I've often thought it might be an easy way out for me in times of despair – but oh, the thought of being rodgered up the jacksy by a bloke's red-hot poker... I'm staunchly anti-pain.

'Hello both. I do like gay men but I'm not one myself.' Shut up you prick, you're making matters worse.

It's been a scrappy opening on my part. And worse is still to come. Alongside June, Tom, Alfred (who bears an uncanny resemblance to a leprechaun) and Andy, there sits Kenneth, a tiny weasel of a man with false teeth that move every time he speaks. He's dwarfed by a badly fitting off-the-peg 1970s grey pinstriped suit. Mind you, it must be a struggle trying to get something that looks the part when you're knocking on sixty and have the muscular body of a ten-year-old. And the loose teeth! It'll be a laugh a minute when the oven-baked whole pork fillet Westmoreland on a bed of lentil purée gets mixed in with those dancing dentures. Has he never heard of Polygrip?

'I hold the world record for playing the recorder with my nose,' Kenneth tells the table in his broad West Country accent. Somerset I'd say at a guess, but it's hard to tell; he's barely able to keep control of his gnashers. I wonder if he knows how to play 'Pop Goes the Weasel' on a Rolf Harris Stylaphone? It could almost be his signature tune.

'They've got a mind of their own those bloody teeth,' whispers Alfred to Andy. Good to know I'm thinking along the same lines as the puffs. Top marks to Dale Winton; he's turned the gay man into the housewife's choice thanks to his *Supermarket Sweep* and six balls on the lottery.

Kenneth's going to be quite a character. He's in Equity. Had a part selling cucumbers in the failed TV soap opera *Albion Market*. (I thought I recognized his well-worn weasel-like features. Now I know why. He's off the television – a hero of the small screen.) Early indications suggest *Albion Market* was his finest hour, except for the recorder of course. He also played a dead tramp in *Casualty*.

Just two left to come and our table is full. No sign of me hitting the jackpot with this lot. Not a possible love affair in sight. But there's still time yet. You just watch. Anthea Turner and Zola Budd will walk in next and the night will be rescued just as I was about to throw in the towel.

I had a big thing for Zola Budd in the 'eighties when she broke record after record in bare feet, before hacking down Mary Decker in the Olympics with a Norman Hunter type follow-through. I once went to cheer her on over 3,000 metres on the indoor track at RAF Cosford, convinced I would be her proud husband come the 1982 Olympics in Los Angeles. I used to stay up half the night dreaming of how David Coleman would put me across as 'the man behind Zola's surge to glory', or 'the man who made little Zola's Budd blossom'. The cameras would pluck me out in the grandstand, beaming with pride as the band played Britain's national anthem. Zola would stand on top of the podium and the nation would weep. Zola made me realize why women throw their knickers at Tom Jones. I would have happily slung a pair of my pants in her direction as she belted barefoot down the final straight. After all, I was groomed for a career in athletics myself. Might have gone all the way if I hadn't dropped my baton during the 4 x 400m relay at the county trials.

Meekly I sit still, sandwiched in between June and Alfred. It's no good. I'm quite possibly the world's worst small talker, despite my incredible thirst for useless titbits. I'm a dab hand at why Penelope Pitstop always finished on top of the Ant Hill Mob in the way-out *Wacky Races*. Ask me why we never saw Mrs Honeymon's husband in *Camberwick Green* and I can give you a two-hour briefing. I'll talk for England about Jack Russell, the greatest cricket wicket-keeper who ever lived (and my all-time hero). But otherwise, I can never seem to get the right sentence out at the right time. Like Donny Osmond. I wonder if that's what he meant when he recorded 'Make the

World Go Away'. I feel just like him sometimes, although I haven't got his teeth (maybe I could borrow Kenneth's).

As per usual, I'm left buggered in the conversation stakes. I can almost see myself heading for disaster. Every time I open my mouth, I wait for my foot; like a good bus, it's sure to be along very soon.

'So Alfred, are you *Sound of Music* or *Sunset Boulevard*?'

Alfred looks straight through me. I've flopped again. They all hate me. I can feel myself retreating into my little shell. I'm on the table from hell. Trapped between the devils and the deep blue sea.

'No, we're more *Eurovision Song Contest*, aren't we Alfred,' Andrew titters. Well, it's more like a tiny chuckle. A chuckle-ette.

'Oh yes love, we'd go any lengths to see Clodagh Rodgers' "Jack in the Box".'

'Lucky Jack,' says Andy with another of his tiny titters.

'I liked Sandie Shaw with her "Boom Bang-a-Bang",' I say, desperately trying to keep together the threads of a conversation.

'It was Lulu, you twat!'

What a cheek. Kenneth the Weasel Man has just called me a twat. And I was only trying to keep the conversation alive.

'What was Lulu dear?' asks June – Mrs bloody Julie Andrews.

'Lulu was "Boom Bang-a-Bang",' says Kenneth. 'Now Sandie Shaw was more of your…' he very delicately lifts his two index fingers as if to conduct an orchestra, then he bursts into song: ' "I wonder if one day that, you'll say that, you care." '

Andy and Alfred join in: ' "If you say you love me madly, I'll gladly be there." '

Blow it – I'm up for a bit of a *Euro* singsong. They're not leaving me stranded in *Eurovision* no man's land; after all, I still remember raising the roof when the girls from Bucks Fizz had their skirts ripped off from under their noses while they were still trying to make their minds up. Hats off to the two lads I say. That's what you call striking while the iron's hot.

Julia Dingley, who lived three doors down, got her mother to make her a Bucks Fizz skirt. Velcro and everything. She wore it to the church bazaar that spring, but she said we couldn't rip it off because she was only ten. Anyway, I'm off the substitute's bench and straight into the action: ' "Like a puppet on a string." ' We're all at it now bar Tom who's sat back with a face like a robber's dog. ' "Like a puppet on a do-do-do-do-do string." '

Good. The mood of the table has taken a turn for the better. Suddenly, we're all getting on like a house on fire. Andy titters, and Alfred gently slaps Andy's arm Larry Grayson style and then nods at me in approval (I think he likes me, after all). Kenneth slumps back down to wait for his mushroom ravioli, Tom's still lifeless and June clasps her hands in glee. For one short cruising moment, table 69 is the life and soul of the party. Thank you Sandie Shaw. Your bare-footed European frolics have not been in vain.

'Tom collects Jessie Matthews memorabilia. And he's absolutely obsessed with Sonny and Cher,' says June, bending over to whisper softly into my left ear, as if to apologize for her husband's complete lack of interest. 'It's a case of anything he can get his hands on with Jessie, and he's got every Sonny and Cher record from "Little Man" to "I Got You Babe". We've got a room full at our house.'

'Jessie Matthews?' Never heard of the woman.

'Oh, you know, the Dancing Divinity.' She starts to sing. ' "Let's do it. Let's fall in love." '

Oh yes, it's all becoming crystal clear.

June's in full flow, 'She was the queen of the British musical. You know the one. Famous for throwing her cares over her shoulder.' I suppose it beats throwing your underwear at Zola. 'Irving Berlin described her as the female Fred Astaire. Terrible business in the end though. She finished up on the wireless playing the lead role in *Mrs Dale's Diary*. Awful waste. She'd have been the greatest superstar of the century but for one tragic weakness. Men. Rampant she was, ruined her in the end.'

How the hell can you have a whole room full of Sonny and Cher? I think to myself as a whole army of waiters emerges, like ants from the kitchens ready, willing and desperate to serve the hungry masses. Anyway, June's played straight into my hands. I know a bit about Sonny and Cher, and I'm about to become the table's information highway.

'Sonny Bono. Mouse-like voice, sheepish smile, became a congressman. Didn't he die in a nasty skiing accident?' I drop my voice not wanting to offend Tom.

'Yes,' says Alfred, quick to butt in. 'Police reported it was a quick death – just like his solo career.' He's in hysterics. Tom hasn't heard, thank goodness. He doesn't seem to be listening to anyone.

Kenneth's too busy on the food. It's easy to understand why. It's a gastronomic extravaganza, and there's me, a bubble and squeak man. Just study the evidence. There's royal Greenland smoked halibut with dill mayonnaise, guinea fowl terrine, trio of melon pearls with ginger...and that's just for starters.

Let's think. Food? Superb. Company? Mixed. There's Mr Weasel Man Kenneth with his teeth and nose shenanigans (although on the plus side he did sell cucumbers on *Albion Market*); the two puffs (one of them is a gay leprechaun – that's got to be a first in anybody's book); June (Mrs Julie Andrews); Tom (Sonny and Cher); and me. And here's the final two in table 69's rich and varied tapestry: Kevin and Kate.

Kevin barges his way in like a dumper truck; a big, loud, know-it-all Yorkshireman. He's making a big entrance like a politician on his way to the podium to make a keynote speech to the party faithful. If there were any babies in the Monte Carlo, he'd probably stop to kiss them.

Just what we need. Mr Mouthy meets Mrs Do-re-mi-fa-so-la-ti-do (it's my personal tribute to June's love of Julie Andrews). Kate is mysterious. Small and timid, but she's quite perfectly formed in the bust department, and sexy in a 1970s suburbia sort of way. She looks like Thelma Ferris (married to Bob in *Whatever Happened to the Likely Lads*). Short, black, neat hair. Almost continental. Prim and proper, yet underneath she's probably simmering like a dormant volcano, waiting to explode like the taste of a sautéed charlotte on the tongue. It's all in her eyes. I'll watch her like a hawk just in case. Probably goes like a rabbit when unleashed. And she's come to dinner with *The Phantom of the Opera* scrawled on the right breast of her blouse. At least June's found a buddy.

'Did you see it with Michael Crawford or Dave Willetts?' she asks, prodding Kate's nipple. (I bet she's got nipples like hubcaps when she gets going.)

'We've seen 'em all,' booms Mouthy Kev. 'We were there on opening night at Her Majesty's Theatre in the West End. I've got a programme signed by the whole cast to prove it. We're close personal friends of Sir Andrew Lloyd Webber, aren't we flower?'

Flower? Kiss Me Kate never struck me as a flower. What sort of a flower shall I put her down as? A Lady's Slipper (win me and wear me)? Or maybe a Lily of the Valley? Too early to say. For all I know she could be an innocent Daisy. On the other hand she could turn out to be Deadly Nightshade. Pear Blossoms (she looks like she's got a blossoming pair from where I'm sitting)? Or Passion-flower? Carnation or Candytuft? Sweet Pea or Shamrock? The list is endless.

Any road up, Mouthy has dampened our early party atmosphere – and he's not stopping there.

'This is our eleventh cruise,' he announces, bold as brass. He turns to Kenneth, looks him distastefully up and down and decides to address me instead. 'We've got a bloody suite you know. Statesman. With bath...*and balcony*!' Time to take stock. I've finally met the Magnificent Seven but there's no sign of Anthea or Zola. If it wasn't for bad luck, I'd have none at all.

'Hello, I'm Roger the waiter,' chirps another little, yet jolly Indian man who seems to have appeared from nowhere – just like the shopkeeper in a Mr Benn cartoon. 'I'm here to see to your every need in the food department.'

'Roger the Waiter.' I'm thinking out loud now.

'Chance would be a fine thing,' replies Andy. Alfred titters, it's the same sort of titter as Andy but there's more spunk in it. Alfred's titter is definitely bordering on the chuckle.

By the third course of this opening Gala Night tour through the wonders of modern day cuisine, I'm struggling to fit any more in. In the food department, I'm ready, steady, stuffed! It's no surprise. They all warned me. The highlight of a cruise is the food, they said. But I defy anyone to eat the lot. Full English breakfast with a mound of fried potatoes, morning coffee with biscuits, five-course luncheon, afternoon cream tea at four with salmon and cucumber sandwiches, the occasional on-deck barbecue, seven courses for dinner...and then a midnight pissing buffet. Hattie Jacques will have to be winched off when we get back to England.

My mate, Dr Roland Rotherham would love this. He's a food historian; knows everything about good grub all over the globe. I say he's my mate but he's more of a colleague really. We draft him into the office to go over any potato facts that need verification. Lovely man. Used to serve in the Household Calvary looking after the troop's mascot – a goat called Treacle. When the goat died, he ate it as a sort of tribute; nice touch, I thought. He says the bravest man in the history of the world was the first one to say: 'I wonder if you can eat that?' Just think... Stuffed heart. Tripe and onions. Who the hell thought about sticking it into his (or her) gob first? According to Dr Rotherham (I call him Rolly) there's a great delicacy in the Himalayas. It's a type of radish finely shredded, stir-fried in sesame oil and served up with…braised monkey's rectum. It's a well-known food fact. Imagine that – tucking into an ape's arse. Must taste a bit like a savory polo mint.

I'm surprised Rolly hasn't tasted it for himself. He's eaten almost every animal that ever lived, including a zebra curry, which he brought into the office (I was queasy for a fortnight, but I've never had the greatest stomach). He reckons that stuffed dormouse is absolutely delicious but I stopped him bringing that in. Swears by chopped date with spring onion and a little breadcrumb for the stuffing. Pokes it up the dormouse within a few seconds. It's like skinning a rabbit to him, but he always warns: 'Do make sure they're dead first or else they'll squeal like hell.'

Gets his mice from the local butchers by all accounts. Dr Rotherham would wipe out a whole continent for saddle of rabbit in a plum sauce, although in the olden days anyone caught poaching rabbit would either have their eyes put out with a hot sword or their tongue bored through with an iron. And for the record, braised pelican with fresh apricot is much nicer than swan. Another food fact. Yes, pelican. Dr Rotherham's eaten them both and prefers the pelican because he says it tastes like a cross between goose and turkey. Swans, by all accounts, are too stringy.

'Excuse me, I'm skipping the coffee.' It's the end of the evening for me, and I bid a fond farewell to table 69. June's involved in a full-scale debate with Mouthy Kevin over the words of 'My Favourite Things' – a *Sound of Music* classic involving raindrops, apple strudels, kittens, bee stings and schnitzel with noodles (although not, according to Kevin, in that order). It's time I was off.

Now here's a problem. My stomach's started to turn. Am I pissed or is it the motion of the ocean? Shall I head for a Motion Discomfort Bag or just go and get my head down? On closer examination, I'm certainly on the sway, but so is the bloody vessel. In fact it's starting to move big time (it's called 'pitching' if you're into cruise terminology). I might just have hit on something here. The golden rule of cruising: no matter how pissed you think you are, you're never as pissed as you think you are. Brilliant! But we can't all be pissed and there's not one passenger walking in a straight line as I head down the immaculate corridors flanked on both sides by fake antique paintings. I decide I'm sober – it's the ship. And, if it gets any rougher, the discomfort bags are likely to get a real rollocking.

Oh Lord. There's Mouthy Kevin and Kiss Me Kate on the picture board outside the Golden Penny One-armed Bandit Room. We all had our photograph taken with ship mascot Cyril the seal as we walked up the gangplank. To coin the football phrase it's a 'Nice one of Cyril', but Kev looks like one of the puppet characters from Michael Bentine's *Potty Time*. Big bushy moustache, no neck, big face – a bear of a man really. Probably squashes Kate if they ever have it away between the sheets. What am I talking about? Of course they have sex. Four times a night I'll bet. He'd say they were the undefeated shagging champions of Scarborough. The earth doesn't move when they do it – there's a flipping landslide. I'll bet a pound to a pinch of snuff he's hung like a donkey as well. It's that big you could knock a foot off and still have enough for a baseball bat.

Despite my slight stagger, I'm halfway home, and, although I don't know it yet, I'm about to stumble upon another beauty of the modern cruise. The art of eavesdropping. I'd never considered it a participation sport before. But on a boat, you can't help but dip your toe into the water. There's a golden nugget to be found every time you prick up an ear.

'She's gone all the one way since she had her back passage done, you know.'

Two elderly ladies are talking on the pale blue easy chairs dotted around the corridor to break up the line of fake antique mahogany furniture. One's bent double (probably a martyr to her arthritis), the other has a face like Huckleberry hound... It's Stoop and Droop.

'Couldn't get out before the man came round to examine her entry.' Stoop's doing all the talking. 'I was trimming my bush on top of the gas meter when out she came as large as life... It's finished she said, come and have a look. Well, you know me, I'm one that keeps myself to myself as a rule, but on this occasion I was round there like a thunderbolt. The whole world knew about her back passage so I wasn't interfering. Well, I've never seen crazy paving like it. And she still had enough room to keep the greenhouse. Well, you know how her husband likes to sex his cucumbers.'

I like the look of Stoop. She's a female version of Albert Steptoe. We had a woman at the end of our street like that. Used to drink Lemsip and vodka, and she'd never give you the ball back when it went flying over her hedge. The poor old soul went mad in the end. They sent her to a lunatic asylum after complaints from the neighbours. She spent six months clattering her skirting-board with a spanner she had christened Stuart. Unbelievable, I know. Why she called her spanner Stuart heaven only knows, but it must have rubbed off on me a little. I've got a screwdriver in my bottom drawer named Sandra.

I tried to invent a board game after 'Maddy' as the kids in the neighbourhood called her. It was based on Cluedo, but never caught on. In fact, some of my so-called pals said it was the biggest flop since floodlights were invented for Subbuteo table football (they were far too dim and didn't focus enough light onto the right part of the pitch – most frustrating, and a constant source of controversy in the playground). I don't want to dwell too much on the past. As far as I'm concerned, my 'mad woman at the end of the street' days are over. But, thanks to my chance meeting with Stoop and Droop, I've decided to fine-tune my eavesdropping skills should boredom set in during the holiday.

Finally I'm heading for the safety of Deck F and my cabin, almost overwhelmed by a day full of ups and downs. I've gone from Hattie Jacques' backside, to some old lady's back passage via a homosexual leprechaun, Julie Andrews, Kiss Me Kate and the cucumber seller from *Albion Market* (a.k.a. Kenneth the Weasel Man). It's been a roller-coaster of emotions. And my only hope of a holiday romance, and possibly marital bliss so far… Miss bloody Cruise Bore. That's unless Jessie Matthews turns up. I like her style. Slippery knickers and prepared to throw all her cares over her shoulder. I'm going to be like her for the next few days. Up Jessie! That's my toast for this evening. Up with Jessie and down with slippery knickers!

'Let's do it… Let's fall in love.'

3

Chris de Burgh. It was definitely Chris de flipping Burgh.

I've woken up with the words of 'Ship to Shore' ringing around my head (it's the name of the cruise company, see). You know, 'Ship to shore, answer my call'. For one minute of blind panic I was scrambling around in my brilliant brain for the singer, and then it came to me in a flash. Chris de flipping Burgh. 'Lady in Red, is dancing with me, cheek to cheek.' (Number one in 1987.) That's me in a nutshell. A heart full of song, and a mind full of useless information. Oh yes, I'm also a coward. I got scared during the night as the *Perfect* ploughed its way through the ocean. I'm sure I felt a slight swelling down below at about 3 a.m. I remember thinking, 'We're on the sodding sway again.' The fake antique mahogany wardrobes began to creak and I wondered how I would cope should we go down all hands on deck.

He's got a lot to answer for that bloody Leonardo DiCaprio and his *Titanic*. I'm thirty-seven years old and I'm starting to get the jitters when night falls. Mind you, the sea can be a bit frightening and I'm certainly no Jacques Cousteau when it comes to water. I liked Jacques. I remember, his ship was called the *Calypso* and John Denver made a song about it. See, I'm at it again. The useless information king defends his undisputed world crown.

Danny brings tea at 7.30 a.m. The clocks have gone forward an hour and I don't know whether I'm in the Co-op or the Home and Colonial. But, one thing I have noticed – they're very big on biscuits. Every time Danny appears, he brings another mini-packet of oatmeal. I shall be sick to the back teeth of oatmeal by the end of the week. I bet Kevin and the mysterious Kiss Me Kate are tucking into chocolate bourbons in their Statesman Suite 'with bath...*and balcony*!'

According to the radio, you are what you eat on the biscuit front. I didn't catch the whole conversation because my wireless shares the same plug as the electric tin opener and I wanted to open a tin of tongue for lunch. Mind you, it was worth it; I like a bit of tongue first thing on a Saturday afternoon. Anyway, nice people eat Nice biscuits, of course. Football agents and car dealers are more your Jammy Dodgers, while television presenters prefer your Custard Creams. I'm more Malted Milk – you know, the oblong ones with the cows on. I don't really know what that makes me. I suppose I could've been a dairyman in a previous life (although I've never really been one for grappling with a loose teat first thing in the morning). June's probably a shortbread. Let's face it, anyone with an unhealthy obsession for Julie Andrews has got to be at least two slices short in the Mother's Pride department. Tom's more Ginger Nuts. Alfred and Andy are Boudoir Fingers. Kiss Me Kate would probably go for a cream horn while Mouthy's a fig roll.

I always thought the black bit on a fig roll resembled a mouth, used to have hours of fun with them at school. In my opinion, they were only bettered by chocolate marshmallows in the 'playground food fun' category. Here's the game. You held two marshmallows a distance apart. One was German and the other was English. You smashed them together with force. One always stayed intact while the other got a right hammering. A German victory was shrugged off. An English win was greeted with a roar from the assembled half dozen or so hard-core followers of marshmallow mangling.

My mind's meandering. I'll have a shower now, then at least that'll be one thing out of the way. Shouldn't think I'll have a poo for at least another day and a half. (It's always the same when I'm travelling. Sometimes I can go the whole week without sight nor sound of a good clearout.)

Oh bollocks. There's a mirror in the shower. 'England's last hope?' More like Bob Hope (pre-Dorothy Lamour of course). Or in my case, 'no bloody hope' – especially where holiday romance is concerned. I'm losing my hair and it's coming out through my nose. (Must ask Kenneth about nasal hair; he's bound to know considering what he puts his nostrils through in the pursuit of musical perfection.)

Malcolm's Log. Day two. It's Friday, June 20th and this is a 'Day at Sea' according to the *Nautical Newsletter* that has arrived courtesy of Danny. Today my search for Mrs Potato Head could take me to Nicola's handicraft club in the Mermaid Suite. (They're making a *découpage* doorstop. She hasn't got a prayer. We'll be back in Southampton before some of these old fossils have mastered a pair of scissors and a photocopied daffodil.) This sounds more interesting: 'Line dancing with Linda in the Paradise Ballroom'. Some think there's a 'lustful undertone' to line dancing. Can't see it myself. Just a gaggle of geezers who failed miserably at the military two-step, but can just about muster a 'kick-ball-change'. There's always 'Bridge for Beginners with Barbara in the Terrace Lounge', or Daphne with her port enhancement talk on Gibraltar in the Hippodrome Theatre. So much to see, so little time to see it. Is it possible I will return to England with my true love? Or will I be back at my desk with my new project: 'The delights of a Desiree'?

Look at me. I've suddenly come over all sentimental. I'm starting to miss my desk! Although, it's no wonder when you think about it. There's a young lad who's just started and I'm convinced he wants to step into my shoes. I call him 'Pimple' on account of the fact that he's got an extraordinary blemish-free complexion. I can see him now, drinking tea out of my *Mary, Mungo and Midge* mug (although I've told him straight: if he touches my 'Windmills of North Yorkshire' calender, he's dead). It's an important week back home as well. The regional heats of the national mashed potato wrestling competition are taking place. It was Dicky Cox's idea and I think it could go down a storm. Instead of grappling around in mud, the contestants – Dicky suggested topless women – attempt a half nelson in a ring full of mashed spud. Delightful if you ask me.

Speaking of wrestling, whatever happened to Kendo Nagasaki, the masked wrestler who appeared with the likes of Big Daddy and Mick McManus on ITV's *World of Sport*? Saturday afternoon was made for wrestling when I was young.

Kendo made a lasting impression on me. He was my early sporting role model, heaven only knows why. They always used to say that he wore a mask because his face was horribly disfigured. Then, one day, he was on the receiving end of a right bollocking from Sandy Savage the Sunderland Slasher. Kendo was chucked out of the ring where some old lady with a flying fake crocodile-skin handbag ripped off his mask. The crowd in our house gasped. I was expecting the elephant man, yet underneath the mask was just some ordinary bloke. Life sort of began to go downhill from that moment on. It was my second biggest disappointment after discovering there was no Father Christmas. That's the real turning point in life. It's the beginning of the end.

Dicky was always a big grapple and groan merchant, yet he was never sucked in to the Kendo Nagasaki scam. He's as sharp as a tack, that's why they made him head of forward planning. It was an obvious move – after all, he came from the world of television. Used to set up the contestants on

Celebrity Squares. They say he also had a brief spell with Nicholas Parsons on *Sale of the Century*, but that job ended quite abruptly after a mysterious incident with a dolly bird from Potter's Bar, a mink coat costing £1.50, and a swift diddle during the quick-fire round.

Oh, there's another thing. He's convinced that unicorns exist. He's got this mate from Finland, Oscar Arss, who reckons he's got photographic evidence. Swears he's seen a living unicorn wandering around one of the many wooded hills in his homeland. He's got the pictures but he won't reveal his findings to the press, for fear of being labelled a madman. He's a multi-millionaire this Arss, yet he spends all his time chasing unicorns.

Dicky keeps trying to persuade me to go on holiday with him to Finland on the off chance we might bump into one. I've pencilled it in for next year, even though, deep down, I think it's all a load of poppycock. Can you imagine it? Me, looking for unicorns in some remote Finnish forest alongside Dicky Cox, Oscar Arss and his wife, who everybody calls 'Horse'. I don't know why she's called 'Horse' because her real name is Cynthia. All I really know about her is that she can burp the National Anthem. It's her party piece. Never right, if you ask me, yet I'm planning my next big trip with them all. My nerves are in shreds just thinking about it. After all, I've got enough on my plate with the holiday I'm on.

Alarm bells begin to ring in my head. It's not really fair. My mind is already in a state of gross flumuxation. Now my stomach's started to turn, and it's all because I've got to book my outings today – just realized. It's shit or bust in the tours department and I still can't decide whether to take a chance on 'Rome in a Day' or the 'Hidden Delights of Corsica'. Maybe the Dolphin hunt off the coast of Italy would be more romantic when I've found Mrs Right. And what the bloody hell am I going to do about Barcelona? In all there's five stops on this magical mystery tour: Gibraltar first, then the pretty port of

Propriano in Corsica, on to either Florence or Pisa from the port of Livorno, then Rome, a drop of Barcelona and home. For now I'll settle for the 'Highlights of Gibraltar' and 'Rome in a Day'. The rest can look after themselves.

I'm still thinking about my tour options on the way to breakfast. It's an easy route this time, just three stops in the lift. No chance of getting all mixed up like the night before. And, fortunately, I've missed the pensioner's rush hour (seven till eight as a rule – they can't get out of the habit of getting up early). Two Indian men are cleaning the mirrors that cover three of the lift walls from head to toe (great for sex, awful if you look like death first thing). I'm almost overcome with the smell of Pledge Amber Lemon Clean when, fortunately, the lift doors open. Just in time as well. Another couple of seconds and I'd have keeled over. Shame. I might have gone down in history as the first man to die from polish poisoning.

I'm still trying to remove the faint whiff of Pledge from my right nostril when I stumble upon Kenneth the Weasel Man. He recognizes me straight away.

'Hello Martin.' He's pleased to see me. Arm outstretched.

'It's Malcolm actually, Kenneth,' I reply, but it hasn't sunk in. He's wearing the baggiest of baggy shorts I've ever seen (mind you anything would look baggy when you've got legs like twigs. The last time I saw a pair of pins like that they were dangling out of a nest).

'I've been thinking,' he says. 'We should have shacked up together in one of them Dutch-friendly twosomes and paid half the price.'

Oh God, can you imagine – Kenneth and his free-for-all false teeth. I wonder if he takes them out at night or if they just give up the ghost and fall out themselves.

'Anyway,' he continues, 'you should have stayed a bit longer last night. We had to go through every song from *The Sound of* flipping *Music*, *including* the one about the female deer.'

I try to intervene with the second line about Ray being likened to a drop of golden sun, but I haven't got a hope. Mr Weasel Man is in full swing:

'I once auditioned for Captain Von Trapp you know. Amateur dramatics of course, nothing professional, but always useful if you want to keep your hand in. Ended up playing one of the Nazis. The bastards didn't like my "Edelweiss".' He's off again, attempting the first half a dozen bars of 'Edelweiss' while strumming solemnly on an invisible acoustic guitar. For my money, it's quite a magical moment – but then, he is a professional actor. He stops to laugh and gently pats me on the shoulder. I think he likes me. In which case, I'll like him back.

A pair of posh knobs studying the picture board turn with a distasteful look. They disapprove of our antics. After all, you'd never get singing and laughing on board the Canberra. 'Riffraff,' whispers the gentleman smartly clad in beige slacks and boating plimsoles. His wife half-nods in agreement. They're the cruising old school.

'Pair of upper class prats,' retorts Kenneth in a sort of a tit-for-tat manoeuvre.

'Anyway, I'm off to the line dancing with Linda. Why don't you come along and strut your stuff? It's the best place for a bit of spare on these things,' he adds quickly regaining his composure. It was only a minor knock-back from the snobs and he's quickly turned the other cheek (probably had composure control knocked into him at drama school).

As for me, I'm strictly off limits as far as trading insults is concerned. Anyway, I'm more interested in Kenneth now. 'The best place for a bit of spare!' I could only half concentrate because old weasel features was leaning towards me and I was afraid of his teeth falling into my top pocket. But from what I can gather, he's on the pull as well. Now if I can't beat *him* in the race for a bride then I might as well join Alfred and Andy on the other side of the fence.

No sooner has Kenneth made off for breakfast followed by a quick shimmy in the ballroom, but the gruesome twosome – Stoop and Droop – take their seats by the picture board. Just where I'd left them the previous night. We're only two days into the holiday and already people are marking out their territory. This was going to be the elderly ladies canking patch and that was that.

Stoop, the one with the Albert Steptoe features, is a fair way behind Droop who has already slumped into her easy chair with a sigh. Droop herself is no oil painting. And she looks even worse in the cold light of day. Face like a shire horse. In her younger days she would have been a dead cert for Dicky Cox's twice yearly 'ugly bird conquest'. I think he's obsessed. He leaves no stone unturned to seek out the most hideous ladies. The girl who had her make-up supplied by the NHS on account of her awful face was a positive delight compared to Petunia Morris, who was so ghastly that Dicky had to cover her head with a sheet when they went out for a drink in case he bumped into anyone that knew him. He was afraid of a backlash from his mocking mates.

'I won't sit down, I'm not stopping,' says Stoop. She takes a seat. 'Look at me,' she adds mopping her forehead. 'I'm sweating like a glass-blowers arse!'

I've found a snap of me with Cyril the Seal on the picture board. Poor shot. I look more like Dorothy Lamour *post*-Bob Hope. Still, I'll pretend to study it while putting my newly found eavesdropping skills to good use. And I'm on fertile territory. Droop's well into another fable:

'When Mrs Coulter two doors up was having her trouble, I told her to pull a bit harder on the little knob – it always did the trick for me, although I had to have a man in to show me the ropes.'

What's this? Either plumbing trouble or how to achieve the ultimate orgasm.

For me, it's time for breakfast – but there's yet more tittle-tattle in the queue for a full English (it's unlike me to be eating so heartily in a strange place. It must be the sea air). The couple I saw before with matching tank tops are now decked out in colour co-ordinated T-shirts with identical pale pink slacks. She's holding court while trying to scoop a spoonful of baked beans onto her already bulging platter.

'Imagine that,' she says as her husband overstretches for the brown toast knocking half a dozen wayward beans onto the side of the counter. 'Clarence and Trisha getting divorced... And they've only just had a new kitchen fitted.'

In a bid to grab hold of the last piece of brown toast myself, I almost cut their conversation dead, but I've decided to skip the beans as a sort of a tribute to Clarence and Trisha. I don't like to hear of yet another marriage hitting the rocks. I'll concentrate on the button mushrooms instead.

No sign of Cruise Bore this morning, although I am joined at breakfast by another friendly threesome from the Bloxwich Musical Society (it says so on their T-shirts). Now here's a belting trio. Two blokes who haven't got long left and a woman in a wig. It's the most remarkable crop of hair I've ever seen: a tumbling mound of curly blonde locks; a sea of cotton wool separated only by a hairband perched precariously somewhere near the middle. She looks like one of the Hair Bear Bunch.

I'll include her in the wife stakes. Contender number two: Mrs Hair Bear Bunch. Getting on in years – not a real contender, more of a wild card for amusement purposes only. Accompanied by her two old gentlemen. They're very much like the pair who used to hurl abuse at the Muppets from the Royal Box. Mrs Hair Bear Bunch is quick to engage me in conversation:

' "A fiddler on the roof. Sounds crazy, no?" '

Oh Lord! Here we go again. It turns out she's president of the National Old Fiddler's Association. It's a sort of fan club for the musical *Fiddler on the Roof*. An appreciation society. I'll be halfway through my sausage, egg and brown toast and she'll start up with, 'If I were a blasted rich man'.

'I've seen it over seventy times, all over the world,' says Mrs Hair Bear Bunch. 'Once knocked around with a man who played one of the Russian soldiers in the film. Never had a line, but he was definitely in it. Danced during the alehouse scene when Tevye got arseholed with Lazar Wolf just before the daughter married Motel the Tailor.' She elbows me in the ribs. 'You know.'

Of course I do. Seen it a dozen times myself.

I'm sure there's a film in this somewhere. The Hair Bear Bunch meet the Muppets fiddling with themselves on a roof – must alert Steven Spielberg. He could add Stoop and Droop and virtually the whole of table 69 for good measure. It could be Kenneth's greatest hour.

The Hair Bear Bunch mob is gearing up for Norman DeVine's 'Whistle-stop tour through the West End' lecture, although there's trouble in the ranks because the oldest of the two blokes wants to attend the Gibraltar port enhancement talk. I don't think Mrs Hair is married to either of them. Probably dabbled with the pair of them in her time but now she's definitely old, free and single.

An unexpected surprise awaits me back in the cabin. A photocopied sheet of the *Daily Mail* – the top stories, on board, every day... Marvellous. Pimple, the new boy at work, reads the *Daily Mail*. But then he would – he's an agronomist. They've brought him in to study the feasibility of creating a British Potato Museum, although Dicky Cox thinks it's all a load of bollocks. He says the only interesting fact about the potato is that one appears on the official crest of Botswana. (We're pretty sure it's a Russet.)

I've decided to skip Nicola's handicraft classes and I'm not in the running to pick up the tricks, or trumps of the bridge trade. It says in the *Nautical Newsletter* that there are

53,644,737,765,488,792,839,237,440,000 possible deals in a game of contact bridge so the chances are you'll never get two deals the same in a lifetime. To be bitten by the bridge bug is to enter the bamboozling world of the games, slams and rubbers. Now I like the idea of games and rubbers but I'm not one for trumping, so Barbara's going to have to manage without me.

The Log needs an early cruise boost, so I'll start in the most unlikely of love haunts – the library. Talking of logs, I'd better stay in my cabin for another couple of minutes; that usually long awaited first holiday poo is about to make an unexpected early appearance – must have been the raspberries steeped in Drambuie with chocolate sauce.

As I prepare to curl out a good seven-pounder, a catchy little slogan just above the toilet catches my eye. It reads:

> If it hasn't been through you –
> don't put it down the loo!

It's all about blockages. By the looks of things they're very strict on what you can flush away. The words are emblazoned in red across a rather large, stooping backside. In my opinion, it's rather tastefully done – a subtle way to deal with the subject. I'll write it down later on and see if I can adapt it for our next potato blitz.

Clear out complete, yet I'm bunged up again. This time I can't manoeuvre my way out of the lift. I've run into the old codgers and they're barring my way to an easy exit. These pensioners could prove a problem as time goes on, but they did fight the Germans on the beaches so I'm prepared to give them the benefit of the doubt at this stage.

The library is the expected washout. Just some scrawny old bint desperately putting the starting touches to a mammoth jigsaw. I'll make a note of it. Mrs Jigsaw Puzzle – a sexual desert probably, but buy her a 5,000-piece epic for Christmas, and it'll keep her quiet till Easter.

If the inside of the boat was all shipshape and Bristol fashion, the outside is just as impressive, and the decking is polished and scrubbed to perfection. I wonder if this is where the idea for wooden floors came from? Some unflappable Swede from IKEA came on a cruise and thought, 'Yes, that would go nice in my hall.' Hey presto. Within six months, he's made a mint. He lets the cruise line know and they stick up a painting of Bjorn Borg in honour of unflappable Swedes throughout the world. It all fits in.

The swell of the sea has died down to a mere ripple. The Motion Discomfort Bags have disappeared from the landing. The sun's breaking through, glistening off the gleaming white of the ship that's towering above the waves like a tower block. I'm aboard the monster of the sea. Things are starting to hot up.

Nobody's taking the plunge in the kidney-shaped swimming pool however. Wise move, there's still a bit of a chill in the wind and the motion of the ocean is causing a ripple in the water, which occasionally takes the form of a mini tidal wave, lashing over the side of the pool walls and onto the well-scrubbed decking below. If I'm brave, I might take a paddle when the temperature starts to soar, but for now I'm staying dry. I wouldn't stand a chance in the midst of a mini tidal wave. As I've said, water isn't my strong point – and swimming has always been an uphill struggle. I battled for nearly three years to win a red braid at school. I could barely manage a width when my mates were dressing up in pyjamas and diving for bricks at the bottom of the deep end. I did like Marine Boy on the television when I was little (used to chew magic gum – his best mate was a dolphin). But when it came to taking the plunge myself, I was always less than keen. I just wasn't born with adventure running through my veins.

One or two hardy souls have taken to the sun-loungers. They've carefully positioned themselves in the small patches of direct sunlight close to the side of the ship. No wind, unbroken sunshine, but still pullover weather for the worshippers.

It was once considered that potato juice was the perfect treatment for sunburn, while raw slices of spud were put on broken bones to heal them. And another thing. Many think it's an old wives' tale, but take it from me; a spud in the pocket really does cure toothache. Don't worry, I'm not obsessed by potatoes, but you do pick these things up at the British Potato Marketing Board.

I'm moving around the ship faster than a piece of greased weasel dropping. It's my day of exploration. I'm checking out the gaff from top to bottom and already I can sniff action. I'm right…it's kicked off big style in the Paradise Ballroom. The sensational seventies glam sound of 'Wig Wam Bam' (The Sweet) is booming out across the dance floor. Half a dozen are dancing themselves dizzy, while attempting to wrap their legs around a line-dancing classic. I think they're attempting the Poor Man's Shuffle while Linda belts out her orders:

'Come on,' she yells. 'Practice makes *Perfect* – if you'll excuse the pun!'

It's a well-trodden path for Linda, probably been telling the same gags for years – but her wisecracking has, at least, raised a giggle from Kenneth the Weasel Man who's having a real go. It's enthralling. He's so thin that when he turns side-on he looks like a piece of cardboard. Yet still his little feet are going ten to the dozen. He's trying to be the new Michael Flatley when really he bares more of a resemblance to 'Michael Row the Boat Ashore'. But, all the time, his eyes are firmly fixed on Lovely Linda the Boot Scooting Baby.

From where I'm standing, she's quite a stocky thing. More Charlie Dimmock than Dame Margot Fonteyn. And she sweats a lot too. Not a natural by any stretch of the imagination. I'd say her boots were made for walking rather than for tripping the light fantastic. But she's still way out of Kenneth's league. He's living in cloud-cuckoo-land. He can't possibly think he's going to have a snowball's chance in hell with her. Can he?

Miss Cruise Bore is also on the floor with mother and father. It looks as if she's got her fan step mixed up with her rolling grapevine. She laughs and flicks her hair – first girly thing I've see her do. She's definitely a woman, even though I've decided she must have her locks tended to by Sweeney Todd. She just doesn't seem to care what she looks like on top. Could do with a shampoo and set if you ask me. A blow-dry at the very least. And I've found out where she gets her Cruise Bore T-shirts from. The on-board shops are full of them. *Perfect* T-shirts, *Perfect* bathrobes, *Perfect* hats.

Perfect knickers! An erect mast on the port side, and a smiling Captain Fletcher on the starboard. The *Perfect* way to spend your day – sat on the skipper's face. (I must make a technical note of this. It's a possible marketing idea.) 'And remember,' I'd have printed on the arse end, 'if it hasn't been through you, don't put it down the loo.' I'm desperate to use that phrase somewhere. It's been playing on my mind since I first stooped to conquer!

Lovely Linda's spotted me lurking in the doorway. 'Come on,' she bellows, as half a dozen heads turn around to see what all the sudden excitement is about. 'There's still room for a couple more on the dance floor.'

It's my signal to hotfoot it straight out of the door with a sort of embarrassed half-wave of the hand as if to signal, 'No thanks love, I'd rather sit this one out.' How humiliating. I've been caught red-handed. I'm no better than a peeping Tom. From now on, I'll be labelled as the 'line-dancing letch'. I'd better keep a low profile for the rest of the day. I leave the Paradise Ballroom in shame as the dancers quickly get back to their pivot turns, body rolls and slides. Anyway, it's almost noon and time for the Captain's message from the bridge. By all accounts we're in the Bay of Biscay. They reckon it can cut up rough around these parts but today the sea's like a mirror.

Mirror, mirror on the wall – where's the best bird of them all?

A short-cut through the reading room reveals a row of pensioners slumped uncomfortably in a line of large easy chairs. It's the closest I've ever been to death row. True to form, they're all sound asleep. In fact, on early indications, the whole ship is either (a) eating; (b) drinking; or (c) cat-napping. Anyway, they're starting to get on my nerves, these old folk. Maybe we should shackle a few and flog them with the cat-o'-nine-tails like they used to in the olden days at sea. It would certainly liven things up a tad before we get to Gibraltar. That reminds me, it's very nearly afternoon and my only hope of an early tickle on my fancy is a bloody slide show. Otherwise known as the Gibraltar port enhancement talk.

At least it's popular. There's quite a queue at the Hippodrome Theatre and the place is done out like a mini palace. I've always said you can't go wrong with beige and biscuit for a colour scheme – and the Hippodrome's got it by the bucketful. Beige carpet subtly complimented by biscuit-coloured seats. And a crystal chandelier lights up the fake antique paintings on the wall. (I've cleverly adapted an old Charlie Pride hit. See, I told you. Some of my best friends are songs. A friend in need is very often a song, indeed.)

Undaunted by my ballroom balls-up, I'm going to take potluck and sit near the stage. It's quiet as the lights dim, then, suddenly, like a bolt out of the blue, she emerges from the wings. Daphne. The Port Enhancement Queen. I gaze square on at the woman in front of me. Daphne's a bloody Kerr's Pink on legs (it's my favourite variety of potato. Ideal for boiling, baking and roasting).

The theme from *Love Story* enters my head; always does when romance is in the air. Immediately I picture the two of us walking over golden sands, blistering sun high in the clear blue sky, sea gently lapping at our bare feet (it's the Zola Budd influence again). We've got two children, giggling as they dart in and out of the water trying to avoid the breaking waves of the clear yet warm water. We're in love and the world has suddenly blossomed like the spring snowdrops or daffodils, butterflies or bees. The sailboats and fishermen, things of the sea. 'All Kinds of Everything.' (Dana.) I could never work that line out, 'Things of the sea.' It doesn't even rhyme nicely with 'bees'. Always had it down as a bit of a cop-out line. Anyway, Daphne is my chick. She's my 'thing of the sea'. I'm planning the wedding reception already. I'm lingering on the moment when our lips touch for the first time. That split second when you realize she's surrendering to your charms. Within days we'll be soul mates – I know it.

Mind you, I thought that about Lucille Bullock, a girl who roared very briefly into my life...and then made a sensationally swift exit. I couldn't even claim she was my girlfriend but I fancied her sure enough – as soon as she arrived at the British Potato Marketing Board. She'd got wild blonde hair like one of the girls from the pop group Bananarama. She'd also got a plum job in design, and before lunch-time, I'd got designs on her. I thought I was in for a romance usually reserved for fairy tales and pantomimes.

She was my beauty. I was dead keen on becoming her beast. She was my Goldilocks. I was her...three bears! It never even got off the ground. Dicky Cox told me she was a weirdo. He was right. Lucille flipping Bullock made the national newspapers when she tried to stab the vicar's son with a pair of secateurs.

I knew she was heavily into the Roundheads and the Cavaliers (or as she used to insist, the Royalists and the Parliamentarians). Used to go to all the group meetings and re-enact battles. Anyway, from what we could make out, she went bonkers at an agricultural show in Colchester during a battle re-enactment sketch. She was on a high the week before because she'd landed the role of the Masked Lady (something to do with Lady Fairfax, who was the wife of the chief Roundhead. I never really did get to the bottom of it).

It all happened just yards from the ladies of the Townswomen's Guild. They were busy clearing away after a satisfactory day's work on the white elephant, assorted bric-a-brac and used foreign stamps stall when, out of the blue, the Masked Lady burst out of the battle scene and made straight for the vicar's son crying, 'For my king and country.' He spent four hours in intensive care, and he'd only gone to exhibit his prize-winning marigolds. I never even got to ask her out for a drink.

Daphne's different. Blonde shoulder-length hair, just turned thirty by my reckoning and she has the face of a cherub. Looks as if she's got a bit of Czechoslovakian in her. Mysterious. Shoulders broad, but her eyes are warm and friendly like two chestnuts roasting on an open fire. It's fate. Bloody fate I tell you. This woman stands head and shoulders above Miss Cruise Bore, Mrs Hair Bear Bunch and Mrs Jigsaw Puzzle. I've found the object of my 'Desiree'. The holiday, my little chicken giblets, is just beginning to take shape.

Daphne prospects: she's been around the world and visited every port from Southampton to Singapore. My travel nerves need never surface again. I'd be totally safe and secure in her beautiful hands. Looks as if she's used mild green fairy liquid all her life. Where else would she get hands as soft as those? Maybe her hands have never touched dishes – she might hail from a family of Czechoslovakian big knobs. Lived through the civil unrest of the iron curtain and now looking for a man to put some Weston-Super-Mare into those eastern groins. Daphne plus points: intelligent, beautiful, looking to settle down (OK, I'm guessing but what else do I have to go on after one glance?). Overall mark out of ten: an encouraging eight. If she fancies me it will soon rise to the perfect ten.

If this was *New Faces* (1970s talent show with Derek Hobson, Arthur Askey, Mickey Most and Tony Hatch), she'd have top marks for star quality and presentation. She'd be the new Lenny Henry. If we were ice-skating it would be perfect sixes from the Russian judge, with five point eight and five point nine from the rest of them. Daphne can be my Jayne Torvill. I'll be her Christopher Dean. Together we'll dance the Bolero.

I'm that pleased with myself, I could do a triple salko with a double toe loop over the rocking-chair. She enters, stage right to a ripple of applause. And what a mover. She glides like one of my old Corgi rockets. That's clinched it for me. I knew it from the very moment she came on. It was something in the way she moved that attracted me like no other lover. (Shirley flipping Bassey.)

4

Congratulations Daphne, you've gone straight in at number one.

She's stormed up the hit parade quicker than Musical Youth when they passed the dutchie from the left hand side in September 1982. It's a phenomenal rise from out of nowhere. 'It must be love, love, love.' (Madness.) It is madness as well. I've gone all limp and mushy. I'm withering before her very eyes and she's only halfway towards the overhead projector. Of course, it's far too early to start withering. Besides, I have an appalling track record at these sort of events. I once pooed myself during a slide show at school about fossils. The thought of it still haunts me to this day.

It was all very exciting at first. The science teacher, Mrs Crowe, thought she was breaking new ground when she proudly produced a new fangled machine which automatically slotted the slides into the projector at the flick of a switch from a round circular plastic container perched on the top. Very quickly, things started going wrong. First Mrs Crowe pressed the switch too hard, dropping three slides in quick succession, which meant the picture was out of sync with the commentary. Then I started to get stomach-ache. Before I knew where I was I felt a nasty squelching in my Hong Kong Phooey briefs. Within minutes I had a pair of pants half full of poo. It was one of the most distressing days of all time. I stuck it out for the rest of the lesson but the kids knew someone had started to smell. Even Mrs Crowe looked at me funny when I walked out of the classroom desperately trying to look normal while attempting not to dislodge any of the contents of my already uncomfortable and overloaded underwear. I remember writing in my Soccer Stars diary: 'I think I might have to kill myself.' I'm not expecting to poo myself today, though. And it's wrong to get sidetracked by negative thinking. This is going to be the port enhancement talk to end all port enhancement talks.

My imagination begins to run riot. At the moment, Daphne and I are lolling around in the jacuzzi on the Sunshine Deck without a care in the world. We're head over heels and we don't care who knows it. I throw out an amusing line. She throws her head back with a cute yet controlled burst of laughter before feeding me a section of overripe nectarine.

It reminds me of when I took What's-her-name (my only girlfriend to date, remember) on our first afternoon out – fishing for chub on the River Severn. There I am setting up my carbon fibre rod (a brand new telescopic one, so it was just a case of pulling it out and casting it straight in) when suddenly, playfulness took hold of me and I tossed a wriggling pink maggot into the lap of her skirt. She screamed with delight as I squeezed the last of my lead shot onto the line (three-pound breaking strain because the chub got quite forceful around those parts). Whatever possessed me to act in such a manner I shall never know. But I've marked the episode down as one of my slushiest moments ever. I expect I'll have to go a long way to better it.

I must come clean about What's-her-name, even though it was such a nasty business. Her actual name was Claire, as in 'Clare, the moment I met you, I swear'. (Gilbert O'Sullivan. Her parents were big fans.) She was shorter than me, a little too plump for her own good, with bleached blonde spiky hair. A good catch by anyone's standards, I thought. I was never in love with her. Not in a full on sort of way, I've never really known full on love – it only exists in my wildly romantic fairy tale head. She never said she loved me either. Not once. But she was the first female that ever showed the slightest bit of interest in me so I felt duty bound to ask her to marry me.

And believe me, Claire was no run of the mill, fly by night character. With her, it was access all areas! Unfortunately, sex was never a big selling point for me. I was inexperienced, whereas she'd been a bit of a 'loose drawers Doris' if the rumours were to be believed. Looking back I was on a hiding to nothing. I should have initiated Dicky Cox's 'trump test' from the word go. 'Malcolm,' he used to say. 'There's only one way to sort out the dead certs from the driftwood. Cock your leg up and fart in their face on the first date. If they raise a titter then it's game on. If they squeal like a pig – fuck 'em and forget 'em.'

But I thought she had everything going for her. Imagine little old Spud pulling Britain's finest female Punch and Judy artist – and believe you me, nobody could perform the 'crocodile stealing the sausages' scene with the panache that she achieved underneath that little red-and-white-striped canopy. Apparently she had the perfect fingers for puppetry and, believe me, she knew how to use them. She performed miracles with Old Red Nose (that's what they call him in the Punch and Judy College of Professors – she was a fully paid-up member). Every time we'd finished in between the sheets, I used to look her straight in the eyes (hazel if I remember rightly), and bark out the immortal, yet somehow romantic line: 'That's the way to do it!' She'd look back at me confused yet, I thought, satisfied.

We met on the New Potato Tour of Britain, on an open-topped double-decker. (*Double Decker*s. Another great 1970s television programme... Not such a good chocolate bar.) Together we cruised the length and breadth of the country promoting our home-grown crop. I finally asked her out on a thundery July day. I'll never forget it. We'd pulled up outside one of the big supermarkets in Coventry where she was drafted in to entertain the children. I was head over heels.

Unfortunately, nerves took the better of me on our first date. I couldn't eat my freshly prepared chicken and chips in the basket at the Plough the Fields and Scatter Pub in Rugby. Finished off by throwing it all up in the car park, but she didn't seem to mind. Our first bonk was even more of a nervy affair, but I seemed to get the hang of things as time went on. I don't know to this day whether or not she ever had an orgasm. Never got round to asking the question straight out. On the quiet, I don't think many women do, you know. Anyway, after five short months, the shit hit the fanny.

I could sense something was wrong when she started to get up early on a Saturday morning to queue outside Terry 'T-bone' Taylor's – a local butcher made famous for his award-winning pork and leek sausages and home-made scotch eggs. He had a place next to Flopsy Wright, the travel agent on Tyne Street. I ask you. No self-respecting woman queues outside her 'friendly' butcher's shop at the weekend unless she's got more than half an eye on the minced beef behind the counter. I was even left to prepare my own tongue sandwich.

Don't get me wrong, I enjoy a lean fillet more than anyone, and there's nothing quiet so pleasurable as a bit of stuffing up the parson's snout on a Sunday lunch-time, but I should have smelt a rat. My dad Walter (as in 'Walter, Walter, lead me up the altar') was a connoisseur of the British faggot. When she brought home half a pound of bloody vegetarian faggots I should have realized that the game was up. I mean, vegetarian faggots… It's enough to make a grown man weep.

Not long after that the bombshell dropped. I got her a Punch and Judy gig at the Hamsley High School spring fair. Usual form: white elephant, assorted bric-a-brac, tombola, home-made cakes and, as a big climax, an Irish dancing exhibition from a team of young *Lord of the Dance* hopefuls.

It was blisteringly hot. I remember one of the ladies on the country produce stall had to be treated for sunstroke. Like any self-respecting kettle, I was boiling my head off too. Taylor, the butcher, had put up a well-hung goose for a 'Guess the Weight' competition. While I was fondling his bird for a bit of a flutter, he was doing exactly the same with mine in the little red-and-white-striped canopy attached to the Punch and Judy theatre.

Noticing that there was a gang of fidgeting preschool children sat cross-legged waiting for the show to begin, I made my way round to the slit at the back of the canopy where, quite frankly, my world fell apart. There she was, knickers round her ankles. Terry had got his hands rammed in between bra and breast, and she was loving every second – that's what hurt more than anything. Word has it she even won the well-hung goose that day. She's probably stood behind his counter as we speak, pumping pork and leek into another batch of award-winning sausage skins. The blackboard outside his store boasted: 'It's not the skin, it's the meat you slot in.' Some thought it vulgar.

I slipped away from the sad scene that wretched afternoon – and out of her world. I cried for days. I was under the doctor for a fortnight. He had me on sleeping pills. Margaret and Dicky did their best but I was totally inconsolable. Dicky told me to forget all about her. 'She's a buffet bird,' he said. 'Men just help themselves.'

Thankfully, I'm yanked back to real life with a jolt. Daphne is about to start. And what a start:

'Hello Ladies and Gentlemen, and welcome to my port enhancement talk.'

Here's a lady who certainly knows how to put a sentence together. She'd have no problem in the small-talk stakes. In fact, when she talks, it's like 'Poetry in Motion'. (Johnny Tillotson hit in 1960. Got to the top of the hit parade.)

'Over the next forty minutes, I'm going to show you the ins and outs of Gibraltar – a beacon which divides Europe from Africa and provides the only link between the Atlantic Ocean and the Med.'

She's almost orgasmic in her delivery. The divine Daphne hasn't put a foot wrong. I'm mesmerized. In my eyes, she's more of a dancing divinity than Jessie Matthews would ever be.

'The surrounding landscape is simply riddled with caves and crevasses. It's all nooks and crannies. Over 140 have been discovered so far and tomorrow some of you lucky folk will get a glimpse of just a few of them.'

Bollock me square. She's talking to me. Pound to a pinch of salt I'm one of the lucky folk. I'm about to stare into one of Daphne's famous nooks and crannies. Bound to. As fortune would have it, I'm booked on the trip to the highlights of Gibraltar so I'm bound to get a sniff of St Michael's cave. Daphne says it's a unique auditorium for ballets and concerts. Wait a minute... Concerts. It's just up June's street. She'll probably be there as well, belting out a couple of verses of 'Supercalifragilisticexpialidocious' in honour of her great hero Julie Andrews. She might cramp what little style I have – but then again, she might shift one or two of the hanging stalagmites as well, and that'll be worth the trip money alone.

I've decided June's hyperactive. Shame really because Tom is a sort of hunched but maturing Clark Kent; so meek and mild – never speaks. (I'll try and bring him into the conversation tonight. Question him on his Jessie Matthews collection while he's sat at table 69.)

Our Port Enhancement Beauty gets into full gear. She's off like a steam train, caressing her remote control projector lever to reveal the hidden beauty of the hundred-ton gun and the apes that roam freely in the hills, pinching food. She's certainly no Mrs Crowe in the projector-handling department. In fact, if Daphne had been in charge of our slide show on fossils, I almost certainly wouldn't have pooed myself – I'm sure of it. Wet myself, yes, but that wouldn't have been such a nasty experience. A minor setback, rather than a Brenda Burston-type blow to my youthful upper jaw.

The talk is over and she glides off to the applause of the crowd. Well, there are only about two dozen of us now, and a good fifty per cent of them have fallen asleep halfway through. One old bloke got up just before the finale on the Moorish Castle because he was complaining of hunger pains. He pissed off for afternoon tea in the conservatory. Daphne exits stage left. Suddenly the stage is bare and I'm standing there with emptiness all around.

I'm in a sort of haze as I wander out onto the decks. I'm thinking about my Czechoslovakian willow stick. I should have brought it with me. Dicky Cox gave it me as a present from Prague, where, by all accounts, men use them to wallop the girl of their dreams. It's a great honour for a lady to be beaten by a willow stick over there. The more lashings they receive, the more desirable they are. It's more than acceptable for a young single lady to return home with a back full of whip marks. The beautiful girls get beaten to a pulp while the ugly ones get off scott free. Dicky met a girl with thirty lashes on her back one day. She wasn't that pretty but every time she was hit she would give the bloke a 'special present'. It was her way of keeping up with the Joneses.

I think willow stick beating will catch on in England one day. I certainly treasure mine and long for the day when I can get it out and thrape an unsuspecting maiden for all she's worth. Can you imagine if I'd got it handy today? After the port enhancement talk, I could have marched onto the stage at the Hippodrome Theatre and given Daphne (who I'm convinced is at least three parts Czechoslovakian) a right good old hammering. She'd have fallen for me there and then, while the crowd cheered every strike. As luck would have it, I've left my Czechoslovakian willow stick at home.

Out on the decks, things are beginning to get quite lively. No wonder. The sun's out and it's getting quite hot under the collar. I'll sunbathe for the rest of the afternoon while the servants wait on me in the beer department. I'll just lie down and think of Daphne.

It's actually quite unsettling having these folks wait on you hand and foot (I swear they'd give you the droppings off the end of their nose if you asked them). I've decided I should have been one of life's servers. I'm much happier giving than receiving. Can't stand birthdays and Christmas – much happier on 'ordinary days' when the pressure's not on. Not realizing, I take my plastic glass back to the bar *and* pick up an empty bag of prawn cocktail Hula Hoops to place in the bin. Point proven. I was put on the earth by the good Lord to place other people above myself, and here I am being waited on willy-nilly. Life's all wrong sometimes. (Maybe that's the key; I think I'm worthless. Unworthy of a woman to call my own. In football terms, I'm always two down with ten minutes to go where the opposite sex is concerned.)

No. Don't spoil it. The day has turned out fine. Things are going well, better than I've known them for a while. The crowd on table 69 are interesting and enjoyable; I've found Daphne, the future Mrs Malcolm; I'm in the lap of luxury and the sun is belting down. If this were England, tomorrow's newspapers would call it a 'scorcher'. They'd have a picture of two half-naked lovelies on page five. Thongs and little more.

Daphne in a thong... It's too much to take in. I'll retire to my rocking-chair for a good old-fashioned swing. Anyway, I've got some preparing to do. Tonight is a formal evening. It's all dickie bows and frilly shirts. My dinner suit has been pressed for more than a fortnight. In dickie terms at least, I'm ready and waiting.

My cabin boy Danny, is waiting in the corridor as I get back from a semi-roasting. ('Oh Danny Boy, the pipes, the pipes are calling.') Before long he's brought my double scotch. Tonight could be the night. I'll scour the Monte Carlo Restaurant, pick out Daphne and prepare to pounce. It's going to take a cunning strategy to pull this one off, but I'm good and ready. I'm that full of confidence, I could skin an eel.

En route to the Monte Carlo, I spot the huge behind of Hattie Jacques making off towards Alexander's Bar. I'm amazed at her wide berth. Now there's an animal that would take some skinning. The explorer David Hempleman-Adams could take her on as his next great challenge. The quest to circumnavigate Hattie Jacques' arse in a hot air balloon. I can see the book now: *At the Mercy of the Winds*. I don't want to bump into her again; she pisses me off blind. I overheard her spouting off on my walkabout this morning (at this rate, I could be on course to represent Great Britain in the world eavesdropping championships – I've taken to it like a duck to water). Hattie was harping on to a couple of old-timers. She was telling them about the 'good old days' when her mother used to take her cruising on the old SS *Perfect*. First Class. 'We had six inch shag pile while the commoners had to make do with lino,' she said, adjusting her extra large bikini strap to reveal the full extent of a sunburnt bingo-wing-type upper arm. 'It's not like that today, of course,' she added in her ghastly pomp and circumstance tone. 'It's all shag on this boat.'

I think I'll avoid her. I'm onto the poop deck and up the stairs on the outside of Deck Seven. Good manoeuvre, but then, I was always very agile. Agile yet, by a strange quirk of fate, ungainly into the bargain. A sort of Olga Corbett crossed with Sir Norman Wisdom. ('Don't laugh at me 'cause I'm a fool.') I'm pleased I've taken the scenic route. I stop for a minute to take in the back end of the ship. It's far more beautiful than the back end of Hattie Jacques. I can almost feel my vigour being renewed. For the first time ever, I've got my fist firmly clamped on the udder of life and I'm steering my destiny out of choppy seas and into calm waters.

No wonder I'm buzzing. The SS *Perfect* is at its best from here. A bloody great vessel powering its way through a massive expanse of ocean. Neither sight nor sound of land. A great white froth as far as the eye can see where the *Perfect* has cast aside the so-called dangers of the deep, like a toddler throwing a cuddly clown out of a cot. I'm on the world's most unsinkable ship, I'd put a pound on it. No wonder Leonardo DiCaprio was so taken with the front end of the *Titanic*. It gives you an awesome power surge when you're dangling over the beautifully manicured railings and staring at the sea below. It must be twice as exciting when you're grappling close-up with Kate Winslet's rear end. No wonder he thought he was the king of the flipping world – who wouldn't be?

I wonder. Can love really blossom on board a big ship? Out of the blue, off the cuff. If it can, when's my ship coming in? They say all the nice girls love a sailor, but what happened in the nursery rhyme when a sailor went to sea, sea, sea? I'll tell you what happened. All that he could see, see, see, was the bottom of the deep blue sea, sea, sea. Not so much as a sniff of 'How's your father'. Came back empty-handed.

Rub-a-dub-dub, three men in a tub. There's another disaster. The title indicates some form of homosexual activity on board. The butcher was probably the life and soul of the party. Terry bloody Taylor all over again. But why was he shacked up in a friendly threesome with a baker and a candlestick maker? In a tub? The whole scenario seems a little far-fetched to me.

What about Bobby Shafto? He went to sea with silver buckles on his knee, but he had to come back before the girl would marry him – it says so in the rhyme. No love on the ocean wave for him. But then, what did he expect wearing silver buckles on his knees? (Plenty of shafting when Shafto returned if the girl in question is to be believed, but again, no fun when he was afloat.)

The Owl and the Pussycat. Here's a sure-fire banker. They went to sea in a beautiful pea-green boat. And they were definitely in love. Took the pig's ring from out of his nose and were married next day by the turkey who lived on the hill. How a pussy shags an owl I shall never know. And what do they produce? A pussy that cries 'T-wit T-woo'? Come to think of it, Dicky Cox once dated a girl with a singing pussy. Used to open her legs and perform 'Pearl's a Singer' by Elkie Brooks. She was quite a lady. Word had it, she could blow out all the candles on a birthday cake in one go – using her vagina! Performed it in front of an enthralled crowd at her granddad's seventieth party. Dicky was there to witness it with his own eyes. He's a great man is my mate Dicky – you could write a book on him.

No. The owl and the pussycat have proved my point. The rubber ring of true love *can* float happily on the deep blue sea. Daphne's my owl and I'm her pussycat. I can see it now. I'll be stood here on the railings before too long looking up to the stars above and singing with my small guitar:

'O lovely Pussy, O Pussy, my love,
What a beautiful Pussy you are, you are, you are
What a beautiful Pussy you are.'

5

I'm stunned.

Malcolm's Log. It's Saturday, June 21st. Day three on
Perfect. First I find Daphne. Then, for the first time, I
experience the delights of an Orgasm, a real home-
made Orgasm. Then sadly, out of the blue, just when it
was all starting to look so good, things turned terribly
ugly on table 69. Let me explain...

After my tremendous boost from the port enhancement talk, I was on a roll. I was into my dinner jacket
and away for a formal evening in the Monte Carlo.
Avoiding Hattie Jacques and bursting onto Deck Seven, I
stopped for a quick one in Alexander's Bar. That's where
I had my first Orgasm. The whole ship's potty about
them. It's a cocktail: Amaretto, Kahlua and Baileys given
a good shake over ice and strained into a glass. Beautiful.
I had two – one after the other. For the first time in my
life, I know what it's like to have a multiple Orgasm, and
I hadn't so much as laid a finger on the banana-flavoured
condoms.

I'd planned the evening to perfection. I was cock-
sure I'd bump into Daphne in the restaurant. If not
there, I'd decided to make a beeline for the Golden
Penny Arcade. I'd gone through it time and time again
in my head. She'd be down to her last token when I'd

stretch over, deposit a golden nugget into her empty slot and – jackpot! Three cherries in a row. That was the plan – fail safe – but I hadn't accounted for the bombshell in the Monte Carlo Restaurant, which knocked me completely off my stride. Well, it would anybody. It all began to take a downward plunge when I took matters into my own hands on the 'let's break the ice' front. It backfired big style…

'Evening June,' I said, deciding it was my turn to take a firm hold on proceedings. 'This is your *Sound of Music* starter for ten and *no* conferring.' I realized immediately that I was beginning to sound like Bamber Gascoigne, but I surged on nevertheless. 'According to the song, finely penned I might add, a batty bint of a nun climbed a tree and scraped her knee.' For a moment I'd captured everyone's imagination. I was peforming well. 'She also danced on her way to mass and whistled on the stair,' I added teasingly. Here comes the best bit, I thought to myself about to deliver the question. 'But what did she have underneath her wimple?'

'Curlers in her hair,' bellowed Mouthy.

Sod him, the bloody loud-mouthed git. He'd even got the cheek to wear a white tuxedo and black sparkling dickie. Looked as if he didn't care who he trampled on.

June sat stunned. She'd known the answer, but the loud one had stolen her thunder and I sensed her mood of despair, like losing the cup final on penalties after the opposing team had equalized in injury time. Awkward silence. Kenneth the Weasel Man intervened, his two index fingers aloft. He was off again: ' "I'm gonna wash that man right out of my hair." ' How a line from *South Pacific* was going to save the day at that crucial stage I shall never know. And it didn't. Things were bad – and got worse. Far, far worse.

'We're swingers you know.'

Knockers, knickers, knackers, clackers. June, thinking that I was now her bosom buddy, decided that, after knowing me for just two nights, she was going to bend over and reveal her darkest sexual secret with a crafty whisper in my right ear. Swingers. June and Tom. Of all people. I blame the system. It's all to do with the lack of sex education in schools. No wonder the over-forties have turned out so badly. They were brought up on Janet and John and the Woodentops. A recipe for sexual mayhem.

She hardly strikes me as a sex queen. All fidgety and spindly, she reminds me more of a twiglet. And she's got a face like a radish; always flushed. She'd be well suited as the new face of 'Permaglow'. She's a devotee of Julie Andrews, and on top of that, she seems such a well-to-do lady, always hyper with her fast talking yet slightly squeaky just-outside-Luton accent (every sentence finishing with a laugh).

Couldn't have heard her right, I thought. I took stock and looked again. She smiled a knowing smile, then gently touched the top of my thigh. I could feel myself suddenly jerk – an involuntary reaction born out of both surprise and anticipation.

'It all started when we joined the naturist club at Saggy Bottom,' she explained. 'It's only two and a half miles from where we live, and it's run by a lovely couple – Maureen and Ben Dover. We only did it to bring Tom out of himself. It seemed a good idea at first, you know, as these things do. Then one thing led to another and suddenly we were in full swing with a couple from the former Soviet state of Lapvia.'

Oh Christ Al-flipping-mighty. I bloody did hear right. June and Tom. Swingers. They take part in these no holds barred, all-in bonking affairs with any old Tom, Dick or Harry. Mrs Julie Andrews and Mr Sonny Bono let it all hang out in group sex sessions. Oh My Sweet Lord. (The late, great George Harrison.) The thought of Tom's Dick while Harry has it away with his missus. Anyway, she meant Latvia – but I was too dumbstruck to put matters right at the time. Unless she was on about Lapland. No, too cold for sexual activity of the group nature. Besides, it's the home of Father Christmas, and I can't see him and Mrs Christmas getting it on with Rudolf and Mrs Red-nosed Reindeer.

Panic sets in on two accounts. Count A: Latvia! Of all places. The country that once elected a potato as its president. Based on that fact alone, I had them down as fine, upstanding folk. Count B: and far more crucial to my mind. Did she tell me because she wanted me to get involved in her dirty tricks campaign? Andy and Alfred, the two puffs arrived – just in time.

'You've missed *South Pacific*,' I told them hurriedly.

'Oh,' said Alfred, before bursting into song. Half decent voice as well: ' "Some enchanted evening, you may see a stranger, across a crowded room." '

Damn me, they're all at it. Everyone wants to shag a stranger tonight. I tried to calm myself down. Alfred was just getting into the spirit of things. After all, this is the Magic of the Musicals theme cruise and most of the Monte Carlo Dining-room had just returned from a Norman DeVine whistle-stop tour through the wonders of *Seven Brides for Seven Brothers*. There you are again. I'll bet they were all at it. Different brides bonking different brothers. They didn't sing 'Bless Your Beautiful Hide' for nothing you know. Filth.

What about Mrs Hair Bear Bunch? She's probably having it off with both Muppets (hope she keeps her wig on for sex). She's already confessed to knocking around with one of the extras from *Fiddler on the Roof*. No wonder he danced at the alehouse just before the first daughter married Motel the bloody tailor. He'd probably just had a session with the queen of the cotton wool hair and half the Russian Communist Army.

Well bugger me. I was beginning to think the unthinkable. Maybe this musicals business is just a cover-up for the 'Tits Out for the *Titanic* Swingers Club'. Lord heaven above and help us. I tried keeping my end up. I tried to pretend nothing had happened; it's called a stiff upper lip.

Roger the Waiter galloped up to the table. He had a new mate to help him – Donald. He wasn't as confident as Roger, looked a little downtrodden (shades of Manuel in *Fawlty Towers*). Mouthy does his best to crack a gag every time the pair of them appears – and he's particularly keen on Marlene. Lovely girl, serves wine and remembers everybody's name. As for me, after the June scandal, the evening went by in a cloudy haze. The thought of her going at it hammer and tongs with a lusty Latvian was just too much to bear. To make matters worse, I think the puffs had had a row. Alfred had a face like a fiddle.

For safety's sake, I concentrated on Kenneth and his 'blowing the recorder with his nose' world record. Thirty-six hours apparently on one of the main streets in Shirehampton near Pill, Somerset. He told me that Pill is the home of the Wurzels' longest serving member and, as a tribute, Kenneth had ended his marathon stint with a medley of Wurzels classics (well, they were the kings of pitchfork pop in the 1970s). He started off with 'I've Got a Brand New Combine Harvester', and by the time he'd got to 'The Blackbird Song', the gathered crowd were in raptures. All the local papers covered it. Amazing really, I could only ever play one tune on my recorder: a dodgy rendition of 'London's Burning', and I sent the house mad trying to get it just right.

'I'm going to have a crack at playing the clarinet next – through my bottom,' said Kenneth looking rather pleased with himself. I don't know if he's serious or not. It looked as if he was. 'I'm already halfway through "Stranger on the Shore". If I can perfect it, they've offered me a slot on television. You know, *Don't Try This At Home*. You see Martin,' he continued, ' "Music was my first love. And it shall be my last." '

We sang together (anything to lighten the table 69 mood): ' "Music of the future. And music of the past." ' (John Miles.)

My porc à la Normande went down a treat. Mouthy Kevin and Kiss Me Kate had grilled whole trout with almonds and nut-brown butter. June went for the coq au vin. A thought raced through my head. One more day at sea and then these barmy buggers would be let loose on Gibraltar. I hoped they'd locked up their sons, daughters – and monkeys. Of course, Mouthy knew Gibraltar like the back of his hand. Been there a dozen times, had close personal friends in all the best haunts and 'wouldn't touch one of those lousy tours. Me and the Mrs are doing it our own way.' Kate looked into his eyes adoringly. You could tell she was clearly besotted by the loud one. But then, what did I know? After all, anything could happen after June and Tom's rocket. It's made me question my judgement. Kate's probably shagged the whole of the Barnsley football team – and the kit manager's wife.

Hang on, she was about to let fly with her maiden speech of the voyage. God help her, and all who sail in her.

'Kevin raises a lot of money for charity through the badminton club. He loves his badminton, don't you love.'

For the first time on table 69, Kevin proudly nodded and kept his gob shut. He knew he was on for a compliment.

'He's won trophies galore. Got a special set of drawers for his shuttlecock.'

Hardly an earth-shattering opener from Kiss Me Kate, but I was grateful for any tiny morsel to deflect from the swingers' stunner. She wasn't finished by a long stretch; went on to give us a mini lecture on how Mouthy Kevin had made a fortune from manure management. In terms of well-rotted horse dung, there was no one to touch him north of the Watford Gap. By then the evening was slowly turning into a shambles. Here was the score so far: Tom and June are swingers; Mouthy Kev is a manure management entrepreneur who keeps his shuttlecock in a special set of drawers; and Kenneth the Weasel Man is trying to get on the television by playing the clarinet with his arse.

I decided to switch off and concentrate on Daphne. I'm convinced she'll be my tour guide in Gibraltar. We could both sit on the cliff top tossing Walkers Salt and Vinegar Crisps to the hungry apes. This time I was ready for love. Well, I thought I was. I'd only ever romped with What's-her-name. Oh, I'd almost dabbled with a small mousy-haired thing at sixth form college who fantasized about having oral sex with a giraffe, but that hadn't gone anywhere. In my view, she was a raving nutter. Then of course, I'd fancied the loopy Roundhead that flipped with the secateurs. That's it in a nutshell. The sad and sorry tale of my love life. Just goes to show, sex with a spud doesn't work.

The thought of dating Daphne kept me company for the rest of the night, but she was nowhere to be seen on board. So much for me trying to fill her slot in the Golden Penny. I even checked the Paradise Ballroom. Nothing. Only Stoop and Droop dancing the quickstep, which was quite a feat considering there's hardly an ounce of movement in the pair of them (it's more like the soft shoe shuffle). Mrs Hair Bear Bunch was also a keen fan of ballroom dancing by the looks of things. She'd taken the two Muppets through the waltz and the military two-step before they'd all settled down for an orange juice. No sign of an Orgasm for those three. They were poised like coiled cobras in wild anticipation of the Gay Gordons.

Ballroom dancing. It was pure comedy. Half a dozen hapless couples having a go at the Mayfair quickstep. I'm sure one bloke got his Mayfair mixed up with his Old Kent Road. He didn't know what day of the week it was. Another young lady was at sixes and sevens as the tempo quickly switched to a number one. She was so stiff, it looked like she was dancing with a number two lodged in her pants. Another old-timer was slumped over the shoulder of his younger partner. Full marks for spirit. He had death written all over his face, yet he was still dancing.

It was a dance floor disaster, but unwittingly, the two left feet brigade gave me the best titter I'd had in a long time. I was starting to loosen up, I could sense it. All the same, I didn't hang around too long at the doors of the Paradise, for fear of a repeat of what had happened earlier in the day when I was spotted trying to get a furtive peak at the line dancers. So, despite the slim chance of bumping into the delightful Daphne, I decided to give up on the whole sordid affair.

But even in the middle of the night, I found myself tossing and turning as the wardrobes begin to creak again. June and Tom. Swingers. The thought just would not budge from my brain. And as for the rest of them, it simply doesn't bear thinking about. Thankfully, morning broke. (No wonder Cat Stevens made his name singing about it. Sometimes the break of a new day can be a welcome relief.) I opened the curtains that had been hurriedly thrown over the picture window the night before. Beautiful view. More sea. That brings me up to date...

...And I'm still stunned.

Oh Danny Boy delivers the *Nautical Newsletter* and oatmeal biscuits. At least you can rely on some things in life. He's always there, on the stroke of 6.30 a.m. It says in the newsletter that it's still not too late to join Nicola's Handicrafts Club and take home a lasting souvenir of your trip to sea. *Découpage* is suddenly starting to sound like a safe option. Especially when you consider that tonight it's the Captain's Ball.

Reminds me of Dicky Cox. Whenever he was on a promise with sexy Sandra on reception, he'd sidle up to me with a smug look and declare, 'It's on! Tonight. Me and Sand. Big Ball at Beaver Castle.' It was his way of telling me he was getting his leg over and he'd follow through with one of his snorting laughs. If he came in the following morning singing 'Down at the Old Bull and Bush', I knew he'd been there (or thereabouts).

Dicky has many claims to fame: *Celebrity Squares*, *Sale of the Century* and his mate who reckons he's found a unicorn frolicking around on the wooded hills of Finland. He also boasts about his brush with the tiny weightlifter, Precious McKenzie (Bantamweight Commonwealth gold medallist three times. I think he also struck gold in the Commonwealth flyweight division in 1974). By all accounts, Dicky once saw Precious McKenzie lift Frank Bough over his head in a BBC bar. I said it couldn't happen on account of the fact that Frank Bough looked a big bloke. But if Dicky said he saw it with his own eyes, you couldn't really dispute it. He prides himself on his honesty. 'Honest Dicky, the punter's pal – that's me,' he used to say. Reminded me of his truthfulness at least three times a day.

Oh well, never mind the Captain's Ball. Without doubt, the highlight of my 'Day at Sea' is going to be the port enhancement talk on Propriano. Delightful Daphne is at it again, unlocking the hidden jewels of the Gulf of the Valinco and one of Corsica's most important sailing harbours. It's wetting my appetite just reading about it in the *Nautical Newsletter*.

I can't get to breakfast quickly enough. And this morning, I'm joined by a new pair. Rosemary and Roger who run a ferret rescue centre on the outskirts of Reading. It's called The Berkshire Ferret Welfare Group. They hand me a leaflet. It's a new organization aimed at the sole purpose of ferret welfare.

'Didn't Richard Whiteley once have his finger severed by one of those buggers?' I ask, in between mouthfuls of brown toast, sausage, bean and egg yolk (I never eat the white of an egg; never have and never will).

'Yes, but they've had a terrible press,' replies Rosemary, concerned. 'We've had Tyson for fourteen years. He's a champion racer. Would have competed in Europe but he trapped his tail in the pipe at his last big meeting. As long as they're castrated and rubbed constantly with oil, they're no trouble.'

I wished they'd done that to Terry 'T-bone' Taylor twenty years ago. Then the vegetarian faggot-making wank-stain might not have stolen my girl. (I wonder if June was covered in ferret oil when the lusty Latvian was preparing to swoop on her crisp apple strudels.) It says in the leaflet that ferrets are intelligent, extremely playful, very clever, never dull, easily trained, clean, fun to be with, mischievous and they don't sweat – they just pant. I'll use that description if I ever sink to the depths of a lonely-hearts advert.

Roger and Rosemary run their own boarding-house for absent ferret owners.

'It's like a five star hotel,' says Roger, who's hopelessly dressed considering we're in the Mediterranean. He's wearing a thick knitted navy sweater. Underneath you can just make out the collar of a grubby magnolia and pink marble effect shirt. He smells of stale ferret.

'The little darlings live like kings and queens when they come and stay with us,' says Rosemary, insisting I get the low-down on her animal hotel. 'They've even got their own swimming pool with diving board.'

It doesn't take me long to realize that Roger and Rosemary have what appears to be an unhealthy obsession with ferrets. They even trade in ferret clothes.

'It's the latest thing,' explains Roger. 'Tuxedos, top hats, commando jackets with matching rucksacks, cowboy hats, even Santa suits for the festive ferret. And sleeping sacks for when they go to bed. We've got sixteen ferrets in all, including Pip and Squeak who we show. The ferret is the pet of the millennium.'

Despite their incessant ferret talk (and, of course, Roger's smell) these two are a nice couple. Besides, I think they take pity on me and, call me quirky if you like, receiving sympathy has always been a favourite pastime of mine. They've invited me to be their guest at the Captain's Ball later on and Rosemary says I could even adopt a ferret. Esmerelda gave birth to nine kits just before they left.

Slowly my mind is becoming less muddled. In the words of the great Johnny Nash, 'I can see clearly now the rain has gone.' When I get home to lovely Lichfield, home of the Lady Rosetta (beautiful little number of a spud with red skin, pale yellow flesh and a pleasing flavour), I'll be either porking Daphne, or on a promise with a castrated ferret called Malcolm. My fate, it seems, lies with the sea gods.

I'm still considering my options after breakfast. My shorts are on and I'm pointing my face sunward in a desperate attempt to get some colour before the port enhancement talk. Fortunately for me, Stoop and Droop are sat within eavesdropping distance. Droop (face like a shire horse) is lecturing Stoop (bent double; resembles Albert Steptoe) on the ups and downs of ailments. I just caught the back end of Mrs Freakley who'd 'had it all taken away down below'. Now, the conversation has moved on to warts.

'They've always been a mystery to me. A law unto themselves. I was covered. Thirty-nine warts spread over two hands,' says Droop.

I've heard of the thirty-nine steps, now I'm going to get chapter and verse on the thirty-nine warts, and I can't wait.

'I tried all sorts of cures. The butcher told me to rub a bit of steak on them, bury the meat and when it went rotten the warts would fall off. Didn't work. Before the steak went off, it was dug up by the dog next door. Then I tried nailing a snail to a tree – nothing. It was just an old wives' tale. I washed them in the morning dew, put a stone in a matchbox and threw it over my shoulder, rubbed them with silver... Still nothing. The old man didn't touch me for months.'

Stoop intervenes. 'It depends on the warts really. You get flat warts, common warts and viral warts. All different. Anyway, I was always told to stick a pin in the wart, then put the same pin in an ash tree while singing, "Ashen tree, Ashen tree, pray buy these warts from me." '

'Cobblers!' barks Droop (she's the more forceful one of the pair). 'In the end I found Albert the "wart charmer". Marvellous, he was. Just looked at my hands and mumbled a sort of spell. They'd all gone within three days. People came from miles to see him. Some thought he was a witch. Snuffed it in the end and took his wart charming secrets to the grave.'

'Whooping cough!' interrupts Stoop. (They're challenging for valuable talk-time.) Droop looks bewildered, but there's no stopping her fired-up friend. 'They used to say the cure for whooping cough was to sit on a donkey with your face to its tail, and eat a roasted hedgehog.'

It's interesting stuff and has helped to pass a good thirty minutes (although I couldn't work out why Droop nailed a defenceless snail to a tree to rid herself of warts. As for the poor donkey and roasted hedgehog, words fail me).

It's funny but, at home, I'd never dream of 'tuning in' to two old dears rabitting on. I'm in a world of my own most of the time. In fact, I rarely talk to a soul. I reckon, in this day and age, people only make an effort to talk to you if they want something out of you. Being friendly has gone right out of the window. Making conversation is now called networking, and the art is to squeeze the last drop of blood out of everyone you talk to. If they're of no use, you cut and run.

I'm of little use to anyone on the networking front, so I never attract much interest. If I'm at a function, people ask my name, then my job...and then they piss off within ninety seconds when they realize I've got nothing else to say. I dream of being able to hold court, of having a small group hang on my every word, but I don't think I've got it in me. My diabolical ability in the small-talk stakes buggers me up every time. Only a fool breaks my ninety-second rule.

On a cruise, it's different. If you're not listening to someone else, there's an endless stream of folk wanting to have a natter with you. There's nothing else to do unless you're into bridge, line dancing or *découpage*. Study the evidence for yourself. There's been Stoop and Droop, the matching couple, Mrs Hair Bear Bunch and her two elderly gents, Roger and Rosemary the ferret pair, Alfred and Andy on table 69 along with Kenneth the Weasel Man, June and Tom the swingers, Mouthy Kev and his wife Kiss Me Kate. I've got more friends than I've ever had in my life and I've not even been on board two full days yet. And sure enough, just to prove my point, it happens again. Before I've had chance to smear myself with my complimentary bottle of suntan oil, I'm caught by another conversation seeker. She's got me. Hook, line and sinker.

'Hello. Is your wife sitting there?'

She's a slightly built lady. I saw her coming from the starboard side of the SS *Perfect*. Within seconds she's introduced herself as Alison. And I've explained that she can lie there if she wants to because there is no wife.

Alison sits beside me on the poop deck. The sunbeds are laid out in a neat line, the waiters are poised and raring to serve. For a moment I consider her as a wife contender. But she's got too much of a pointed head. Looks like one of the goblins in a Noddy book. I wonder if she was born with pointed features or if she just began to develop them over a period of time. It might be a disease. One day she could wake up to find out she's turned into a spike. I'll call her Mrs Cocktail Stick, and enter her in the Log. Shagability: one. There's every chance she could break in half. Overall mark out of ten: two and three quarters. She picked the extra up because she could see I was in no mood for romance, and therefore, she quickly turned the conversation round to doll's houses.

Mrs Cocktail Stick is a miniaturist. Apparently, these are people who spend all their money on collecting doll's house furniture. She tells me she's just finished building her own Victorian cottage out of MDF. All she needs now is a thunder-box for the back.

'Thunder-box?' I ask, trying to keep the conversation flowing.

'Yes,' giggles Mrs Cocktail Stick. 'It's what they used to call their shit-houses in the olden days. Victorian women used to swear by an hour on the thunder-box after a day's hop picking. You must have heard of it.'

Shit-houses! She's turned out to be quite a game old bird, Mrs Cocktail Stick. I can tell she's desperate for a holiday romance, but I can't possibly take her seriously as a wife contender. I've got Daphne to think about. And there's still the burning issue of Tom and June nagging away at the back of my mind. I'm getting nervous about our first port stop as well. Just when I'm getting used to life on board a cruise liner, the bloody thing has to pull in to port and I'm faced with yet more problems: What does a tour consist of? Who will I sit next to? (*Please* let it be Daphne.) At least they deal in English pounds in Gibraltar. That means I don't have to confront those miserable bleeders on reception to hand over my travellers cheques.

And another thing. I haven't come into contact with any children yet on this boat. Are they confined to their cabins because it's a Magic of the Musicals themed trip (codeword for sex-crazed swingers)? It reminds me of a scene from *Chitty Chitty Bang Bang* when the love interest, Truly Scrumptious, turns to Professor Potts after his car has landed in Vulgaria. 'But there are no children here,' she says as Jeremy and Jemima scarper into Benny Hill's toy shop only to fall prey later on to the most evil man of the century – the Child Catcher.

I'm heading for the port enhancement talk humming 'Hush-a-Bye Mountain' as a tribute to Chitty. This is going to be a good day, but I'll make it a priority before we dock at the rock. I'll make sure I find the children.

Soon it's time for the main item on today's agenda. Daphne is about to slap it on the table with her talk on the joys of Corsica, and I'm out for a front row seat again. Preferably the same seat as yesterday. I'm quite superstitious in that way.

It's getting warmer as well. A clutch of old fogies has nabbed the sun-loungers on Deck Seven and they're clearly getting set for a day in the sun (don't care about skin cancer these lot, they've lived through the Normandy Landings). The matching couple are also poolside in identical floral swimwear. Him in skimpy trunks. Her in beached whale-type full-on bathing suit. After the port enhancement talk, I'll lie in front of the terrace pool and watch them all while getting pleasantly pissed. I wonder what colour pants Daphne's got on today. Red – bound to be – and thongs into the bargain. I've grown quite fond of the thought of Daphne's thongs. Phew! What a scorcher.

'Play it cool,' I think, as Daphne makes her way to centre stage at the Hippodrome Theatre. I'm not going to push it. I'm going to let it happen naturally. Anyway, she's bound to be at the Captain's Ball tonight, looking for some handsome hunk to sweep her off her feet during the gentlemen's excuse me, so it's a good job I've packed an extra dickie.

Almost the same two dozen have assembled including Miss Cruise Bore with her 'I'm riding along on the crest of the wave' T-shirt. Probably the only ride she's ever had. (And anyway, didn't cropped sleeves go out in the seventies?) Wait a minute. Mrs Cocktail Stick is a late entry. Hope she's not going to turn into my stalker after one brief encounter on the poop deck.

Daphne begins. Propriano is an ideal bridge between the beaches and the mountains. Sounds a bit too much like Lyme Regis to me. Anyway, I'm hungry. It's Saturday dinner-time and I could murder a tongue sandwich. Daphne stops for a second. She looks straight into my eyes and smiles. I smile back, although rather hesitantly – maybe our minds were locked simultaneously in a tongue-sandwich type of moment. My heart skips a beat, I'm starting to perspire. It's all happening just the way I'd dreamed. I don't want to speak too soon, but I think I've pulled the port enhancement girl. It looks very much as if Daphne is mine for the taking, and I've done it without even flashing my willow stick. Amazing, when you think about it.

I spend the whole afternoon waiting for the evening to begin. I'm fifteen and a half years old again, but this time I'm on the starting blocks, ready for my great love journey to begin. Stand aside Brenda Burston, I'm getting ready to burst out of my sexual shell – and it's long overdue.

Back in my cabin, I'm still in high spirits, leaping around the room like a gazelle. I even spray deodorant around my groin. I brought it especially for the trip along with the banana-flavoured condoms. 'Sea breeze' it says on the can. I'm not sure. Smells more like sea*weed* to me.

Table 69 is in full swing. On second thoughts, I'd better not use that phrase after the revelations of the night before. I've decided to put the antics of June and Tom behind me for a while and go all out to woo the woman of my dreams. Nothing's going to sidetrack me tonight. I'm focused. I'm blinkered like a well-trained thoroughbred about to dart out of the stalls at Sandown Park. In musical terms, 'This is the Moment.' (Dr Jeckyll and Mr Hyde.)

The puffs are back on form. Alfred's moaning about the keenness of the cabin stewards: 'I only went for a poo and bugger me, he'd come in to turn down the bed sheets. Well, there was Andy stark bollock naked, going over my two-piece with his travel iron. You can't imagine what I thought when I heard the pair of them squealing like castrated voles!

I just had enough time to yank down my winceyette; still got half a roll of toilet paper jammed up my arse.'

According to Alfred, Andy is obsessed with ironing. He's a fully paid-up member of the Extreme Ironing Club. That means he takes his ironing board to some remote far-off place: up a mountain, on the piste or on a white water raft and does his ironing. It's the missing link between household chores and dangerous sports.

'He's a thrill seeker, through and through,' Alfred explains. 'He once pressed a dozen shirts and four pairs of slacks while mounting Everest. He got the bloody board out halfway up, then suddenly produced a tin of spray starch. They still talk about it at the Extreme Ironing council meetings. His main ambition is to get it up on the Great Wall of China. Imagine that. They'd see his ironing board from the moon.'

June tries to switch the conversation to the musical *Brigadoon*, but Kenneth's getting overexcited at the far side of the table. He almost loses his teeth for the umpteenth time when he proudly boasts to Mouthy Kev that he was once auditioned to play the role of James Onedin in *The Onedin Line*. How they chose the dashing Peter Gilmore over Kenneth the Weasel Man I shall never know.

'Just think Kelvin. I could've got my hands on Annie Webster's crow's nest.'

'It's Kevin, you daft prat,' retorts the loud one. It's a bit harsh in my opinion, but it's comforting to know Mouthy Kev has a contender in the 'seen it, done, it, got the T-shirt' category.

The conversation has turned to holidays of the past. It always does when you're away from home in a crowd. First, there's a graphic account of when Alfred took Andy up the Arc de Triomphe. Then it's Andy's turn. 'We once had a holiday in Austria,' he says.

Kenneth's gone quiet. Austria reminds him too much of *The Sound of Music* and the low point in his chequered acting career when he wanted to be the Captain and ended up playing an amateur Nazi. Andy's ploughing on down the Austrian route.

'I got the ironing board out halfway up the Schattberg and Alfred had a blow on one of those Alpine Horns. You know, the big long things. Couldn't get a note out of it could you love? I told him at the time, you're hardly a "Little Boy Blue"! Now, he *was* a horn blower. Legendary!'

I'd never considered Little Boy Blue as a gay icon, but I suppose it's obvious when you think about it.

Andy starts to recite the nursery rhyme: ' "Little Boy Blue, come blow your horn. The sheep's in the meadow, the cow's in the corn." ' He's rudely interrupted by Kate who's extolling the virtues of Doris Day in *Calamity Jane*. Kenneth raises his fingers. I'm braced for a burst of the 'Black Hills of Dakota', perhaps 'Windy City' or even 'Once I Had a Secret Love'. But no. Should've guessed.

' "Oh, the deadwood stage is a-rolling on over the plains," ' he begins, but we're all struggling for the second line. June saves the day, galloping ahead like Champion the bloody Wonder Horse. She squeals: ' "Whip crack away! Whip crack away! Whip crack away!" '

I'm galloping through my baked fillet of red snapper wrapped in parma ham. For me, the main event of the evening, my lords, ladies and gentlemen, is about to begin. The Captain's Ball. It's my big chance. In the blue corner, Mr Potato Head, sent crashing to the canvas in his last bout after a savage Mr Punch and a crushing upper-cut from a well-hung goose. Record: one encounter, one miserable defeat. In the Kerr's Pink corner, delightful Daphne. Well-travelled, sophisticated, possibly half-Czech blonde bombshell, yet warm and friendly in the eye department. Seconds out. Round one. Malcolm, you shall go to the ball.

I wonder why they call a dance a 'ball'. I must look into it when I get home. Ball research. It's an absolute must. Surely the most famous of them all was Cinderella's. She lost her glass slipper there. It's fairy godmother talk for losing your virginity. You ask anyone in fairyland. It's even in the fairy godmother handbook and every self-respecting wand-waving wench reads that. The entry goes something like this: 'V for Virginity. The loss of virginity is often referred to as losing one's glass slipper. (See also Cinderella.)' That's why she lost track of the time. She failed to notice it was near midnight because Prince Charming was giving *her* a pumpkin (if you see what I mean). By the time she looked at the clock, she'd well and truly lost her 'glass slipper' – the handsome prince had got his sticky fingers on it.

If I can think of ten famous balls before I reach the Paradise Ballroom, then tonight I'm going to lose my glass slipper...to Daphne. (I know I'm not technically a virgin, but it's the same sort of thing.) Alan Ball (footballer with squeaky voice); Kenny Ball (and his Jazzmen); Bobby Ball (comedian with red braces; one half of Cannon and Ball; *Rock on, Tommy!*); Michael Ball ('Love, love changes everything'); Lucille Ball (Star of *I Love Lucy* with Desi Arnez); 'The Ugly Bug Ball' (I'm starting to struggle now and I'm in the lift. Not long left); Screwball (it's an ice-cream).

Balls. I'm three short and I'm in sight of the double doors that lead to the Paradise Ballroom. I can hear the resident band playing 'Tie a Yellow Ribbon Round the Old Oak Tree'. The din is becoming louder. Andy and Alfred are lurking just outside. They're probably waiting to make a big entrance.

'Hello boys, big night tonight.'

'Oh yes,' says Alfred. 'I simply adore balls.'

Andy butts in excitedly. 'I don't know if it's me, but the Captain's Balls seem to get bigger every year. How he does it I shall never know.'

Alfred, determined to retake centre stage, swiftly takes me to one side. 'Andy's got three you know.'

I'm puzzled.

'Balls, love. He's got three bollocks,' Alfred's determined to tell the story. 'He's well known for it in Brighton. They call him a miracle of modern science. Andrew and his famous bollocks. They all talk about it on the south coast.'

That's it then. Andy's three famous balls, added to my seven makes ten. By an extraordinary stroke of good fortune, my glass slipper is as good as lost.

6

So, Andy's got three bollocks! It's only just started to sink in, but it soon sinks out again as the atmosphere of the ball starts to take me up a couple of notches on the romance-o-meter. In fact, it's simply oozing love in the Paradise Ballroom. In the words of the song, 'The balls are swinging, for me and my girl.' (Or was that the bells are ringing? Same difference.)

It's not a bad place either. I was a bit on edge following my disastrous door-hovering display during the line-dancing session, but I shouldn't have worried. The Paradise Ballroom, when bathed in half-light, is quite a classy joint. They've certainly come a long way since the days of the Wheeltappers and Shunters Social Club. It's all greens in here. Lime green on the skirting, frog green on the walls, pastel green shag pile on the floors and pea green on the ceilings. (I once had a poem printed in *Look-In* magazine entitled, 'Watching my dad shell the peas.' It was one of my greatest triumphs. I won a leather briefcase.) Above the dance floor hangs a giant mirror-ball adding that extra bit of sparkle to what's an already glittering occasion.

No sooner am I through the door than I'm offered a stiff one on the house. The agenda of the evening seems to be gin and tonic, whisky and dry, or orange juice. Alison (a.k.a. Mrs Cocktail Stick) is on the floor already. She's attempting the foxtrot with a man who's far too flabby for his own good.

Got to be twenty stone if he's a pound. Mrs Cocktail Stick stumbles for a moment and then giggles. I think she's just hit it off with a new holiday romance, and he's the Pillsbury Dough Man. Strange that, when you consider that Mrs Cocktail Stick is an ardent miniaturist. I wonder if he's aware of her tiny thunder-box.

Mrs Hair Bear Bunch is also tripping the light fantastic. By the looks of things, she's a ballroom dancing fanatic. Tonight she's taking it in turns with her two Muppet escorts from the Bloxwich Musical Society. Turns out she's quite a dear old wench. When she's not fiddling with herself on the roof, she sells the Salvation Army newspaper *The War Cry* on the corner of Cradley Heath market every Saturday morning. She may have the wig from hell but she's obviously got a good turn of wrist for tambourine playing. She hasn't got a bad turn of foot either. Like a swan with a poor hairpiece, she scampers effortlessly across the dance floor as the foxtrot turns into the Gay Gordons. (Dicky Cox gets a big ball at Beaver Castle. I get the Gay Gordons at the Captain's Ball. There's no justice in this life.) Her two Muppets, eager for a slice of the action, are trailing well behind.

There are still one or two stragglers on the floor, but overall, it's a display far removed from the shambles of the other night – a complete turnaround. Perhaps too polished in some areas. One couple are showing off rotten! Look at them. Mr and Mrs *Come Dancing* Latin American regional finalists 1978. Mind you, they are attracting some very envious glares as they make their way through a stunning rumba. She's very precise and directional in her movements. He thinks he's Wayne Sleep. They glide across the dance floor like a pair of peacocks making sure that everyone marvels at their every shimmy. They're both sporting a bouffant hairstyle and fake orange tans, white shoes for the gentleman and high stilettos for the lady. They're immaculately turned out – the man from

C&A meets Dorothy Perkins. I turn away. It's my own one-man protest to the pair of twinkle-toed tossers.

I was once labelled 'twinkle-toes' at school. Not for dancing – for hedge-hopping. For a short spell, after I'd grown out of marshmallow mangling and before I started taking notice of girls, hedge-hopping was my favourite hobby. It was all about diving, as elegantly as possible, into a well-manicured bush – and coming out the other side relatively unscathed. (You got the odd cuts and grazes, but that was part of the territory for experienced hedge-hoppers.) We had a circuit mapped out from Macey's corner shop to the newsagents. Nine hedges in total.

My prowess in the world of hedge-hopping was legendary. 'Fatty' Barrett was my only serious rival, but I left him standing on one glorious evening when I conquered all nine hedges. He could only muster three and a half before he was called in for his tea. From then on, it was Malcolm 'twinkle-toes' Williams – king of the hoppers. Unfortunately, my glory days were short-lived. As fences and walls began to replace good old garden greenery, hedge-hopping slowly died out. It soon became a thing of the past. Had its day, just like Tide washing powder. Anyway, the headmaster said he was going to come down hard on hedge-hoppers after a series of complaints from the residents.

Back in the ballroom, Mouthy Kev is busy chobbling on his nuts. He's bumped into an unsuspecting couple near the bar. You can hear him a mile off.

'I like Gary Wilmot. The wife likes Gary Wilmot. My bloody pussy likes Gary Wilmot.'

No wonder he's so big in manure management; he talks enough of it.

'I'm telling you, Wilmot's a bloody genius. Best performance of "The Lambeth Walk" I've ever seen. Anyway he's a close personal friend,' he continues.

'You smell nice tonight Kate,' I say, trying to make polite conversation. Of course, I'm really only using her as a foil. I've got one eye on Kevin and Kate while the other scours the room looking for Daphne. Sometimes I'm shocked by my own ruthlessness. I don't know where it comes from. Still, Kate's overwhelmed by my compliment.

'Oh, you *are* a chicken Malcolm. Did you hear that Kevin? He says I smell nice. It's my Charlie Girl, love.'

Point A: I've never been called a chicken before. Still it's better than Mr Potato Head. Point B: didn't Charlie Girl perfume go out in the 1970s? June's spotted us and she's making a beeline for me. Tom's in tow.

'Hello my little blobs of beef dripping. Isn't it nice we're all sticking together? I reckon there'll be a few lasting friendships come out of this cruise.'

Interesting. One moment I'm a chicken, the next I'm a blob of beef dripping.

Half of me wants to smile politely and agree, the other half's begging me to tell this perverted old bag to piss off if she thinks I'm going to drop my trousers for an orgy on Deck A. I decide to smile politely and agree. Where June's concerned I'm definitely ninety per cent chicken, and proud of it. (That makes me ten per cent beef dripping, just about right for my age.)

'It's Tom's birthday on Tuesday.'

She turns to whisper in my ear. I don't know why she's whispering. Tom never seems to be listening.

'I've got him a belting present. A copy of Sonny and Cher singing "Love is Strange"; it's his favourite. They recorded it when they went under the name of Ceaser and Cleo. It's worth a fortune. Never released in England. I've got it hidden away behind the Tampax in our bathroom. I hope he doesn't go fiddling. When he opens it, you'll probably hear him yelling. Even on your floor.'

She's starting to turn on me. I can sense it.

'Did you know you're only one up from the crew's quarters? I bet you can almost hear them splicing their main braces.'

Now she's started to giggle.

That's unfair. I'm going to stand up for myself. Fight my corner. Anyway, the scotch is starting to kick in. I'm going to blow June's murky world into little pieces.

'So June, let's start at the very beginning.' I'm told, in Julie Andrews circles, it's a very good place to start. 'This swinging business. It's a bit on the dirty side for a nice couple like you and Tom isn't it?'

I meant the question to be a bit more hard-hitting but I'm no Jeremy Paxman when it comes to confrontation. In weed terms I should've auditioned for the remake of Bill and Ben.

'Oh, it's quite discreet really,' says June. She's hardly on the defensive. She's quite happy to have it all out with me. 'You only get involved with people in the same income bracket as yourselves. It keeps out the dirty-willy Dereks! Anyway, everybody's at it these days. Before we came away we had a lovely knock with two cooks from Bishop's Cleeve. Claude and Suzanna. He's heavenly when he gets going with his rolling pin. It made my eyes water just watching him perform. It's all in the wrist, you know. Mind you he'd been under Michelle Roux when he was a young man. They reckon his filo pastry was the best in the country.'

She laughs uncontrollably for a few seconds. You've got to give it to her for sheer bravado. She's a brazen hussy dressed in vicar's wife's clothing. Imagine the scene, a swinging foursome with Julie Andrews, Mr Sonny Bono, Fanny and Johnny Craddock.

'No,' she'd recovered from her tittering fit, 'you only live once so you might as well take the bull by the horns. Tom spent most of the afternoon titivating Suzanna's "laa-laa" with a toothbrush. He's quite non-contact really.'

In the name of healthy children's television, thank heavens he wasn't ramming his Tinky Winky up her Laa-Laa. It's all quite surreal. She's telling me the whole sorry saga as if the four of them shared a quiet afternoon cuppa accompanied by a slice of apricot tea loaf in some quiet Cotswold tearoom.

'Mind you,' said June. 'They cooked us a smashing spag bol to finish off the evening. Do you know, I can always tell when a woman wants it up her Ginger Rogers. Take that Kate on our table, she's gagging for it. It's written all over her face. I'd get in there while the going's good if I were you. Give her a good lampooning up the Gulf of Mexico. That'll give the lifeless old windbag something to talk about.'

Gulf of Mexico? Ginger Rogers? She's lost me. The woman's turned from a harmless if a little eccentric *Sound of Music* fan, into a sex beast in just two days. You can't blame such a momentous mood swing on the sea air, can you? And what about poor Suzanna spending the whole afternoon having her beaver tickled by Tom's toothbrush. Did Sonny and Cher ever do a version of 'O, Suzanna?' If they did there's no doubt Tom would be humming a couple of verses while he was down there. 'Oh Suzanna, won't you marry me. 'Cause I come from Alabama with a toothbrush up your tree.'

Alfred and Andy arrive in the nick of time. They've got a habit of cropping up when I most need a 'get out clause'.

'What were you saying about spaghetti?'

Alfred's pissed as a newt. I've noticed how he gets it down him on table 69. Drinks like a fish. Marlene the Wine Girl puts two bottles of Jacob's Creek aside every night for him. I need a quick reply here, and I think I've got one.

'June was just saying how too many cooks don't necessarily spoil the broth.'

Does he know I'm covering up for her wild and wicked ways? Shall I tell him that Ginger Rogers is gagging for it up her Jacob's Creek? Look at me, I'm a wilting violet. I'm getting confused and mixed up... And this was supposed to be my big night.

'Oh, Andy knows how to cook.' Now Alfred's taking the bull by the horns. 'He's very domesticated. All I have to do is drink the sherry and walk the shitsu. Mind you, he's got to be good in the house. He's got a son. Eight. Why he called him that I shall never know.'

Hysterics all round. I'm late to see the joke but I feel forced to give a complimentary snigger anyway.

'You should see his Yorkshire puddings rise,' Alfred's in his element now. 'I've never known anyone like him for making sheer magic out of a couple of eggs and a drop of plain flour. I stand open-mouthed some Sundays. He has to yank me off and drag me into the utility. They just seem to come up before your very eyes.'

A good cook and three balls. No wonder Alfred's prepared to splash out to keep hold of his dashing young partner. Looks like he can turn his hand to anything – even extreme ironing.

Alfred leans over to whisper. 'Between you and me, I've told him not to take the ironing so seriously.'

That'll be last night's row then.

'He doesn't go anywhere without a tin of spray starch. I told him, it's just not healthy. That's him though, and I'm not going to change him. I said to his mother when I married him, he can turn his hand to anything in the kitchen, but when it comes to do-it-yourself, he's buggered.'

I'm just about to tell him about my mate Dr Rotherham. He's the one who spouts off about braised monkey rectum in the Himalayas. I wonder how Alfred would fancy an ape's arse on a Sunday afternoon. It would be enough to make his eyes water. Unfortunately, I'm unable to interject. There's no stopping our leprechaun-like friend now. He's in full flow, and the conversation's moved on to his ex-partners. It looks like I'm going to get the full works. He is quite amusing though. Apparently, he once had an affair with a man who read the shipping forecast on Radio Four.

'Absolutely bloody obsessed, he was,' Alfred tells me. 'After sex, he used to compare me to a gale warning. I can hear him now, randy little bugger. If it was a decent dabble he'd sip on his gin and tonic and say "Portland Bill" – he always thought his erect willy looked like a lighthouse – "south-west, five to seven at first. Veering west occasionally gale eight. Moderate to good." Imagine that, having your performance compared to a bloody shipping forecast.'

I think my performance would be more akin to the Test card transmission.

Oh Lord, I've seen her. She's here. Alfred will have to make way. I can feel my attention veering off south-west. Just seconds ago I was north-easterly three or four. Now Daphne's in the room and I've gone from Test card transmission to Portland Bill in one fell swoop. Gale force eight and rising. That's what she does for me.

She goes to sit in a quiet corner of the room sipping gently on her gin and tonic, smiling sweetly at anyone who happens to catch her eye. We're like two peas in a pod that way. I move slowly but steadily towards her, picking a couple more complementary whiskies off the overladen trays. (Extravagance in the extreme this. Must remember to give generously to a third world charity when I get home just in case Him Upstairs is watching.)

Drat and double drat. Daphne's been cornered by Miss Cruise Bore. She's probably going to ask her about tossing her threepenny bits into the Trevei Fountain when we get to Rome. (They all do it. Chuck a coin over your shoulder and it's a cast iron certainty you'll return.) I'll bide my time and wait until the moment's right. But I can't wait forever. I'm three sheets to the ever-increasing wind. It's all the free booze. Too late, I'm within striking distance of the pair of them. They're deep into a conversation but what the hell; I'm on the point of no return. I bowl my first googlie.

'Hello, Daphne. I enjoyed your talk on Gibraltar yesterday, and I was also at the P-P-Popliarmo.'

Shit, my powers of speech have deserted me just when I needed them most. If we were in a boxing ring, the referee would have stepped in to save me from further punishment. The crowd would have booed me off the stage for not providing credible opposition.

'Propriano.'

Daphne saves me from an embarrassing first round knockdown. But I'm still pinned firmly to the ropes. It's like Mike Tyson brawling with the man from the Mr Muscle adverts. My confidence has gone and Miss Cruise Bore's looking at me as if I was an overused punch-bag. My legs are starting to buckle. I can feel myself heading for the canvas.

'If you want to see any more of me, I'll be in Gibraltar tomorrow.'

Now you're rambling like an old fool. Of course you will you arsehole. The whole fucking ship will be in Gibraltar tomorrow. Undaunted, I'm determined to finish my speech, despite Margaret Chandler's law of holes: 'When you're in one, stop digging my little scrag-end.'

'I may bump into you there. We could nibble on a plate of braised monkey's bottom, or have a drink in your fanny. Sorry, I mean crannie. Now, if you'll excuse me, I'm going to sit with a towel wrapped round my head. I've got this rocking-chair in cabin number F153. I can think better with a towel around my head when I'm rocking to and fro, I'm a bit funny like that.'

Great speech Mr Potato Head. It's no wonder women flock to worship at your altar.

Disgraced, I turn to leave, yet, like in a bad dream, my co-ordination has gone and within seconds, I'm over. Soon I'm stumbling around at Daphne's feet. I'm on the floor, just me, an empty glass where my drink used to be and the six-inch pastel green shag pile. A small amount of whisky and dry sinks slowly into the carpet while two ice cubes sit stranded just inches away. A waitress arrives at the scene to try and help me up, but, seeing the whisky stain, she leaves me abandoned and instead produces a small tin of Vanish upholstery cleaner from her skirt pocket. I'm on my backside while she's on her knees rubbing away at the stain. Imagine that, I'm less important than a stain. It's taking cleanliness too far in my opinion, but I'm in no mood to remonstrate.

Wait, I might still win this bout on a split-decision sympathy vote. She might think, in a bumbling sort of way, that I was the cutest thing since Eamon Holmes, the king of early morning television. Rooted to the carpet, I find the strength to pick up my head. From out of nowhere, a stupid drunken grin appears on my stupid drunken face. I'm sort of acknowledging the fact that I'm a wanker, but, for some unknown reason, I'm prepared to give it one last shot. Even now, I still think I can repair the damage, despite the fact that I look like a pissed-up Freddie 'Parrot-face' Davies.

'I've got a Czechoslovakian willow stick at home!'

It's my last throw of the dice. My final attempt to nail the girl of my dreams. I feel, despite the fall, I've done well. Given it my best shot. But I might as well have been nailing a snail to a tree. It's all too little, too late. Daphne is back talking to Miss Cruise Bore. She bows her head in a 'now where were we before that drunken tosser butted in' sort of way.

'Do you know, I long to be a man,' says the Port Enhancement Queen, looking deep into Miss Cruise Bore's eyes.

It's the killer blow, like an upper-cut to my glass jaw. I'm out for the count. Daphne's a lesbian, and I'm still trying to claw my way up from the floor.

Bliss, the resident band, strike up with *Una Paloma Blanca*.

It's the worse case scenario. Daphne's a lesbian and she's pulled Miss Cruise Bore right under my bloody nose. Talking of noses, Kenneth the Weasel Snout seems to be getting on well with Linda the Stocky Boot Scooter. From my position, floundering around on the shag pile, I can see them laughing out of the corner of my eye. He's rammed his fingers into his mouth to stop his teeth falling into his gin and tonic. If he shags her before we get off the boat I'm walking the plank.

So much for my ten famous balls. I've just dropped the most famous ball of them all. And what about the owl and the pussycat? I can almost feel them rewriting the words as I speak: 'They howled as the little twat went to seed on the beautiful pea green shag.'

The night's in tatters. Now don't get me wrong, I'd pay good money to watch Daphne perform a lesbian act, even if it was with Miss Cruise Bore. But not tonight. It's too much to bear. The party's just beginning and I've made a fool of myself in front of the most beautiful woman on the ship, who turns out to be on the verge of shagging another woman. I wonder if Miss Cruise Bore wears an 'I lick the stamp on the other side' nightdress? Is Daphne about to plunge headlong into her Gibraltar straits? Has June turned me into a sex-crazed loon?

Kevin and Katie have taken to the floor with Andy and Alfred just in time to do the Spanish Hustle, June and Tom are on the hunt for a gang-bang and Hattie Jacques has got her sticky fingers on Captain Fletcher's compass. Her husband has got the skipper's hat perched on top of his squirrel-like head.

Dejected, I drag myself off the floor and begin to make my way sadly towards the exit. Even by my low standards, this will surely go down as one of the most shocking performances of all time. Paul Nicholas has got a lot to answer for. You know the one. Long curly blond hair. Heartthrob who starred with the thin woman in *Just Good Friends*. It was him who had a hit with 'Dancing with the Captain' in 1976, and now they're all at it on board the good ship *Perfect*. (Anyway, I preferred the follow-up, 'Grandma's Party'.)

The final straw. Rosemary and Roger, the couple that own the five-star ferret hotel, are desperately trying to get the hang of 'The Birdie Song'.

'Good evening both.'

I'm gallantly trying to pick up the pieces of my broken heart. The night that began with such promise has ended in carnage. As far as I'm concerned, it's a complete and utter farcical shambles as per bleeding usual.

Rosemary (lovely woman, even though she's as mad as cheese) grasps my hand. I was always a big hit with older ladies. 'If you'll be my Fred Astaire, I'll be your Ginger Rogers,' she says, attempting a sexy smirk.

I think it's time for bed.

7

I met Val Doonican once.

I'm awake. It's Sunday morning. They've just played a peal of church bells over the ship's tannoy to get us in the mood. Next we'll be having the late Thora Hird lead us through Psalm 23: The Lord's my Shepherd, I'll not want. He makes me down to lie. Where was he last night? He was supposed to leadeth me through the pastel green, to the quiet waters by. As it was, I went arse over tit on the shag pile.

I'm in my rocking-chair thinking of the nice moments in my life. It's an emergency damage limitation exercise to combat the carnage caused by my drunken performance in the Paradise Ballroom. That place is rapidly becoming my bogey room. It's jinxed as far as I'm concerned; has been since day one. They can stick their six-inch shag. I'm not setting foot in the place again.

Any road up. Val 'Valentine' Doonican was the undisputed king of the rocking-chair. He's also a very nice man. Enormous in his day. Ronan Keating meets Daniel O'Donnell. And the songs? Every one a gilt-edged classic. ('Paddy McGinty's Goat', 'Delaney's Donkey' and 'O'Rafferty's Motor Car'. There are three for starters.) We met out of the blue, after a charity concert that was heavily backed by the British Potato Marketing Board. I waited all night to shake him firmly by the hand. I used to swear by his variety show on a Saturday evening, so what an honour, when he took the time to have a chat. I was expecting him to shrug me off, but no. He was the exception that proved my ninety-second rule.

He told me that, as a boy, he used to steal jam-jars and sell them to the local grocer at a penny a time, just so that he could afford an outing at the picture house to watch his all-time hero, the singing cowboy Gene Autrey. His life changed in just seven minutes. In 1964 he was offered a slot on *Sunday Night at the London Palladium*. After the show, entertainment impresario Val Parnell came over, shook his hand and said: 'Tomorrow you'll be a star.' And he was.

This 'star overnight' business has just started to happen all over again. After years of struggling, television's 'new talent' department has found a massive new lease of life. Eat your heart out *New Faces*, *Stars in their Eyes* and even *Opportunity Knocks*. There's an even bigger monster on the scene. The new overnight sensations, the new Val Doonicans, are being created by shows like *Pop Stars*, *Pop Idol* and even *Big Brother*.

I love them. I became quite addicted to *Pop Idol* – held a party for the final and voted for both of them because I thought they'd done equally well to get that far. Dicky Cox said I was a twat because one vote cancelled out the other and I needn't have bothered at all. But I was quite insistent.

I discussed the whole thing with Dibble the Muffin Man at work. He delivers sandwiches, crisps and home-made cakes to our office every day. He's called the Muffin Man because that's his job (his business is somewhat unimaginatively called Dibble's Snacks and Savouries) and, like the Muffin Man in the nursery rhyme, he lives in Drury Lane. Margaret Chandler, who'd wandered over to buy her usual rhubarb and ginger bloomer with extra mayonnaise, said I should go in for the follow-up to *Pop Idol*: 'Bone Idol', the search to find Britain's biggest layabout. (I think she's secretly jealous of me.)

Val Doonican (Valentine to his friends) was different. He's from the old school. The days when you only became famous if you were the very best in your field. You'd be found

without the need to audition with ten thousand others before
the television masses, and you'd stand the test of time.

I even plucked up the courage to ask him about the
rocking-chair. Apparently, it all started when a lady folk
singer appeared on his show that was recorded, in the early
days, in a converted church in Manchester (here I go again,
the king of useless information). Anyway, the show's director
decided she should sit down to sing her big number. They
sent down to the props room and some bloke came back
with *the* chair. She started to sing, but the soundman picked
up a dreadful creaking noise coming from her bra strap as
she rocked. To cut a long story short, she finally did the
number standing up, but the director already had a beautiful
shot of the rocking-chair bathed in a pool of light so he told
Val to use it for his closing number. He sang the song, said
good night and the credits came up.

Where's my seven minutes that will change my life forever?
Where's my rocking-chair moment; a stroke of luck that will
help me make my mark on life long after I've gone?

I liked Val. I bought his album after we'd finished talking
and played 'Elusive Butterfly' over and over again. Daphne's
proving to be the most elusive butterfly of them all. Maybe I
should have gone straight in with my Val Doonican story last
night. It just might have saved the day. Anyway, I only caught
one line of her sentence. I've probably got it all wrong again.
My mind was clouded by the free scotch. She's no lesbian.
She was just trying to satisfy Miss Cruise Bore's lust for
'same-sex sex'. (Wouldn't surprise me one iota if the old
tomboy drove the other bus and was desperate for a pull on
Daphne's remote control projector panel.)

Maybe Daphne swings both ways. Lord, there's so much
swinging on this boat it's a wonder the bastard thing doesn't
topple over. Imagine us all capsized just off the coast of
Gibraltar. It'd be like *The Poseidon Adventure* all over again.
Who would survive? Mouthy Kev for one. He'd slip the

Captain a backhander to bail out first, using the ill-gotten gains of his manure management empire. Rosemary and Roger, the ferret duo, would be the sad couple who decide to spend their last seconds in bed reciting the Lord's Prayer, holding hands, and thinking of their soon-to-be orphaned ferrets. Tom would be too busy meddling with June. Probably have a feather duster to her Ginger Rogers. Almost certain goners those two. Kenneth would be the unlikely survivor, although I wouldn't bet on his teeth making the journey. And I'd be the hero. Helping everyone else off before settling down with Norman DeVine and his assembled orchestra to serenade the poor buggers who would be clinging on to the candelabras without a hope in hell. I can visualize it. After a couple of verses of 'Sit down, You're Rocking the Boat' (*Guys and Dolls* if I'm not mistaken), I would turn with a Tommy Steele-type misty look in my eye and announce: 'Gentlemen, it's been a pleasure singing with you tonight.'

Enough. We're in port. It's our first stop. The great limestone rock of Gibraltar is waiting outside my picture window. I'm going to start afresh. In the words of the great Val Doonican, I'm going to 'walk tall, walk straight and look the world right in the eye'. (They just don't make them like that any more.)

Malcolm's Log. Day four.

I don't know why I'm bothering with this diary thing. I'm no Bridget Jones. Won't even read it when I get home. Still, it's keeping me company.

It's Sunday, June 22nd and things have taken an unexpected turn for the worse. Once again, I let myself down badly in the Paradise Ballroom but I'm not going to let it affect my quest for romance with the dashingly beautiful Daphne, even though she could be a lesbian. She

might even have spent the night with June and Tom
having her Gulf of Mexico lampooned with a toothbrush.
I shall never be able to pick up a toothbrush again
without thinking about Tom and Suzanna – the cook
from Bishop's Cleeve. I bet her 'laa-laa' had never received
such attention. *No!* I'm determined not to write myself
off. I'm going to pick myself up, dust myself off and start
all over again (Frank Sinatra song about a little old ant
trying to move a rubber tree plant... And everyone knows
an ant *can't* move a rubber tree plant).

No big breakfast for me today. I'm like June that way. For
both of us, the Sunday morning fry-up is off limits. 'I only
have a muffin first thing on a Sunday,' she told me last night
while extolling the virtues of 'free love'. (Maybe I should
introduce her to Dibble the Muffin Man. It's got the makings
of an explosive combination, especially when she sees the
size of his treacle tarts.)

Anyway, it's land ahoy! I'm on Tour A which means I get
a special fluorescent pink badge with 'Tour A' written on it.
I've been told to report to the Hippodrome Theatre and wait
for my number to be called, so that's exactly what I do (never
really been the type to go against the grain). I'm sat behind
Stoop and Droop who've gone for Tour B. Cable-car and
shop till you drop. Won't be long before Stoop drops; she's
going faster than the Leaning Tower of Pisa as it is.

Droop's already in full flow, and I'm rapidly becoming a
serious contender for the next Olympic eavesdropping gold
medal.

'She's got a phobia of birds,' she says, struggling for her
next breath. 'She had a robin's nest in her arch. Stopped
her watering her hanging baskets. Well, you ask Alan
Titchmarsh. Once you've neglected your baskets for a couple
of days they're buggered. They went all limp and saggy. Now

her husband had much more luck, had tits flocking around his fat balls but he could never get them into his box.'

Stoop intervenes. 'My neighbour's just the same. Great tits swarming around his nuts but he can't entice them into his wife's nest for love nor money. It's worrying him to death.'

'I'm not surprised!' Droops back in charge. 'Tits have dropped by twenty per cent since the bustards moved in. They're on their way out, it said so in the paper.'

From what I can gather, Droop's not just an expert on sagging tits. It seems she's well into *all* birds. Her late husband was a pigeon fancier. Used to take her to Belgium every other weekend to sell his squeakers (apparently, that's the name you give to a baby pigeon, but I've never seen one, and I don't know anybody who has). Anyway, just outside Antwerp, they hold a sort of pigeon car-boot sale every Sunday. You just set up your pasting table, and once the man has been around with his little ticket machine, you're in business.

'The Belgians are the masters. Make a fortune they do,' says Droop. 'I once saw a yearling' – a middle-aged pigeon – 'change hands for two hundred and fifty quid. It's the squeakers and the yearlings they go for; the old birds are left on the shelf unless they're of good stock.'

Stoop intervenes: 'I've got a good daughter. Takes me to Winchester every other month. She's a vegetarian, although she will eat beef, and the occasional lamb chop.'

I think she wants to change the subject. She's either fed up with the pigeon talk, or trying to compete with Droop in the outings department, although, once a fortnight to Antwerp must beat an occasional trip to Winchester in anybody's book.

As I'm waiting to be called for my outing, I notice a poster advertising tonight's entertainment in the Hippodrome. And I might go. Norman DeVine and Perfection (the ship's dance crew) take us on yet another whistle-stop tour of the musicals. It's called 'Water in the West End – from *Singing in the Rain* to the *South Pacific*, riding on a *Showboat* down the "Ol' Man River".' Very clever Norman. I'll try to be seated before 9.30 p.m.

I've seen some of the Perfection dancers wandering around. Half of them look as if they've come on board to get a good meal inside them. Tragic really. You spend three years starving at drama school because you can't afford to eat. After drama school you starve some more so you can dance behind some trumped up C-rated celebrity and make him look half decent. Ten years of abuse and starvation, then you're thrown on the scrap heap because you're getting too fat! Ridiculous. Ten years of hard work for nothing. Spend five minutes on 'reality' television and you're the biggest thing since Zsa Zsa Gabor. The world's gone upside down if you ask me.

'Tour A!'

A uniformed lady holding a megaphone tightly to her over-glossed lips has given us the nod...and it's developed into a major cavalry charge. The pensioners have been mobilized and they're down the stairs like shit off a shovel. No wonder the bloody Germans surrendered. They wouldn't have a snowball's chance in hell against this mob. And what are they all so desperate to claim? The front seats on the tour bus. You would never have guessed those four places were such a valuable commodity. But I swear some of these old timers would kill for them. It was always the back seat when I was a youngster. Now I'm just happy to get a seat at all.

Mrs Cocktail Stick (a.k.a. Alison the miniaturist) is on my minibus, with the Pillsbury Dough Man. They're canoodling like teenagers. It's definitely the start of a new romance. He's wearing canvas shorts that are far too tight for his own good. You can virtually make out everything he's got. A most ugly sight if you ask me. He turns to say hello.

'I'm not a love walrus. But I know a man who is,' he says, and laughs. Mrs Cocktail Stick laughs too. Must be their new lover's code. At any rate, they've totally lost me.

There's a fleet of these white minibuses snaking their way over the country's main airport runway. When you visit Gibraltar you have to drive over the runway. Imagine that at Heathrow on the last Saturday in July. Still, no runaway planes coming down the track here. We're on our way to the main attractions: a rock and some monkeys. If this were the Himalayas we'd be stopping halfway to stir-fry their bottoms with shredded radish. Oh no! Monkey's backsides. Reminds me of my speech from hell last night. (Daphne didn't get my point. She was never going to. She doesn't know my food historian pal.)

I'm glad we're only staying half a day. Despite the nooks and crannies, it's more than enough and I'm not really in the mood. In truth, Flopsy Wright, the travel agent, *had* warned me. 'Gibraltar?' he'd said. 'Load of shit.' To be fair, St Michael's cave, as the delightful Daphne suggested, *was* an unexpected pleasure. As a rule, I wouldn't be turned on by the thought of a stalagmite, but the atmosphere of the place had me enchanted for a good three and a half minutes. True to form, it was dark and drippy, but it was also mystical in a murky sort of way. 'Good cave!' I mumbled to myself as I left. Otherwise, the apes entertained to order, and as for the 100-ton gun... Seen one cannon, seen 'em all.

I did spot Miss Cruise Bore and her father, studying the Straits of Gibraltar on a map that was situated on a mound of earth overlooking the sea. I thought, yes you dirty bleeder. No wonder you're full of beans after full-on lesbian sex with Daphne right underneath your mother's snout. *No!* It didn't happen. Keep telling yourself it really didn't happen.

The shopping opportunities are good, especially if you're after one of those Lladro figures the women bring back by the wheelbarrowful (and there's me, still trying to flog my Capi de

Monte fisherman at the car-boot sale. Of course, I've got no chance. The tip of his rod has snapped leaving an open-mouthed carp high and dry in the water with no visible proof that he's actually been caught). The best thing about Gibraltar is the Gibraltarians. They have a real sense of pride. At least Robin did. He was our driver. Cracked the occasional joke as we weaved our way through the narrow streets. He was Gibraltarian through and through. He was also fiercely determined to stay British. Although, for my money, Gibraltar's nothing like the United Kingdom at all. They've got the pubs, but there are no caravan parks. Imagine that in Britain. A place so close to the sea that doesn't cater for caravans. It's unheard of. Absurd!

I'll alert Dicky Cox. We could be on to a moneymaking scam. I could even bring Robin the driver in on the idea. I liked him. In fact I gave him a big tip as I disembarked. Two pounds and thirty-six pence. It was all I had left after I bought a Gibraltar pen with a boat floating up and down the bay. (You may have seen the naked lady version. Tip the pen and her clothes are off. Tip it back and she's dressed in a black swimsuit. Highly recommended for a laugh in the play-ground if you're twelve and three quarters; goes down well as entertainment during the marshmallow fighting inter-mission.)

I even caught a glimpse of Daphne. But she wasn't looking for a nook, or investigating a crannie. She was on the high street, darting in and out of the shops like a woman possessed. And, for the record, she didn't have the contented glow of a girl who's just had a night of lesbian passion in the crew's quarters with a cruise bore-type tomboy. See, I've gone and put two and two together and come up with six.

Like most passengers I've soon had my fill of Gibraltar and before long I'm back on the ship, roaming like a little lost lamb trying to piece together my next move. Can you believe it? Mrs Jigsaw Puzzle's still at it in the library. Hasn't moved, and she's only completed the bottom bloody edge. She's trying to build a picture of sunflowers against a wall. Waste of time. When she's finished what will she have? Sunflowers. She's missed the delights of the Med for a picture of sunflowers against a brick sodding wall.

I once ventured into the jigsaw world myself, although you could never really say I was an enthusiast. *Blue Peter*. If I remember rightly, I had it for Christmas and by Boxing Day it was under my bed, never to be seen again. I don't know what all the fuss is about. I spent thirty-five minutes creating a picture of Valerie Singleton perched on a stool between Peter Purvis and John Noakes, her hand on a cockatoo, or was it a budgie? My memory is slightly clouded. You must realize this was pre-piddling elephant. Even 'get down Shep' was just a twinkle in John Noakes' eye. Anyway, I was more into Peter 'Hot Shot' Lorimer than *Blue Peter* as a youth.

There's prize bingo in the dreaded Paradise Ballroom. This is far more my scene. As a boy, I used to scarper off to the Grand Pier at Weston-Super-Mare with a shilling squeezed so tightly in my hand that, by the time I'd got to the bingo hall, I had the Queen's head imprinted on my palm. I almost developed a nasty addiction to the game one year, owing to the fact that the top prize was a remote control Trumpton fire engine (they were all on it. Clinging to the sides. Pugh, Pugh, Barney McGrew, Cuthbert, Dibble and Grub).

I fell in love with that fire engine and I was determined to win enough tokens to take it home by the end of the week. But I had to be at my best. The bingo caller had the fastest line in patter you've ever heard. Would have given the legendary Ted Rogers a run for his money (you remember *3-2-1*, Dusty Bin, etc.). He used to rattle them off like a machine gun: 'On the blue, four and two; red garden gate, number eight; Ted Heath's den, number ten; five and nine, the Brighton line.'

Of course, the Trumpton fire engine eluded me. I went home with a novelty ornament called 'Piddling Percy'. It was a fat man on a stand. When you pulled his pants down, his penis shot up and squirted you with a narrow jet of water. They were all the rage at one time. It was hilarious for five minutes, but I cursed my missed opportunity to land the big prize. The fire engine stayed in Weston. I was badly affected for a few months. I even considered a career in the fire service but I don't think I'd have been any use on the other end of a hose, or sliding down a slippery pole.

I could never work out why firemen are the only professionals who use a pole to get to work. Why is a pole exclusively for their use? Ambulance workers have to get to work in a hurry; where's the pole? Police officers? No pole. What a great way to break the ice in the delivery suite if the midwife slid down her pole just before your waters broke.

Back in the bingo hall, Hattie Jacques is sat concentrating. Now there's a turn up for the books; (a) I'd have thought she'd have been following some tour guide around the Moorish Castle in a last-gasp attempt to drink in every last cultural drop of our first port stop; and (b) surely Bridge with Barbara is more up her street. I bet she's hard to beat with a good trump. She looks as if she's sweating. Probably waiting on number 88: two fat ladies, you and your mother.

'House!'

Hattie Jacques has lost out. The matching couple, resplendent in identical mauve shell suits, have beaten her to the prize. They were waiting on 'Two little ducks, 22'. I realize that I'm lurking in the Paradise Ballroom doorway again. It's becoming a nasty habit, so I'm off before they can try to pull me in for the next game.

Before long, it's 'Bingo!' for me. I've found the children. They're in the Woody Woodpecker Club on Deck Five. Dozens of them all glued to their computers. Now here's a thing. Maybe I could reinvent child labour. It was all the rage in Victorian times. Only I wouldn't send them up chimneys. I'd hire them out to teach old fogies how to use their computers. Do parents realize there's an absolute fortune to be made from their offspring? In my view, the five- to thirteen-year-olds are the world's greatest computer wizards. Just hire them out for an hour or two before and after they go to school. Within a few months they could become the biggest earners in the family. That's it! I'll launch the 'Diddy Dot-com Men' and earn myself a tidy little fortune. I can see the adverts now: 'Net an Infant for your Internet' or 'Boot-up Babies 'r' us'. It's a winner, I reckon.

There are complimentary 'good ship lollypops' in the Woody Woodpecker Club. Shirley Temple would have been as pleased as punch! And talking of punch, they're trying to set up for a Punch and Judy show – if they can prise any of the little bleeders away from their computer games.

Rather than peering through the double glazing, I've decided to take a casual, yet innocent, wander into the children's den. Oh fuck! Punch and Judy. A memory stirs…and then, a face remembered. I stumble slightly. Almost upended by a toddler trying to gnaw his way through a part-opened box of felt tip pens. (He's done well, the green and the blue are almost totally devoured – they're all over his face. Now he's made a start on the black.) But it's not the toddler who's captured my attention. Far worse. The vacation to end all vacations has suddenly taken a nasty turn. I'm frozen to the spot. I can feel a wave of horrorfulness embrace me. It can't be. Surely. Can it be? It bloody well is, you know. It's What's-her-name. Fucking Claire. (See, Gilbert O'Sullivan was right: Clare, the moment I met her, I swore – and who wouldn't under the circumstances.)

What's-her-name's on the good ship *Perfect*. It's her. I know it. It's definitely her and she's on the good ship sodding *Perfect*. She's on the good ship *Perfect* as the bloody Punch and Judy girl. And I'm on the good ship *Perfect* as well, with her. Well, not *with* her, but with her. On the good ship *Perfect*. With What's-her-name who dumped me three years ago to shag the butcher. The thought of a pork and leek sausage and a well-hung goose goes through my mind. He had his hand wedged between her bra and her breast in the red-and-white-striped canopy. She had her Mr Punch rammed into his knackers. The lady who bust my heart into a million pieces has been here, with me, all the time.

Do I run? Has she seen me? Do I dart back to cabin F153 and order a couple of large ones from Oh Danny Boy? No. I'm standing my ground, and she's within touching distance. I feel a surge of bravery sweep over me (Val Doonican you see, just thinking about him has given me extra spunk). Before I know what I'm doing, I've gone and said it:

'Hello.' (A Lionel Ritchie hit. Got to number one in 1984.)

Claire looks, and looks again almost immediately. Her jaw drops – odd that, it's usually her knickers that go first. She recognizes me. For a moment she's shocked. I'm shocked too. We stand there trying to absorb the shock. For a moment we're united. We're a pair of shock absorbers. Who would've thought it? Out of the blue, in the middle of the sea, two hearts have been thrown back together as one. Soon, her shock subsides and she's back to her normal self (i.e. couldn't give a monkey's rectum). She looks me square on, hazel eyes and everything. Then, in her own inimitable matter-of-fact sort of way, she yells, 'Well! Go fuck a Penguin. It's *you*. Spud. It's you, isn't it? What the bollocking arseholes are you doing here?'

Lovely girl. Always was. Lost none of her charm.

I'm looking for one of my quick-witted, cutting replies. I'm desperate to show her that I've shaken off her rather substantial knock-back. She'll see I'm a man for the new millennium. I'll show her I've come of age.

'What am I doing here?' I reply. It's a disappointing response. 'Well...nothing really.' Now I've decided to show her my straight bat. I'm going to keep an air of mystery about the man she let slip through her puppeteeringly perfect fingers. 'You remember me then?' I ask. (It's possible she still fancies me.)

'I'll never forget your pink maggot.'

No. She definitely hates me – always has. I've been a standing joke with God knows how many boyfriends. It's Monte Carlo or the workhouse now. I've got nothing left to lose. We stand still and silent for a second. Seems like an hour.

'Did you have the well-hung goose with garlic and herb stuffing or did he force his pork and leek sausage on you that evening?'

I'm unusually calm. Normally at this point I'd be in a total state of dither.

'It didn't last,' she replied. 'It was good at first. He'd bring a pork pie round in the middle of the afternoon. I'd slop on a dollop of mustard while he fondled his award-winning sausage. You know Terry. Hands like shovels but he could turn them to anything when he put his mind to it. But, as time went on, he became obsessed with his steak and ale pies, wanted to scoop another award. I just moved on. Thankfully I met Norman, the musicals bloke. It's a good arrangement. We do this cruise every year before the summer season really gets going; I've got a residency on the beach at Bognor Regis.'

Norman. She's in love with Norman DeVine and his whistle-stop tours through the magic of the musicals.

I think I'm still carrying a candle for Claire. It's her confidence. She's no bad looker either, still a bit too plump and she's still got the spiky bleached blonde hair, but she's worth a second chance. After all, she's the only bird I've ever got my end away with despite two false starts with the barmy bint who fancied oral sex with a giraffe, and loopy Lucille Bullock who finished up behind bars after her nasty encounter with the vicar's son. I still shudder every time I think of Lucille Bullock. Just think, my goolies could have finished up on the end of those secateurs. (I suppose a small tribute must also be paid at this point to the legendary Brenda Burston who, unknowingly, kick-started my sexual career all those years ago; but it's only a passing mention, you understand. She doesn't really count.)

'Anyway, it's lovely to see you again,' says Claire, trying desperately to break the ice. 'Listen,' she's getting flustered. She's trying to salvage something from the ruins of our once promising relationship. 'I've got two shows tonight. You'll remember how good I was with the crocodile and the sausages.' Claire's warming to me, I can see it in her eyes. I'm beginning to see the nice side of her as well. 'I'm off tomorrow though,' she adds.

Here we go Looby Lou! Her sentence ended in a kind of 'we could meet up if you're interested' way. She's going to invite me back to her red and white canopy. I'm going to get the Terry Taylor 'hands like shovels' treatment. But this time it'll be my hand on her T-Bone as she spreads Branston Pickle on my tongue sandwich. The thought has transported me back to paradise for a second.

'Why don't we go the Happy Days Diner for a drink before dinner? There's a bloke on who plays the piano just like Jerry Lee Lewis.'

Can you believe it, mother? I've got a date. This time a real date. Claire and I are back in business at the 50s diner. Tomorrow. Just before the evening meal, watching the bloke who plays the piano like Jerry Lee Lewis. Six o'clock. Deck Seven. The swing-o-meter of love has lunged back in my favour.

Two thoughts suddenly send me crashing back from Branston Pickle on the tongue sandwich heaven. One: what about Norman DeVine? I always had him down as gay. Big flouncy shirts opened to just above his naval, and a tight-arsed walk. Almost a quick shuffle. Short dark hair cropped to perfection. More Alfred and Andy than Claire What's-her-name. Two: didn't Jerry Lee Lewis have a monster hit with his 'Great Balls of Fire'?

It's a good omen. The deal's been struck. Astonishingly, after my golden duck the night before in the Paradise Ballroom, I'm striding out for a second innings. Before long, I'm back in the bosom of table 69. I want the whole lot of them to know that I'm just about to smash a six into the grandstand. I'm waiting to pick my moment, although it's quite difficult to get the timing right when table 69 is in full flow. We're tucking into a plum crumble discussing the great Judy Garland.

'Of course, Eva Cassidy almost bettered her in the "Somewhere Over the Rainbow" stakes,' says Kiss Me Kate.

'Bollocks,' retorts Kev.

'I'm more David Cassidy than Eva Cassidy,' titters Andy.

Kenneth the Weasel Man holds his two index fingers aloft: ' "Bye, Bye Baby. Baby bye, bye." '

'That wasn't David Cassidy. It was the Bay City Rollers, you daft wazzock!' Kevin again. It's a bit unfair in my opinion. He's in a wretched mood tonight and everyone can sense it.

'Oh Kevin. You'll have to excuse him. Something's got him all flustered.'

Kiss Me Kate is quick to cover up for her husband's wayward misdemeanours. (Loyal wife by the looks of things. She has to be with that great King Kong of a man barking his orders every five minutes.)

We move on to a quick game of fantasy film cast. You choose a new line-up in a well-established movie (preferably a musical, they're mad about musicals, this lot). I've gone for a remake of *Chitty Chitty Bang Bang* starring Kenneth Williams as the Child Catcher. Barbara Windsor is Truly Scrumptious, and Sid James is the dad who makes the car. It's more like 'Carry On Bang Bang'. Could be something in that. I'm half expecting Andy and Alfred to create a brand new Willie Wonka.

Willie Wonka! That reminds me of Margaret Chandler at work. She once got very close to a dwarf from the tiny hamlet of Zender on the Scottish borders. Dicky Cox said she was definitely shagging him. And why not? He'd got a fabulous track record. Get this. He was one of the original Umpa Lumpa men in *Willie Wonka and the Chocolate Factory*. We'd just finished our rather successful 'Is there a guy who works down your chip shop who swears he's Elvis?' competition. All part of our great plan to remind the world that you don't just boil a potato. The dwarf won hands down. He surprised everybody at the grand final in Southport with a tear-jerking performance of *Old Shep* done in the style of the king of rock and roll. One thing led to another after his triumphant encore that included both *Love Me Tender* and *Wooden Heart*. Whether she was shagging him or not, Margaret certainly became very fond of him. There was talk they might move in together at one stage, but when push came to shove, it all fizzled out. She returned him to Zender (address unknown by all accounts). Anyway, I'll never forget the day when he walked into our office and produced an original golden ticket he had nicked from the Willie Wonka film set and had framed for posterity. I was most impressed. I reckon that ticket would be worth a fortune on this trip. Norman DeVine would break the bank to get his hands on it.

Oh dear. Him. Norman De-bastard-Vine. I wonder if he's got his hands on Claire's golden ticket in the red and white canopy. No, too busy taking us on his voyage through the watery West End in the Hippodrome Theatre. (I wonder if they've got to three coins in the fountain yet; bound to be on the itinerary as we're stopping in Rome.)

Resisting the Willie Wonka option, Alfred and Andy have gone for Julian Clary and Lily Savage in the new *Me and My*

Girl for their fantasy musical. Might be worth going to have a look at. 'Or anything with Danny La Rue,' adds Alfred. 'We went to see him in *Hello Dolly* and I was in tears for a fortnight. He's still giving champagne at beer prices if you ask me. The man's a showbiz legend.'

'We're close personal friends of Danny La Rue,' Kevin retorts with another bear-like growl.

I'm waiting for His Weaselness to start us off on a verse of 'On Mother Kelly's Doorstep', but he's struggling with the plum crumble and his loose fitting dentures. Alfred's right. Danny La Rue, a showbiz legend. Marjorie Proops once described him as a 'beloved national monument'. In his day they used to say he had the prettiest face you've ever seen on a chap past puberty. And to think Harry Secombe, God rest his soul, once told him to give up the stage and return to his 'proper' job as a window dresser for J V Hutton in Oxford Street.

At the risk of boring table 69, I launch into another batch of useless information:

'Daniel Patrick Carroll is his original name you know. They wanted to change it to Danny Street but there was already a singer called Danny Street so Daniel Patrick Carroll became Danny La Rue, and with the change of name, there came a change of luck. He was given 'On Mother Kelly's Doorstep' by Randolph Sutton in 1969.'

Roger the Waiter appears to collect the empty bowls of plum crumble, when suddenly, Kenneth bursts into life.

'*Tony Christie!*' he bawls.

He's got us all bemused.

'Tony Christie!' he shrieks again. ' "Is this the way to Amarillo?" '

He's becoming insistent.

' "Is this the way to Amarillo? Every night I've been hugging my pillow." ' Kenneth's trying to dance in his chair, while singing a Tony Christie number.

'It's not a musical, you daft old woman,' scoffs Mouthy Kev. It's a bit inaccurate in my opinion. Still, it's Kevin all over. He's getting angrier, but Kenneth thinks he's on to a good thing.

'What a cracker! "Tony Christie, the Musical." That's my fantasy!' He sings again: ' "In the avenues and alleyways…" '

It's the theme tune to *The Persuaders*. (A 1960s detective show I think.)

'I once played a transvestite in *The Persuaders*. Never had a line, though,' says Kenneth, not realizing he's killed the game stone dead.

The entertainment on table 69 is over and I haven't even had the chance to tell them about my hot date. Alfred and Andy are going to chance a pound in the Golden Penny. Kev, Kate, June and Tom are off to the Hippodrome Theatre. Kenneth the Weasel Man is a bit of an unknown quantity after dinner. He slips away into the night (probably stalking Stocky Linda and her team of boot scooting babies in the Paradise Ballroom).

For me it's a toss up between Norman DeVine or the rocking-chair, a towel over my head and a last stiff drink from Oh Danny Boy. I can't stand the thought of applauding Norman DeVine, so the rocking-chair it is. After all, I've got Claire to think about. I keep going over it in my mind. The Happy Days Diner, tomorrow night, 6 p.m.

'I've got to focus my mind on Jerry Lee Lewis and his 'Great Balls of Fire!' Goodness gracious, I wonder if they ever sang that to three-bollock Andy along the South coast?

8

Something tells me something is gonna happen tonight. (Cilla Black. Got to number three in 1971.)

Malcolm's Log. It's Monday, June 23rd. My mind is fixed on my hot date with Claire in the Happy Days Diner at 6 p.m. We've landed in the pretty port of Propriano, but I've hardly had time to gaze out of my picture window, and take in the stunning tree-lined coastal view. Claire's shagability: eight. She's still cute and spiky, and I'll be better off this time around.

Listen to me! This cruise is doing my confidence the world of good. I've given her an eight despite the lurking Norman DeVine. Just think. He's probably having a whistlestop tour round her Gulf of Mexico right now. Still, I was there first. When he arrives at her South Pole, he'll find my flag flying high. And, for your information Mr DeVine, I'm getting ready to hoist my Union Jack again. What the hell. If all else fails, I've still not given up on Daphne the Port Enhancement Queen, despite her now dubious sexual orientation.

The sunshine is pouring through the picture window as Captain Fletcher welcomes me to Corsica. It's a tender stop. The ship anchors itself in the bay while the passengers get ready to pile into motorized dinghys for a good old-fashioned Derby and Joan stampede onto foreign territory. I'll bet one or two of the pensioners are already halfway down the gangplanks, bayonets at the ready. If only they'd got a bloke flogging Stannah Stairlifts on board, he'd make a killing.

I've always fancied one of those stairlifts. In fact, there was a time when Dicky Cox and me thought about going halves on a custom built one for the office. We intended to spend most of the day giving each other rides up the stairs – one in the chair, one on the control panel. We even invented a game to make it more interesting. It went like this: turn the custom-built control knob to top speed then slam on the brake when the passenger's least expecting it. The sudden jerk would be enough to topple him or her out of the chair and onto the stairs below. It was a human form of 'Buckaroo'.

Oh Danny Boy has brought me the usual. Tea and more oatmeal biscuits. The *Nautical Newsletter* has details of a cocktail and karaoke evening with resident band 'Bliss' on the Sunshine Deck tomorrow evening. My new love rival, the dastardly DeVine is running workshops so we can exercise our vocal cords to 'get in to the rhythm of the night'.

Tonight is made for love. Tomorrow it's bop till you drop at the cocktail sing-a-long. I can just imagine it. Alfred and Andy ripping through a version of 'Jack in a Box' by Clodagh Rogers, while Kenneth practices the 'Tush Push' with Stocky Linda the Boot Scooting Baby who's driving him crazy. I wonder if Kenneth has brought his recorder. A couple of verses of 'I am a Cider Drinker' on the Sunshine Deck could bring the house down. Might even take the whole bloody ship down.

The dinghys are filling up. Compared to the good ship *Perfect*, it's a rocky ride as we head towards port. Memories of the mackerel fishing trip off the coast of South Wales come flooding back. Still, it's full steam ahead and, once ashore, the Captain lays out the red carpet: a container full of freshly squeezed cool orange juice and a huge tub of oatmeal biscuits, just in case anybody feels peckish. Hardly likely, we've just polished off a full English buffet-style breakfast, and, if we're back on board by 11.30 a.m. there's mid-morning coffee with home-made chocolate éclairs. How the hell am I expected to fit in another oatmeal biscuit? I'm starting to look like one as it is.

In my humble opinion, and I'm no Alan Whicker, the pretty port of Propriano is a damp squib. A limp lettuce. It may be an ideal bridge between the mountains and beaches but, to be honest, I'd rather have stopped on board listening to Barbara's bridge lecture (today it's 'signalling the legitimate way for experienced players'). Propriano is no prettier than Paignton. But there's far more to do in Devon and I quickly decide to quit this deserted ghost town in favour of a pint in the Champions Bar. I could sit staring at Bjorn Borg holding his Wimbledon Trophy aloft, and dream of a mixed doubles knock-up with Daphne and Claire. I'd come in quickly with a penetrating forehand to Claire's baseline, followed by a neat little lob with Daphne, and a dipping volley down the middle to finish. New balls please.

It's unlikely. I'm getting carried away. And anyway, where is Daphne? She was the prat who told us about the wonders of Propriano. I bet she's pissed off to another part of Corsica. Somewhere with a bit of life. She's living it up, knowing full well she's left us poor buggers high and dry in a Ghost Town. (The Specials. 1981.)

I pass a small section of shingle beach where a group of dads from our ship are busily trying to keep their children amused with a sandcastle-building competition organized by the Woody Woodpecker Club. (Everybody here is from our ship but nobody's told the locals to open the shops on the so-called promenade.) Still, the kids seem to be having a good time, despite the stiff breeze that's gusting in from the sea.

I've got a theory about sandcastles. You can tell the occupation or hobby of the dad concerned by the sandcastle he's trying to build. The architect has carefully constructed a ten-bedroom mansion with matching turrets and a surrounding moat, approached by a sweeping drive that meanders its way from the seashore to the portcullis. The mechanics have built a car with lumps of sand hastily scooped at all four corners to depict the wheels. Discarded lollipop sticks are the controls. If they're lucky, a spare bit of driftwood comes in handy for a gear stick. Those with a bent toward history have subconsciously piled up the sand in a random triangular mound. They have inadvertently built an ancient Egyptian Pyramid. Funeral directors prefer to bury limbs in the ground, while cable layers and gas board men dig holes. They just dig and dig.

It makes me wonder. If they didn't stop digging and finally reached Australia, would they come out feet first and drop off the end of the world into outer space? Interesting. Builders you can spot a mile off. They've built half a sandcastle and abandoned the project to go for a quick pint. Poets and pop stars simply write love letters in the sand. (It worked for Pat Boone. Got him to number two in 1957.) Sportsmen are rather more difficult to track down. That's except for cricketers. Three tall towers attached – bail-like – by a slim bridge.

I bet Jack Russell (my all-time hero) would be a natural in the world of sandcastle construction. He's a cricketer and an artist – the perfect combination. We're kindred spirits Jack and I. If I found him in bed with my wife I'd pull the sheets over him to make sure he didn't catch a chill. I'm a replica of Jack. I'm his other half – his Jill – only I'm happy to stay in the shadows while he, awkwardly, takes the spotlight. Of course he's achieved far more than I ever will. And I'm scared of cricket balls because they hurt when they hit you. And I can't paint pictures. And I've never represented my country at anything. And I haven't got a floppy sun-hat. Apart from that, we're bloody identical.

It's all in the mind, see. Robert Charles Russell, Gloucestershire and England cricketer (he plays backstop), likes his Weetabix soaked in milk for between twelve and fifteen minutes exactly; I like my tongue sandwich on a Saturday afternoon. He remembers everything about his career and life (he's still haunted by a missed stumping off the bowling of David Graveney against Northamptonshire in 1982); I still remember how to play 'Pop Goes the Weasel' on my Rolf Harris Stylaphone.

This man is an inspiration to every youngster in the world because he turned his hopes into happenings. If he hadn't been a cricketer, he would have been prime minister, I'm one hundred per cent sure of it. Sweeping statement, but bear with me, and you'll see what I mean.

Jack had a dream. A stupid, impossible dream. He sat around the dinner table in a council house in Stroud, on a run-of-the-mill Christmas day and pulled the wishbone out of the chicken (this lot were so poor they couldn't afford a turkey). He gazed at the wishbone for a second and said to himself, 'One day I'll play cricket at Lords for Gloucestershire,' just like his hero Alan Knot (another backstop) who he'd watched and admired in the Benson and Hedges Cup Final of 1977; the first time he'd ever seen Gloucestershire in the flesh. This poor, scrawny, grubby haired ragamuffin had no right to play cricket for Gloucestershire. But he did.

Having set that goal, he tried another. What about going to Lords again. This time to play for England. The man went on to play in fifty-four tests and forty one-day internationals. The big knobs in the long room, most of them trumped up twerps born with a silver spoon in their mouths, were soon to be speaking of him as if he were a lord himself. (Please note: trumped up twerps are often like that. Their opinions twist and turn more frequently than a well-rubbed cricket ball. It's their secret of success: find a winner and stick with it. Until you find another winner, then dump the previous winner faster than you can say 'Howzat!') Yet still, Jack Russell remained true to himself. He wasn't going to fall for the charms of the gentlemen who once looked down their noses at him. In the words of the great song, he did it (and still does it) *his* way.

On one cricket tour he ate well-done steak and chips on twenty-eight consecutive nights. He keeps his gloves and floppy hat locked away. If he doesn't know where they are at any particular point, he has a panic attack. I'm the same with my Pan's People paperweight at work. He takes his painting utensils all over the world. As a keen student of military history, when he dies, he plans for his coffin to be placed on top of a Sherman tank, and for his hands to be cut off and placed in his gallery in Gloucestershire. He's that patriotic that he insisted on his wife playing the Queen's speech down the telephone when he was touring in South Africa. Best of all, he blindfolds other members of his family before they come to visit because he likes to keep the whereabouts of his house secret. Only three of his relatives know his home telephone number.

I bloody adore the bloke. He does everything in a 'just so' manner (even the milky tea is just right, and he drinks it by the gallon). Not because he's fussy, but because that's the way he is and he's determined not to change for anybody. He's living his life his way. The man is black and white with no grey areas.

I met him very briefly, just the once, after reading his autobiography *Barking?* I went to Edgbaston on an overcast Tuesday to corner him. And I did. I can remember my speech as if it was yesterday.

'I'm sorry to tell you, but the good Lord has made us twins of the mind.'

As per blooming usual, I felt embarrassment crawling up on me (my Donny Osmond affliction) but I carried on shaking his hand with every word I uttered.

'I feel the same about things as you do. And I'm proud of you even though I don't really know you at all.'

I managed to gabble the words into a sentence as he dashed off the field in between sessions. He was always first off. He looked me square on – I shall never forget it – and said:

'Thank you for telling me that. Don't ever let anyone tell you you're wrong.'

You ask anybody. I've now got the cleanest drawers in the British potato industry. I can put my hand on anything. At home it's the same. I have my own special way of keeping my small semi-detached house in order. Everything's done in my own little way – my own little teaset, my own little tray. My main hobby is pottering about the place, putting things away. (I long to own a bed and breakfast when I grow up. I could even give these buggers a run for their money with a can of Vanish and a tin of Pledge.) It's an undisputed fact. I do things the Jack Russell way. I'm his disciple.

I'm also a disciple of Daphne, and like all good followers, I'll be at her side (well, right in front of her) when the Livorno port enhancement talk gets underway in the Hippodrome Theatre later this afternoon.

Propriano looks much better when you're back on the good ship *Perfect* but I've no time left for gazing. The pressure's beginning to mount and I can feel myself getting the wind up. After Daphne's Italian talk (I won't take much notice because I'm not going to either Florence or Pisa from Livorno), it's Jerry Lee Lewis and Claire in the Happy Days Diner. I might stay there for my evening meal tonight and let the crazy gang on table 69 cope without me. I quite fancy a more casual dining experience. And anyway, there'll be enough excitement tomorrow on table 69 when Tom celebrates his birthday just prior to the cocktail karaoke.

I'm going to sit near the Children's Deck to keep an eye on Claire's red and white canopy. Any sign of movement and I'll be in there like a ferret down a hole (once bitten, twice shy).

It's funny how some mothers love to flaunt their parent craft. One little boy is running around the paddling pool. His mum's making sure she broadcasts his every movement. 'Good boy Jacob,' she booms across the sun deck. 'No, don't touch that rubber ring, it's not yours, it's the little girl's. Do you want a drink now poppet or shall we play with the Mickey Mouse ball? Jacob. That's not yours. Give it back to the little boy. No, he doesn't want to see your winky.' What she's really saying to the assembled bunch of sun worshippers roasting on their sunbeds like chickens on a spit is: 'Look at me everybody. I'm the world's greatest mother. No sign of abuse in my house. I *really know* how to look after children.' Jacob will probably grow up to be a category A prisoner. Overprotection at a young age, see.

There's a little chap of about three in the children's jacuzzi. He's splashing around with two five-year-old girls without a care in the world. And why should he care? It's eighty degrees and he's on one of the world's most luxurious cruise liners anchored off a pretty Corsican hideaway with two birds at his beck and call. I'm tempted to go over and tell him that life doesn't get any better. 'From now on son, it's all downhill.' But he's too young for a Kendo Nagasaki-type let down. I'll leave him to enjoy the moment.

Before I know it, Daphne's on stage. I almost missed the start because I was queuing for a salad roll in the buffet restaurant. Unfortunately, I got held up in a bottleneck of ex-*Canberra* cruisers. It was hell. I was jammed in on all sides (and you can tell them a mile off, always harping on about the good old days. Nothing on this ship will ever be good enough for the ex-*Canberra* crowd). The topic this time was cold beans at breakfast. It's not the first time the beans have been brought up. In fact, the warmth of the early morning bean seems to be a major topic of conversation with the whole ship. They're all obsessed; I witnessed it for myself yesterday. The matching couple forced the head chef to stick his thermometer into the baked bean tray, right in front of their identically burnt noses. It was a hairy moment I can tell you. The whole of the room held its breath...but the beans passed the test and normal service was resumed.

Now I've had a hairy moment myself, rushing from salad roll to Hippodrome Theatre, but I've made it with seconds to spare. It's a good job I did as well. Daphne's noticed me. She glanced my way and nodded as I took my usual seat at the front for the third port enhancement talk of the tour (only Rome and Barcelona to go). She's probably thinking, 'There's the drunken dork who tried to interfere with my night of lesbian lovemaking.'

I sit through the forty-minute talk with half a dozen others. Two of them fall asleep in Florence while a third nods off in Pisa. His head started to lean just as we were arriving at the leaning tower. Before you could say 'cannelloni' he was snoring.

I enjoy watching them crash out one by one, but it must be devastating for our poor Port Enhancement Queen.

There's a new face in the theatre. A man of about fifty. Very neat. He's wearing a blazer despite the heat. Brylcreamed hair, flicked back like a 1950s holiday camp rep. He's far too confident for his own good. He's asking Daphne questions during the question and answer session at the end of the talk. How dare he. Nobody's ever asked Daphne a question on this voyage. I should know. I've not missed a talk. I've sat here and witnessed every cough, splutter and snore. I deserve a testimonial for my one hundred per cent port enhancement presence. And I'm not going to be upstaged by some tosser in a blazer. If he thinks he's going to barge in and take over the whole bloody kit and caboodle, he's got another thing coming. Well-groomed git.

He's probably a leading light in the Rotary Club back home. Dicky Cox can't stand members of the Rotary Club. Hates them more than anything else in the world. (It's a bit extreme if you ask me. How can you hate a Rotarian more than someone who mashes Jersey Mids or microwaves jacket potatoes? They're public enemy number one in my view.) According to Dicky, Rotarians are 'a group of half-baked nitwits trying to prove their self-worth by throwing themselves down the charity route'. He used to say to me: 'Don't ever think they're in it to help the good causes. They are there to boost their own pathetic inadequacies.' He means it as well. He once tried to have the president of our local Rotary Club kneecapped (mind you he was a nasty little worm if I remember right. Ended up running off with the Round Table Chairman's daughter, and she was only seventeen).

Dicky's mate knows a former villain who will kneecap a victim of your choice. I was on the verge of employing his services after the Terry Taylor incident, but I bottled out, and the butcher kept his knees. Mind you, I've kept his business card. It's under my Pan's People paperweight. You never know when you're going to need a good kneecapping service. And, let's face it, it's a snip at seventy-five quid.

Filing out of the Hippodrome, I'm full of hate for the Tosser in the Blazer who's trying to steal my thunder. As a kneecapping candidate, he's a dead cert. Suddenly, there's a tap on my shoulder. It's Daphne.

'I think you're ever so lovely coming to my talks. And I'm sorry if I appeared off-hand at the Captain's Ball last night. I think I'd had a little too much to drink. I was rather tiddily when I got back to my bed.'

Well, here's a turn up for the bollocking books. Daphne is gazing into my eyes, apologizing for her cock-up when I'd been beating myself up all night because I thought I'd made a plonker of myself in front of her and Miss Cruise Bore. I ended up half buried in the shag pile, and she's saying sorry for being pissed. It's the biggest upset since Hereford United beat Newcastle in the FA Cup and thousands of kids invaded the pitch in their green parker coats. You know the ones, grey fur around the hood. Most of them were green but I had a bloody blue one. Typical. And my feet were too small to fit into a proper pair of Doc Martins. I was called 'baby docs' at school for years. But I finally came good and got my own back. I was the first kid to wear a jumper with those crouching skiers going around a band in the middle. Oh yes, I've been fashionable in my time.

Anyway. I'm delighted. Daphne's clearly no lesbian after all. She's decided to make me the object of her holiday passion. Miss Cruise Bore, who clearly wants to sniff around her Ginger Rogers, was just trying to take advantage of her lovely nature knowing full well she was under the influence. Probably been giving the Orgasms a bollocking before she went into the ballroom. Flushed with success, I barge in with the first thing that comes into my head:

'Have you got any Czechoslovakian in you Deirdre?'

Deirdre! I've done it again. I've called her 'Deirdre' when I know full well it's 'Daphne'. How the hell am I ever going to get close to pulling a real woman in my sad and sorry life with slip-ups like that? When it comes to the crunch, I'm left wanting in almost every department. In short, I'm an arseholing wanking git. I think that sums it up nicely.

'I'm sorry, it's Daphne isn't it? Like the girl from Scooby Doo.'

It's the only other Daphne I know. She always went one way with Velma and Freddie, while Scooby and Shaggy went the other.

'Czech? No. But I am half Welsh. What's your name?' asks Daphne, attempting to rescue the situation. You've got to give it to her, she's plodding on even though the cause for some would seem well and truly lost.

It's the question I dread. 'What's your name?' It's a simple enough request but I shall never forget the time I told Lucille Bullock my name. 'Malcolm,' I'd said. She'd roared with laughter. Couldn't believe anyone was called Malcolm in real life. He was the man in the Vicks Sinex Nasal Spray adverts. I'll just have to grit my teeth and answer as honestly as I can.

'Malcolm,' I reply.

'Well Malcolm, it's lovely to meet you. Maybe we can share a drink some time.'

In the words of Victor Meldrew, I don't believe it! I'm nearly thirty-eight and I've had one shag in my life. I come on a bloody ship and now I've had two women asking me to go out with them in as many days. They're practically falling at my feet. (I wonder if it's got anything to do with the cold beans?) I've scored again. I'm like Geoff Hurst at the 1966 World Cup final. I'm Michael Owen against the Germans in München. Every time I touch the flipping ball it goes in. I'll ride my luck. The night is young and Claire is waiting. Like a seasoned juggler, on this voyage, I'm going to keep as many balls up in the air as possible.

'Wonderful,' I say. I'm just about to fix a date when the Tosser in a Blazer butts in with a question about the 'Field of Miracles' in Pisa. I'll give him a bloody miracle. It's a miracle he's still on his feet. I should have laid the swine out for ruining my moment. The man's a total slime-ball.

I once devised a 'slime-o-graph' for the office. Margaret Chandler was top for six weeks running, only to be dislodged briefly by Dibble the Muffin Man who shot straight in at number one for trying to sell marinated beaver rolls. (The dish was devised by food historian Dr Roland Rotherham. It never caught on, and neither did Dibble's snacks.) He clinched the top spot when he arrived at the office one day with a strange twinkle in his eye and, oozing slime, announced: 'Anyone for beaver?' Anyway, they've all just been gazumped. The Tosser in the Blazer has out-slimed the slimiest. He's the new undisputed slime lord. I'm still cursing him and his 'Field of Miracles' when I get back to my cabin. Mind you, it's a minor miracle that I'm still in the ball game as far as Daphne's concerned. It's just a shame she's got no Czechoslovakian in her. My willow beating stick would have been a brilliant ice-breaker.

I'm into my eveningwear early. Six o'clock start, see. And I'm just in time to see the ship leave the port of Propriano. It's a lovely evening. The waiters are serving canapés on the poop deck to the assembled crowd, while our resident band are playing 'Yellow Bird' to the gathered sun-soaked few. (For the uninitiated, a canapé is a small snack, usually resembles a small squirt of Dairylea cheese on a Ritz biscuit and topped with a processed pea, that sort of thing.) It's amazing. Some of the old dodderers have almost changed colour in front of my very eyes. They've gone from light pink to purple in just one day; must have been the wind in Propriano.

I may be a sad cynical old git at times, but even I must concede, the atmosphere is magical. Do you know, I don't think I'll ever take a 'normal' holiday again as long as I live. That's how a cruise hooks you. You're given the best. Everything else will seem like second rate after this.

I'm singing to myself over my Orgasm. (I'm growing quite fond of them.)

'Yellow bird, up high in banana tree.'

The ship leaves Corsica behind. We're full steam ahead for Italy.

'Yellow bird, you sit all alone like me.
Did your lady friend leave the nest again?
That is very sad, makes me feel so bad.
You can fly away, in the sky away.
You're more lucky than me.'

My Orgasm's gone straight to my head. I'm a contented man. For one of the few times in my life, I feel at peace with the world. Tonight is going to be Perfect. Just Perfect.

9

The man's a bloody genius.

Jerry Lee Lewis is at it full swing in the Happy Days Diner. This place has opened up a whole new world for me. He's just rattled his way through 'Sweet Little Sixteen' and 'High School Confidential'. Now the bloke's literally hammering the bollocks out of the piano as he rams into 'Good Golly, Miss Molly'. The sun's gone to everybody's head and the atmosphere is electric.

I think Great Britain would be a marvellous place with three months of unbroken sunshine. Show me a political party that can offer me a Mediterranean summer and I'll show you a cross in their box. Roll on global warming, I say. Despite the scaremongering, I quite fancy the thought of going to work on a camel.

There's a different clientele altogether up here and it's no wonder when you look at the menu. Fish and chips for supper and they specialize in traditional English puddings. There's a glamorous young thing sitting at the bar swinging on her stool. A gentleman who looks old enough to be her great-grandfather is shovelling Spotted Dick into her mouth. She licks her lips and giggles as a crumb of Dick falls into her ample cleavage. It's like watching a mother thrush feeding worms to her young.

It looks like I've inadvertently stumbled upon another fascinating cruise pair. Introducing, at the bar – and swallowing another mouthful of spotted dick – Sugar Daddy and Miss

Sugar Baby Love. ('Sugar Baby Love.' A Rubettes classic.) Maybe she's the ship's high-class hooker. No. Far too common. She speaks with a broad Lancastrian accent, and she's over-bold in her delivery if you ask me. As for the poor old bugger that's grabbing her attention, he looks ninety, but he must be well-heeled in the wallet department. Believe me, it makes all the difference. Money is a great leveller when it comes to pulling a loud-mouthed lassie from Lancashire. (Mind you, she's got a sensational pair of knockers. When she bends down in that dress I can see it all. Young women these days, they don't give a monkey's!)

She's leapt into first place for the 'Knockers of the Voyage' award. She's even on course to pick up a gong for the most daring dress. But she's not my type. It's a wonder the Tosser in the Blazer hasn't got his slimy paws on her well-rounded bazookas. He's up here looking for talent – it's written all over his face – but he'd better keep his eyes off Daphne and Claire, unless he wants his kneecaps blown off in Southampton.

Claire arrives. But I don't get the loving 'it's been so long since you held me in your arms' hug. It's more of a whistle-stop peck that just misses my left cheek. (She's gone all showbiz; it's mingling with DeVine that's done it.) Not the start I was hoping for. Maybe I should divert my attentions to the Lassie from Lancashire after all and concentrate on getting my nose wedged firmly between those beautiful bosoms.

What ever happened to the old-fashioned Triumph bra? The world's number one boulder-holder before the company decided to make bicycles instead. My Auntie Helicopter used to swear by them. (Of course, her surname wasn't 'Helicopter', but she brought me one for Christmas when I was three and, somehow, the name stuck.) While my mind's on bras, it's also worth contemplating the 'Cross Your Heart' which came into its own when it offered to lift and separate. These days they're still after the lift but then it's more a case of 'get 'em bunched up as close as you can', like two crown green bowls around a jack.

On closer inspection, it looks as if the Lassie from Lancashire has had a boob job. They're all the rage with women these days, false bazookas. Some girls don't know when to stop. They end up with a couple of space hoppers stuck to their chest. False dongers? Foul, if you ask me. I'd sooner plump for untampered tit any day, no matter what the size.

No need to ask Claire what she wants to drink. There's no waiting at the bar trying desperately to grab the bartender's attention when you're on board the *Perfect*. Before she's even sat down, the waiter's there with a tray. He's done up like Buddy Holly, but, being Indian it doesn't quite come off.

Claire's as cool as a cucumber. Asks me about life at the British Potato Marketing Board. I tell her everything's going fine. Of course, I'm lying though my teeth.

'And your love life?'

'Oh, that sort of disintegrated when I discovered Terry Taylor's hand under your Playtex. For a man who's got hands like shovels, he's certainly very agile when it comes to squeezing them into tight spots. Years of practice getting his sausage meat into their skins I suppose.'

'Malcolm,' Claire's taking a firm grip on proceedings, 'forget Terry fucking Taylor. He's history, right? He was just a good shag when I needed one. End of story.'

Well, considering I was her boyfriend at the time, that makes me feel a lot better.

'So what about Norman DeVine?'

I don't care now. After an Orgasm on the poop deck and a couple of shorts with Jerry Lee Lewis and the Lassie from Lancashire, I'm throwing caution to the wind. (Sugar Baby Love is definitely an item with Old Father Time. She's got her arms around his waist. The wonders of modern medicine. I bet he's dosed up to the eyeballs with Viagra.)

'Norman and I are business partners more than anything,' insists Claire. 'We've got a lovely arrangement, if you see what I mean.'

I don't, but I agree with her anyway. Oh God. Jerry Lee Lewis is off again.

The Happy Days Diner has erupted into a cacophony of noise as Lewis shifts into top gear. I swear to you, he's playing the piano with his feet.

Sugar Baby Love almost pops out of her dress as she raises her arms to the roof. She drags her head back in a moment of wild excitement. It's probably the only excitement she's had all holiday. (I expect she gives him a blow-job every morning without fail. That's the deal.) Claire meanwhile, has given me no indication of regret. There's no sign of her love light shining in my direction and that's quite disappointing considering I began the night with an Orgasm. What am I supposed to make of it all? She's colder than the breakfast beans, yet she assures me that Norman DeVine is little more than a business associate. Does she realize she's got me dangling like a puppet on a string? (Back to night one – Sandie Shaw.)

Maybe I should seek advice from my new friends on table 69. In a strange way I miss them all. They may be a bunch of total weirdoes, but I'm beginning to like them. Even Mouthy Kev has his plus points. So does June. Perhaps she would be able to tell me whether Claire was gagging for a lampooning up the Gulf of Mexico. Or is she more a quick Jessie Matthews up the Fred Astaire? Where's my Auntie June when I need her most?

Claire's gone in a flash. She has to meet Norman in the Crow's Nest. He's got a busy day tomorrow, trying to knock the punters into shape for the grand cocktail and karaoke evening with our resident band 'Bliss'. Bliss on the good ship *Perfect*. I ask you. Did they see us coming? As for me, I'm left alone again, naturally. (Gilbert O'Sullivan. Again.) The high-class hooker is well pissed. Sugar Daddy is in for a *Good*

Night Sweetheart. It's my favourite television programme. Margaret Chandler says I'm one of the good Lord's mistakes. I should have been born between the wars but I came to earth too late. I often ask myself, Why was I born too late? (Poni-Tails. Got to number five in 1958.)

I'm going for a walk on the poop deck. The evening hasn't quite turned into the free-for-all sexual frenzy I'd hoped for. Claire shows more consideration to her puppets than she does to me. Mind you, there's no one who can perform the 'Punch hitting Judy over the head with stick' routine like she can. It's almost as good as her 'Crocodile stealing the sausages' scene. The College of Professors awarded her a Silver Judy at the annual 'That's the way to do it!' bash at a top class London hotel. It was in recognition of her work persuading more young females to become Punch and Judy artists. The top prize, a Golden Nose, went to Professor Gordon Hornblower. Well deserved too. It was a lovely, touching story. One that pulled at everyone's heartstrings:

Professor Hornblower fell into a coma after a rather nasty seaside accident. A carousel horse he was riding, worked its way loose and careered head-on into an oncoming open-topped tram that was making its way steadily along the Esplanade. Good job the lady operating the nearby barrel organ was a fully trained member of the St John's Ambulance Brigade or he would have died on the spot. Right in front of his own Punch and Judy booth. Anyway, after nearly three weeks in a coma, Professor Gordon Hornblower had a vision. Mr Punch came out of a cloud and told him he was going to make a full recovery. Mr Punch, of all people, dressed in a shimmering golden robe and surrounded by Judy-type angels. He held out his hand, Professor Hornblower grasped it and within seconds he was back in the land of the living. It was, some said, a miraculous recovery.

Since then, he's turned his house near Seymour Butts into a Mr Punch shrine. There's a seven-foot nose in the front garden, which he hangs fairy lights on at Christmas for charity. He's got more than one hundred and seventy pictures of Punch in his sitting-room and he's tastefully modelled the porch on his own Punch and Judy booth. Here's the bit that swayed it for me. When you press the doorbell, you don't get a chime. You get a Mr Punch-like, 'That's the way to do it!' Professor Gordon Hornblower has dedicated his life to Mr Punch. There was a standing ovation when he walked up to receive his trophy.

Dinner on table 69 is over. I know because, in the distance, I can hear June singing. I can't quite make out where the sound is coming from but it's definitely June. Her high-pitched squeak is piercing the calm night air. Stubbornly I press on with my gentle evening stroll but, as June gets louder, I get increasingly sucked in. Finally I snap. Like a guided missile, I decide to close her down and pinpoint her exact location. For me it has become a mission – I'm determined to sniff her out (fortunately, I've always had a good nose). Before long, I've developed a cartoon-style creep – but I'm well and truly on the scent. Closer examination reveals that she's unusually out of tune.

Even more unusually, she's at the rear end of the poop deck. Her and Tom usually go for an Orgasm in Alexander's Bar before they turn in. I'll go and surprise her, although not in a Ginger Rogers sort of way, you understand. I'm still trying to piece together the fallout following my rather abrupt evening with Claire. To be honest, I don't think I've got a Bobby Hope of tossing my pink maggot into her lap again. Still, a good few minutes with June should soon cheer me up.

Hold on a minute. My rather pacey, if not a little over-confident, creep has now slowed to a careful tiptoe. It's no surprise, either. I'm met by potentially one of the most horrific scenes I've ever witnessed. It's like coming face to face with

Brenda Burston on the Witch's Hat all over again. If I'm right, this sordid scenario could really get tongues wagging!

With a nifty glance off the outside of my foot, I kick a stray quoit underneath a vacant wooden deck-chair. It's a silly mistake. I don't want to draw attention to myself at this vital stage. I need to be still, almost glued to the spot. Slowly, I tilt my head forward. Then, reality kicks in. Oh no! It can't be. It's too much to take in.

Not tonight of all nights. I'm washed out sexually. I'm ready for my rocking-chair.

Very steadily, I move closer. I'll have another good look, just to make sure. I'm spot on. It's them. They're at it. Just in front of the children's jacuzzi. They're shagging. He's knocking her off.

It's a lovely night. The full moon casts a shimmering light onto the well-scrubbed decking, and yet there they are. Bonking for England. Mouthy Kev is having sexual intercourse with June, and she's singing, well, more like shrieking now. If I'm not mistaken, it's *The Sound of Music* song featuring a yodelling goatherd on top of a hill. Kevin's got his boxer shorts dangling by his ankles. I wonder if those are the drawers where he keeps his special shuttlecock? June's putting every last ounce of energy into a final non-stop yodel.

It's amazing, and it's going on before my very eyes. Kiss Me Kate did warn us. Just the other night she said that something had got Kevin flustered. How were we to know it was June? The dirty old bag is riding the poor bloke raw while, at the same time, attempting to belt out a gutsy rendition of a Julie Andrews classic (although she sounds more like a fading opera singer trying to grasp the high notes while driving over a cattle-grid). What shall I do? Turn a blind eye, or break it up in the name of good honest British decency. I'll cock a deaf one. Anyway, for all I know, Thomas the Toothbrush might be upstairs in the Statesman Suite with 'bath...*and balcony*!' meddling with Kiss Me Kate's laa-laa.

He's probably there right now, giving her beaver a good scrubbing with his well-used nail-brush while Jessie Matthews belts out a couple of songs from *The Midshipmaid* on the gramophone.

It's alarming. I leave table 69 for one pleasant evening in the Happy Days Diner and all hell breaks loose. I'm going to retreat to my cabin, sit in the rocking-chair, put a towel over my head and order a large one from Oh Danny Boy. Let's face it, him and me are the only ones not getting our end away this evening. And even I've had two Orgasms with a yellow bird.

I'm quitting while the going's good. Deck F is my sanctuary. But not for long. There's a stranger in the shadows waiting to capture my attention. It seems the night has one last sting in its tail.

'Pssst. Malcolm.'

I half-heartedly attempt to turn my head. But, if I'm totally truthful, I'm too scared to go the whole hog. It might be the ship's ghost.

'It's me you twat. I'm over here,' whispers a now familiar voice. And it's no spook. It's Kiss Me Kate crouching awkwardly beneath the fire extinguishers like a frightened bunny. I always said she had an air of mystery about her. But hiding on Deck F? I can't help feeling one or two questions need to be asked. Looking on the bright side, at least she's not having her Horseshoe Pass examined by Thomas the Toothbrush.

'Can I see you for a tick, chick?' Kate asks and then giggles at her unexpected ability to make two words rhyme. She's back at it with the chicken business, but she's not behaving in the way I've become accustomed. On the other hand, that might be me. After all, I have just seen her husband having a sexual encounter with June.

'Yes of course you can.' I reply without hesitation, not realizing I could be flirting with danger.

I've let my mild mannered nature rule my head and it's all wrong. Kiss Me Kate's on heat, you can sense it in her eyes.

She's like the woman off the Hi Karate adverts. And within seconds she's making a play for me, as nice as you like – more neck than a giraffe. She might not be a ghost, but I'm pretty sure she's after my goolies.

'Do you want to see my tu-tu?'

First it's laa-laas. Now it's tu-tus.

'Tu-tu? What's that…a dance?' I ask tentatively.

She laughs a seductive sort of laugh and inches ever closer to me with those Thelma Ferris-type 'come to bed' eyes. I might as well face the facts. Kiss Me Kate wants me between the sheets. She's bloody determined by the looks of things. She comes closer still, almost pinning me to the bathroom door. God only knows, I hope she doesn't discover my banana-flavoured condoms. It's all my fault. In a mad fit of overconfidence, I predicted that this night was made for love. But I didn't think for one minute that Kiss Me Kate, the loyal wife, would be heading towards me, licking her lips in cabin number F153 while her husband pole-axes Julie Andrews near the children's jacuzzi.

'I feel like chicken tonight,' sings Kate flapping her arms chicken style. How sad. She thinks she's got wings. Daisy? I got it all wrong. She's Poison Ivy. But I'm buggered if I'm going to be tiptoeing through her tulip. Not tonight of all nights.

She purrs like a kitten: 'I'm damp downstairs.'

How's that for an opening gambit? 'I'm damp downstairs.' Hardly a Hollywood classic. Clark Gable never turned to Scarlet O'Hara when the mansion was burning to the ground and told her straight out that his knob was as hard as the rock of Gibraltar. Just imagine it:

Clark Gable: 'Frankly, my dear, in the downstairs department I'm as stiff as a board.'
Scarlet O'Hara: 'I'm getting a touch of mildew in the nether regions myself.'

I should've ended it there and then. Damp downstairs, Kate? Frankly my dear, I don't give a damn. But I'm too kind. Before you can say *Gone with the Wind*, Kiss Me Kate moves in for a second attack. She says it again. But this time she opens her blouse (it's got *Guys and Dolls* written on the front and 'Luck be a Lady Tonight' emblazoned across the rear). I can see her heaving bosom lurching towards me.

'I said I'm damp downstairs.'

It's time for me to say something. 'Well, can't you get a man in?' I ask.

A limp-wristed response, I know. But she could have been talking about her four bedroom detached in Barnsley 'with swimming pool...*and en-suite changing facilities*!' (Mouthy Kev has told us everything.)

Kate is almost on top of me. Back-peddling for all I'm worth, I collapse awkwardly into the rocking-chair. I fall backwards, then rapidly plunge forwards so my nose is almost jammed between her breasts (and she has got a decent pair, currently lying second to the Lancashire Lassie in the 'best boobs of the holiday' category; looks like it's going to be a ding-dong battle). She pats my head and sings softly: 'Chick, chick, chick, chick chicken. Lay a little egg for me.'

In a state of amazement and panic, I hastily blurt out the first thing that comes into my head: 'I'm sorry Kate, I don't lay eggs. Besides, I'm waiting for a stiff one from Danny.'

That's told her straight. For once in my life I feel like I've given the speech of a lifetime. But I'm still in shock. Kiss Me Kate! The absolute neck of the woman. Doesn't she realize that *not* shagging is the new shagging? And as for Malcolm's Log! What started off as a one horse race (Daphne) has turned into the bloody Grand National. And there's me – a so-called 'chalk jockey'. Stoop and Droop fell at the first fence, never really got under starters orders. Hattie Jacques was an early straggler too. Carrying far too much weight. June? Unseated her rider at Bechers Brook first time round.

(From what I can make out, it's the first time she's ever unseated a rider in her life. She was going like the clappers with Mouthy Kev.) Mrs Cocktail Stick: elbowed at the elbow. Anyway, I think she's gone on to find new love in the shape of the Pillsbury Dough Man. Kiss Me Kate: refused at the Chair. What's-her-name – I mean Claire: starting to tire as we cross the Melling Road for the second time. That leaves Daphne well out in front. But on the evidence of tonight, anyone could be coming up to challenge on the rails.

Kiss Me Kate has realized she's on to a loser:

'We all fancy you on table 69 you know. I'm not giving up. Before Rome, we'll be like two coins in the fountain. I know it.'

'It's three coins actually Kate,' I say, trying desperately to stay friends with this lady. The loyal wife who turned into a sex beast while I was tapping my feet to 'Great Balls of Fire'.

'Well if you insist. Three coins it will be.'

Oh fuck it. She shuts the door on cabin F153. I've just joined the 'Tits Out for the *Titanic*' club. Hattie Jacques was right. It's all shag on this boat. I sit on my rocking-chair with my towel over my head. Tomorrow is the cocktail and karaoke night and I'm in all sorts of trouble. It's not going to be easy for me to get my head down.

10

It's been coming out of both ends of me all night. I'm a nervous wreck. Tossing and turning into the small hours. In and out of the bathroom like a dog at a fair. Welcome to the 'Maison des Lunes'. This boat's got more tricks up its sleeve than David Nixon had in his Magic Box. (David Nixon? He was sort of a 1970s Paul Daniels without the lovely Debbie McGee.)

Dig this. Just a few hours ago, Kiss Me Kate was trying to seduce me in this very room. The mild-mannered, loyal wife had turned into a rampaging bull. Some blokes would have jumped at the chance. I can almost hear June now: 'Go on, slip your Bali High up her South Pacific. Run your tongue over her Oklahoma and watch the wind come sweeping down her plains.' She'd have loved it. Mind you, it was June who tipped me off at the Captain's Ball. She'd already noticed that lust was lurking underneath that *Phantom of the Opera* blouse. And as for her having it away with Mouthy Kev... As proud as a peacock he was, waving his award-winning shuttlecock in front of the children's jacuzzi. I couldn't have been the only one to hear her impromptu rendition of that Julie Andrews classic about the hill and the yodelling farm-hand (the artist otherwise known as a goatherd). It's Tom's birthday today as well. Poor bugger. Left in a room with his toothbrush, waiting patiently on the prospect of a bit of pre-birthday laa-laa stroking. It was him I was supposed to hear wailing in delight, not her, yodelling into the clear night air as the ship sailed on. (Paul Nicholas again, remember? 'Dancing with the Captain.' Got to number eight in 1976.)

And how was the atmosphere in the Statesman Suite when Kiss Me Kate and Mouthy Kev finally got in last night? Was it a planned shag-fest? Did they compare notes? How am I supposed to behave on table 69 tonight? Then there's the cocktail karaoke party on the Sunshine Deck this evening. The way it's going we'll have a full-scale orgy on our hands. It wouldn't surprise me if the Captain was slipping Hattie Jacques a length at the breakfast buffet this morning. And goodness only knows where the matching couple are going to ask the head chef to plunge his thermometer. I've decided I'm definitely a social outcast. I live on the morning side of the mountain, while the rest of the world lives on the twilight side of the hill. No wonder I'm shitting myself.

Malcolm's Log. For the record, it's Tuesday, June 24th. After the delights of Gibraltar and Corsica, it's a 'relaxing' day at sea. I'm too emotionally exhausted to record the events of yesterday. Suffice to say that, on moral grounds, I'm not giving Kiss Me Kate a mark out of ten for shagability. In fact, I'm abandoning my shagability ratings from now on as a mark of disgust. Suddenly, I've gone right off sex.

The *Nautical Newsletter* arrives just in time. Sanity is restored for a moment. It's a good job there's plenty of alternative entertainment to keep me going, while the other randy buggers entertain themselves. The social short tennis is up and running from 9 a.m. followed by a stretch and relax class in the dreaded Paradise Ballroom, 'for those who overindulged the night before'. Most of the flipping ship, if my night is anything to go by. On past experience, if I go lurking anywhere near the Paradise Ballroom today, I'm liable to be carted away and court marshalled, or whatever they do in the navy.

I'll skip the deck quoits on Deck 13 as well. Quoits my arse. It's just a jumped up version of hoop-la. And shuffleboard's just as bad. It's curling without the ice. (After my early and quite unexpected introduction to the sport at school, I once teamed up with Dicky Cox to invent office curling. We used two mops and my Pans People paperweight. It worked a treat.) Anyway, nobody's any good at shuffleboard on this voyage. You can't move for the buggers trying to shunt an ice hockey-type punt in front of your plimsoles.

I'll give Deck 13 one thing. It's very picturesque. There's even a handy little shower and sauna hut just beside the quoits court. Although, why you'd need a shower after quoits is beyond me – you're hardly likely to build up a sweat. I had it down as a handy little shagging den if me and Daphne 'got it on' near the crow's nest and couldn't wait to get down to the 'almost submerged when the tide's in' Deck F.

One of the girls in our Potatoes for Pleasure office entered the British Sauna Bathing Championships last autumn. It's one of Europe's fastest growing sports (could even give extreme ironing a run for its money). The idea is to sit still and upright in the sweltering heat of the sauna for as long as possible. Last one to flake out is declared the winner. Our girl only lasted twelve minutes, twenty-four and a half seconds. The crown eventually went to a woman from Ellesmere Port who was still going after four hours. They had to yank her out in the end. She was suffering from severe dehydration.

It's Takeout Doubles in the 'Bridge with Barbara' lecture this afternoon and Whist Drive in the Champions Bar followed by body conditioning and 'meander a mile' with one of the hosts. What's this? A 'Travelling Alone Get-together' in the crow's nest. 11.30 a.m. I'll make a mental note of it. Deck 13 again. No wonder the shagging den's up there. It all makes sense. There's also a double whammy on the port enhancement talk front. The delightful Daphne is giving us the remaining twosome – Rome and Barcelona. I'll be at both.

Claire proved to be too cold a customer at the Happy Days Diner last night. Should have known. She broke my heart tugging at Terry Taylor's T-bone so why should she have changed? No, Daphne is definitely the object of my love. Pure and simple. (Hearsay; the fallen Pop Stars.) Although I can't possibly contemplate a serious sexual challenge today, not after the events of last night.

Kiss Me Kate has knocked me back a good three years in the bedroom department. Who does she think I am? Some sort of Shuttlecock Sam who drops his pants at the first sight of a heaving Dolly Parton poking through a *Guys and Dolls* blouse? Some men yes, but not me love. I'm more a 'Nine to Five' than an 'Islands in the Stream'. (Both big hits for Miss Parton and her beautiful Dollys.) No. Kate's blown it with Mr Potato Head. I'm not peeling off for some overboiled Golden Wonder.

I'm soon on my way down the corridor. As usual, it's been rubbed, scrubbed, swept and polished. At the entrance to the Paradise Ballroom, there's an army of cleaners waiting to rake the shag pile. There's even a man perched precariously on a dangling bit of scaffolding outside. He's cleaning the picture window while the ship's sailing; must have nerves of steel. Moving swiftly on, as they say on breakfast television, I notice that Stoop and Droop have had their photographs taken with a backdrop of the *Titanic* and I'm up there too, looking a little confused as I pose next to the ship's mascot, Cyril the Seal. Mind you, it was day one and my nerves were beginning to get the better of me. Oh, and there's Daphne, Miss Cruise Bore and the skipper looking radiant at the Captain's Ball. (Miss Cruise Bore – yet another great obstacle in my never-ending quest for romance. Will she get her grubby little lesbian claws stuck into the Port

Enhancement Queen before I strike?) On further investigation I discover a picture of June, Tom, Mouthy Kev and Kate all raising a toast to...well, God knows what. Swingers of the world, possibly.

Finally I reach my destination. It's been a long haul but I'm inside the Hippodrome Theatre and Daphne's radiant. She's soon got all eleven of us going on the main attractions of Rome. I've booked a tour to do the whole city in a day. Basically, the coach drops you off somewhere near the Pope's house and you're free to explore from then on. It's my great travelling adventure of the holiday. My great sexual adventure, if I ever get my appetite back, is Daphne.

Sure enough, the Port Enhancement Queen is on top form. She's soon shifted into top gear and drawn first blood with a small, yet perfectly tuned rendition of 'Three Coins in the Fountain'. She's got the crowd eating out of the palm of her hand. Before you can say, 'Show us your threepenny bits', she's moved on to the Spanish Steps. I might take a stroll up them myself before a quick flick through the Pantheon (Roman for 'round building with a hole in the top').

By all accounts Emperor Hadrian erected the Pantheon in AD 118. He later went on to build up a decent business in the wall building industry until the bottom fell out when the Chinese went one better. Pink Floyd went on to record a tribute to the great Hadrian with their best-selling album, *Another Brick in the Wall*.

I wonder if Andy would settle for a quick ironing session on Hadrian's Wall as a sort of warm up to the great Chinese version? I must put it to him later on. He thinks Extreme Ironing will be an Olympic sport before the Olympics return to Great Britain.

I think ball juggling stands a better chance. And let's face it, he'd be a gold medal cert with those bollocks. (It's amazing how my mind races when Daphne's in mid delivery.) Take Michelangelo, for instance. Designed the dome at St

Peter's Basilica and then got on his back to paint the ceiling of the Sistine Chapel. According to the delightful one (who turns out to be nought per cent Czech, and fifty per cent Welsh) it took him four years, 1508 to 1512. Maybe June should've applied for the job. Four years on your back? No problem.

Finally we're at the Coliseum. Now here's a place for you. Held 55,000 spectators in its day. I wonder how much they paid for a ticket to see a good scrap to the death. The touts would have had a field day. I believe it'll come back into fashion. The ultimate reality television show. The lucky few inside the auditorium will be able to smell blood, while the rest of us sit glued to our screens waiting for the telephone vote on which innocent wannabe should be thrown to the lions. It would be the most compelling Saturday night TV event since they scrapped *Seaside Special* live from the big top of Gerry Cottle's Circus at selected holiday resorts across the United Kingdom. (Mike Batt sang the theme tune and went on to mastermind the Wombles' rise to the top of the charts.)

My mother, the Angel, went to one of those live recordings. Well, half of one. They were doing part of the show from Weymouth and the other half from the continent. Just over the channel in the French port of Cherbourg if my memory serves me correctly. New Generation (the top starving dancers of the day) did a routine to 'Chanson D'Amour' while Sacha Di-bloody-stel sang 'Raindrops keep falling on my head'. You ask anybody. They were television's glory days. I once wrote to the BBC pleading with them to bring back *Seaside Special*, *The Good Old Days* and *White Horses*, but they never replied.

The talk's over. Now, here's a dilemma. Do I linger and let Daphne catch me near the auditorium exit? Will she finally ask me out for a swift one in the Paradise Ballroom? I can see us now, sipping on a pint of Pina Colada while Mrs Hair

Bear Bunch and her two cronies take to the floor with the salsa. I wait… No Daphne. She's exited stage right. It's an awful setback. I can see my love hopes slipping away. Maybe Kiss Me Kate is worth another look after all.

I've got a good hour and a half to kill before the next talk, but just as I'm about to go and join the small crowd that gathers daily to witness the end of the shag pile raking in the Paradise Ballroom (on this boat it's quite a draw), I spot Alison in the Champion's Bar sipping gently on a lemon and lime. (You remember. Mrs Cocktail Stick. An early Spud wife challenger before I abandoned my Log in disgust at the sexual shenanigans of table 69.) She's got a lovely way about her. And I was right. She and the Pillsbury Dough Man met on one of these 'Travelling Alone Get-togethers' in the Neptune Suite. Love blossomed second day in.

'Our eyes met over a game of deck quoits. It was like the song,' she tells me.

'What song? I've got a lovely bunch of coconuts?' I playfully tease.

It's all right. I know I can have a laugh with Alison without her pouncing on top of me like some coiled up cobra.

'No!' She giggles at my joke.

Maybe I should've moved in on her when I had the chance. It would have been different, marrying a lady that looks like a spike. Who knows? We might have been very happy and had lots of little 'spikettes'. We'd have been laughing at Christmas. Just get the Kerplunk out and they would have all felt at home. If the marbles were close to dropping, I could have rammed a couple of kids through the holes for extra security. Alison continues: 'It was like the song. You know. " 'Twas a hot afternoon, last day of June, and the sun was a demon. De-de-de-de-de-de-deer." '

Of course, Mrs Cocktail Stick is talking total pants. Her meeting with the Pillsbury Dough Man couldn't have been anything like that song. (By the way it was Bobby Goldsboro in 1973.) For a start (a) it's still only June 14th, so she couldn't possibly have met him on the last day of June, and (b) in the song, she was thirty-one and he was only seventeen. No chance. They're both well into their forties. Besides, I wonder if she's told him about her miniaturist ways yet (she's the doll's house fanatic). For Mrs Cocktail Stick, size matters. She's got a passion for all things small, yet she's dating a bloke who's got to be more than twenty-five stone. I can't quite weigh it up.

The Pillsbury Dough Man arrives. He's come looking for her. Pleasant enough face; sort of a middle-aged Billy Bunter.

'Hello my little raspberry ripple. Fancy a bit of prize swap on the poop?'

I can't let that one go by.

'Prize swap Alison? You've only just met him. You're not thinking of trading him in for a new model yet are you?'

Now they're both laughing. If only they knew the secrets of table 69.

Prize swap is for the people that have won gifts at the shuffleboard, or jackpot bingo, or deck quoits. Some people have two 'Good Ship *Perfect*' T-shirts. Some have two brollies, etc. So they all get together to swap their prizes.

They depart hand in hand. The Pillsbury Dough Man turns and winks. 'I'm not a love walrus, but I know a man who is.' They both giggle and on their way out, he cocks his leg up, Morecambe and Wise style. That's the second time he's told me about knowing a man who's a love walrus. I haven't got the foggiest idea what he's on about. Still, if it makes them happy, who am I to mock? Incidentally, I'll bet Miss Cruise Bore is at the prize swap looking for another *Neptune* jacket to go with her ever-growing Cruise Bore collection.

Wrong again. She's at the port enhancement talk of Barcelona. I'm staying well away from her. I'm convinced she's trying to pull my Daphne over the other side of the fence. Saw it for my own eyes at the Captain's Ball. But Daphne's not that way inclined. I've got it worked out. Daphne's more a Shirley Bassey. Full-blooded Welsh girl from Tiger Bay. I knew it. The minute she walked in the joint.

Although I've no interest in Barcelona whatsoever, I'll stick it out to see if Cruise Bore makes a move on my chick. As the talk goes on, I find myself thinking how nice it would be to go and find a quaint little Spanish hideaway over-looking the sea and sit there quietly, contemplating the cruise while getting pleasantly pissed. (Pleasantly pissed is good. Pissed as a fart is bad. If you know where to draw the line, then yours is the world and all that is in it. And what's more, you'll be a man, my son.)

I suddenly realize the talk is over and I'm the last one out of the theatre. This time, Daphne's chosen to slip off stage left. It's another giant setback on the love front, but at least I still have the delights of Tom's birthday bash and the cocktail karaoke ahead. Norman DeVine's got the job of knocking the assembled chorus of volunteers into shape. I've encountered his type before. I was once dragged kicking and screaming by Dicky Cox to sign up for the Staffordshire Amateur Dramatics group (SAD for short). They were putting on a pantomime and Dicky fancied the girl playing Cinderella. He badgered me into auditioning for one of the ugly sisters, but I bottled out when I met the director. It took me just fifteen seconds to decide that acting wasn't for me.

I can hear him now, mincing around as if he was about to perform before Her Majesty. 'Come on Malcolm. Get yourself from out of that doorway, and get into a frock. I can't waste time on the uglies you know. My Baron Hardup's pulled out and I've got to knock this lot into shape.' He was pointing at a rather bedraggled chorus line. One was dressed as a pumpkin, while a young lad of about twelve was done out as a clock. He was trying to get his hands to point upwards in a sort of midnight position.

The whole thing is almost too shocking for me to recall. In fact, the memory has sent a shudder through my half-dressed body as I delicately prepare for the evening's entertainment. I'm going to lie down and think for a minute. I'm contemplating, just like Robinson Crusoe did when he rested in his hammock at the end of another hard day on the desert island. I too feel as if I've found footsteps in the sand, only to chase them for a mile and then find out…they were my own. Still, I'm keeping my end up and my snout clean. After all, I've hardly put a foot wrong on this trip. Weasel Man Kenneth and me are the angels on table 69. It's the other lot who should be hanging their heads in shame. Mind you, by now Kenneth might have had his end away with Stocky, Sweaty Linda the Boot Scooting Queen. For all I know, he's knobbed her in between bouts of the Toe Strut.

In the Monte Carlo Dining-room, table 69 is done up like a dog's dinner. There are balloons all around. It's going to be a once in a lifetime occasion. You can just sense it. I'm there first because I want to study their faces. June, Mouthy Kev and Kiss Me Kate. Go on love, open up your 'Luck be a Lady Tonight' blouse in front of your old man and show me your Finian's Rainbow. (I think there was a leprechaun in *Finian's Rainbow*. I wonder if it was one of Alfred's cousins.) I'm going to enjoy myself tonight. I just know it.

I'm in the midst of my usual routine, that of quickly memorizing the menu, then scrunching it up and placing it in my trouser pocket. Dibble the Muffin Man asked me to save him all the menus so he could nick a couple of new ideas. I promised I would, and I am. Although, how he's going to get braised guinea fowl with basil pasta and tomato pistou on a crusty cob, I shall never know. Before long, the sinners begin to arrive. Mouthy Kev, the maestro of manure management is first.

'Hello Kevin.' I greet the dirty bugger with a wholesome handshake unable as ever to upset the apple cart. Alfred and Andy are accompanied by Kenneth the Weasel Man. June and Tom bring up the rear.

'He's had a great day you know!' June's as brazen as ever. I don't know how the pair of them are pulling it off. 'Loved the Ceaser and Cleo record,' she continued. 'Howled like a wolf. Everard, the cabin boy had to pop his nose round to make sure everything was okay. He ended up dropping off an extra packet of Fondant Fancies.'

Now wait a minute. For the first time in my life, I'm not swallowing it. Their cabin boy cannot be called 'Everard', and I'm ready to dispute the matter, birthday or no birthday.

'It's true,' says three-bollock, ironing Andy. 'Me and Alfred had him last year.'

I give up. Any road, how come they get Fondant Fancies? They're only on Deck D. It's only two above us oatmeal peasants. June's back holding court.

'Bought him a Jessie Matthews video as well. *The Man from Toronto*. She really is an amazing woman you know. And if it wasn't for Gertrude Lawrence she'd have been nothing.'

I'm lost again.

'Gertrude Lawrence?' I ask, although I'm thinking, How dare you talk about Tom's birthday when you were going at it like a blacksmith's hammer last night.

'Yes. Gertrude Lawrence was playing the lead role in *Charlot's Review of 1924*. Suddenly she developed the flu and Jessie stepped in. Got rave reviews. Became a star overnight. Tragic. She ended up in *Mrs Dale's* bollocking *Diary*. Still, she was a dirty old ride. Couldn't keep her hands off the men, and that was her downfall. They called her a "person of odious mind" in the end. Filthy little whore. Still, Tom loves her and that's all that matters to me.'

'And do you love Tom?' I ask. I don't know what came over me. It just slipped out. I think I really like the two of them deep down. Although I've never heard Tom say anything more than 'Hello', 'Thank you so much' when his dinner arrives and 'Good night all' when he leaves.

'Me and Tom,' replies June. 'We're the greatest.'

She looks sincere but I can't help thinking that she's pulling my leg. Sometimes I just don't understand folk.

I feel a bit guilty. I fully intended to buy Tom a card, but the shops in the 'Pretty Port of Propriano' were closed. Kenneth, of all people, has produced one out of his inside jacket pocket – it's dicky bows again tonight – and the puffs have made their own out of a sheet of the *Nautical Newsletter*. (Andy and Alfred are very artistic. They own a gift shop in Brighton selling the latest in quilted tissue boxes and nodding meerkats.)

'Oh, Tom. Don't forget to thank Kevin and Katherine for their present. Do you know, he's always wanted one of those electronic toothbrushes.'

Oh Lord. Mouthy Kev and Kiss Me Kate have brought Tom an electronic toothbrush. He'll be tickling laa-laas from here to Barcelona, and back to Southampton. I don't reckon there's a woman on this ship that can sleep safely in her bunk for the rest of the trip. But there's no time for me to get all worked up. The festivities are about to begin.

No sooner have I finished off my purée of pumpkin soup, when Roger the Waiter appears with a twinkle in his eye. He's accompanied by Donald the Downtrodden, Marlene the Wine Girl, and a gaggle of hosts in waistcoats. Even Everard's here. Seems like a nice boy. They perform two quick verses of 'Happy Birthday' and then hastily produce needles from their waistcoat pockets. One by one the balloons around our table are burst. It's Tom's tribute.

In typical Tom style, the man of the moment tuts a tut of approval, raises his eyebrows to the heavens, and then humbly tugs his forelock. It's quite emotional. He half rises to his feet, and then sits back down again before looking at us all and declaring, 'Thank you. Thank you so much.' It's one of Tom's greatest speeches, and we all applaud spontaneously. We love him. He's the underdog of table 69 and I'm almost inclined to give him a standing ovation. But then, I'm the only one who knows that his wife is secretly knocking off Mouthy Kev.

We've decided to stick together for the cocktail karaoke. Kenneth the Weasel Man has gone before his pudding. He's the advance party, making sure we get a good table near the front. I've gone overboard on the Jacob's Creek. The way it's going, I might even do a turn myself. They always said back in the office I should go on *Stars in Your Eyes* as the new Tom Jones. But I'm not so sure. I love the show and I'm very fond of Matthew Kelly, but I couldn't stand the smoke. I'm quite weak-chested in that way.

Mouthy Kev's bought a bottle of champagne for Tom. He insists we all have a glass, including Roger the Waiter, and Donald the Downtrodden. I can't help but get to my feet. 'To Tom.' I raise my glass majestically and table 69 follows suit. Along with table 15 next to us, and table 35 on our other side. For a second I consider this. If the tables closest to us are 15 and 35, how can we possibly be 69? I let it go.

Kenneth, already outside, God bless him, has done his job to perfection. He's stood on a chair calling us to our table near the front of the stage. The Sunshine Deck looks beautiful. Row upon row of fake paper lanterns, swaying gently in the sea breeze. It's a full moon and the cool air makes a refreshing change to the warm sunshine of the day and the hot air of the Monte Carlo Restaurant. Kiss Me Kate glances in my direction and then looks away as she takes her seat on the Sunshine Deck. Oh bloody Nora. I'm sandwiched in between her and June. What a position. Give me Alfred and Andy anytime. Still, I'm more than half pissed, so for once in my life, I'm going to let bygones be bygones. I can tell Kate is embarrassed by her knock-back in cabin F153. She hasn't looked at me all night, and I tried desperately to grab her attention as the champagne took hold during the maple walnut sponge.

June's already started. She's pointing to the Tosser in the Blazer who's gliding his way around the Sunshine Deck like a slippery sardine. I think he's having a bash at the military two-step.

'I wouldn't mind him examining my "Knick Knack Paddy Wack, give a Dog a Bone".'

'Oh June,' I'm ready for confrontation. 'Won't you ever leave the men alone? After all what's wrong with Tom. He's a lovely man.'

'I suppose I'm a bit of a Jessie Matthews,' she laughs.

The penny drops. It's Jessie Matthews. June is playing the role of Jessie Matthews. So tragically obsessed with the opposite sex that she became a 'person of most odious mind'. Tom and June are role-playing. He'll turn a blind eye because he thinks he's married the woman of his dreams. Tom thinks he's married to Jessie Matthews. And in a strange sort of way, that makes everything all right. She's playing the role of the 'Dancing Divinity turned *Mrs Dales' Diary*' to keep the love alive. I've bloody cracked it. I should be a sodding agony aunt.

Well, I think I've cracked it, but normally I'm wildly off the mark on these matters. I'm just about to put my new found theory to the test when Bliss, the resident band, strike up with a verse of *Jesus Christ, Superstar*. The bastard DeVine rushes to the centre of the stage. It's his bloody signature tune. The more I look at him, the more he resembles the SAD's director who had his Baron Hardup pull out at the last minute. And where's his girlfriend tonight? No sign of Claire or Daphne. Looks like DeVine's going Baron in the Hardup department for one evening. Miss Cruise Bore's here with her mother and father. She's run a comb through her hair for a change – it's a major improvement. Mrs Hair Bear Bunch is desperate to get onto the dance floor with her two Muppets, and even Mrs Jigsaw Puzzle has left the sanctuary of the library. They're all here. In the words of Shalamar, 'We're gonna make this a night to remember.' Norman kicks off with a rendition of 'Love is in the Air'. (Well, it certainly was last night.)

'Who had a hit with this song in 1978?'

I'm leaning over to ask Andy and Alfred. There's no doubt about it. I'm in an unusually playful mood tonight.

'Perry Como?' Andy is hesitant.

'Ha! Perry Como! It was John Paul Young, you knob-head.'

I realize the drink may have taken hold so I'm going to keep quiet for the next thirty minutes and let the rest of the night unfold in front of my very eyes. It's not long, however, before I'm back in the thick of the action.

The Norman DeVine choir are on stage. Hattie Jacques is among them.

'Okee dokee, ladies and gentlemen, boys and girls,' says DeVine. '*Okee dokee!*' Bloody hell, he's got a catchphrase. 'This morning, these people you see before you were just a bunch of ordinary folk.'

I can't stand his line in patter. I turn to June. 'Don't tell me he's rebuilt them. He's got the technology. He has the capability to make the world's first bionic musical.' She bursts into a semi-fit of laughter.

By now, DeVine's got the bit between his teeth. He's going full throttle.

'Here they are, with a Magic of the Musicals medley... The Almost Perfectionists.'

Well, you've never seen such a ramshackle load of arse-wipes in your life. They begin with 'Be Our Guest' from *Beauty and the Beast*. *Hello, Dolly!* follows and before long, they're into *Annie* with 'The Sun'll Come Out Tomorrow'.

'It better fucking had,' says Kenneth. 'I haven't paid this much money to go back to Shirehampton as white as a bloody sheet.'

It's happened, it's finally happened! Kenneth is so flustered that his top teeth have fallen into Andy's lap. Andy squeals, mouth wide open with horror. It's his worst nightmare. Kenneth hurriedly grapples with his dentures before securing them back into his gob with one last and desperate finger thrust. Alfred is not sure whether to laugh or cry. He's more concerned with Andy's immediate welfare.

Mouthy Kev lets out a hearty chuckle. 'Daft bugger.' Now that's more like it. Far better than 'daft wazzak'. I think the pair of them are beginning to gel. I follow suit with a jolly little cackle. June titters, and Kiss Me Kate has finally got into the swing of things. Now that Kev has laughed, she feels it's okay to smile a shy sort of smile. Yes, you dirty cow. Not like last night when you tried to straddle me over my rocking-chair. (I think I might make an offer for that chair. My souvenir from the SS *Perfect*.) Even Tom shrugs in a half-laugh sort of way. Andy smiles, and the awkward emergency is over.

The Norman DeVine choir continues unabated. To my amazement, they've gone from *Annie* to *Mamma Mia!* in one fell swoop. Unfortunately, it's not over till that fat lady sings. And here she is. Hattie Jacques has stepped forward to give the gathered masses a chorus from *Cats*. She sounds like one. Struggling desperately to put it across to a crowded Sunshine Deck that's becoming more raucous as the drink wears on. ' "Midnight. Not a sound from the pavement," ' shrieks Hattie. Before too long, she's starting to squawk.

'Ahhh,' says Andy. 'She looks ever so clean. I bet her kitchen worktops are spotless. I wouldn't mind having a sniff around her downstairs cloak either.'

'Someone put the fat cow out of her misery,' replies Alfred. (He's not as patient and understanding.) 'I wonder if DeVine's lot know the tune to "Mouldy Old Dough" by Lieutenant Pigeon?' he enquires.

'That's funny,' I'm back in at the forefront, 'I half expected you and Andy to do a Clodagh Rodgers classic. "Jack in the Box" or maybe "Come Back and Shake Me". Anyway, you can't do "Mouldy Old Dough" because it hasn't got any words. He just growls "Mouldy Old Dough" occasionally.'

'I wish him in the blazer would come over here and shake me,' says June. She's got eyes like a pair of bulldog's bollocks. It's the drink – she's pissed as a newt.

The entertainment's hotting up. Roger and Rosemary are next on. The ferret rescue couple. They're doing 'Save Your Love', the Renee and Renato classic from Christmas 1982. It's a magical moment. Roger, who's wearing another ill-fitting home-knitted sweater, looks deep into Rosemary's eyes. (I hope she's been sprayed with ferret oil tonight. Or maybe he's been castrated as a mark of solidarity to his furry polecat friends.) ' "Save your love my darling, save your love. For summer nights with moon and stars above." '

The whole of our table's on its feet. We're singing our little hearts out. June, who's already got hold of Kevin's right hand, grabs my left hand and lifts it high while Kiss Me Kate takes my right hand and thrusts it skyward. We've linked hands in a triumphant circle and we're swaying to the rhythm.

'I hope you're ready for a big climax, chicken,' says Kate. She's started on me again. Fortunately, the song saves the day.

' "Save your love for Roma and for me." '

'I'll give him "Roma". That Renee never went anywhere near Italy. They filmed the video at Luton airport,' booms Mouthy Kev. June gazes briefly into his eyes. But it's all over in a flash and she looks away (well, it *is* Tom's birthday). 'I should know,' he continues. 'I'm a close personal friend of Renee...*and Renato*! They're still married you know; own a nice little Italian just outside Wakefield. He specializes in curried pasta.'

I'm only half listening. One slushy song and my mind has slipped into romantic overdrive. I wonder if anyone's saving a bit of love for me. Maybe Daphne's watching it all from a safe distance. Perhaps she's studying my every move, waiting to pounce once I get to the Spanish Steps.

The evening is about to reach fever pitch. Kenneth has brought his recorder and he's making his way to the stage amidst roars from his fellow followers on table 69. Andy and Alfred are performing some strange American dance routine as they bark out, 'Go Kenneth, Go Kenneth' while rolling their clenched arms around in an awkward circling motion. Kenneth turns to address the members of Bliss. 'You can go and piss off for a pint lads,' he tells them. 'I might be here some time. I'm a master at playing this thing.'

He strolls up to the microphone and rams the end of the recorder firmly up one nostril (good job he's left his clarinet at home). Within seconds, he's off with 'Brown Girl in the Ring'. It's a winner with the crowd. But most of them are well-oiled by now. Desperate to hang on to the adulation from the gathered masses, he sends the Sunshine Deck revellers into a frenzy with a couple of Wurzel numbers. This is surely enter-tainment at its very best. If Greg Dyke were here, Kenneth the Weasel Man would be an overnight success. It would be the Val Doonican story all over again. Kenneth's in his element. But even he's about to be upstaged.

The Pillsbury Dough Man hauls himself onto the stage. Within moments he's off, writhing around and shaking his rather ample stuff to Chubby Checker's 'Let's Twist Again'. Mrs Cocktail Stick's going mad. (She's got to watch her step tonight. It's a cocktail evening. Someone might try to stick a cherry on her head and dunk her.) There's flab all over the stage as the Pillsbury Dough Man attempts to get down, and back up again while keeping in tune. To be fair, he's not a bad singer. And he's giving it absolutely everything. The perspiration's pouring off the poor fellow, all in the name of love. What can topple that? There's only one thing. The highlight of the night... Me.

'Tonight Matthew, I'm Tom Jones.'

I first performed it at the British Potato Marketing Board Christmas Party 1987. They're still talking about it. Like a fool, I'd mentioned it discreetly to June. She swore solemnly not to tell anybody, yet within seconds she's dragging me from the comfort of my plastic chair, yelling at the top of her already high-pitched voice, 'He's Tom Jones.'

At first I refuse, then refuse again. Kenneth is reassuring. 'Look you prat,' he says sympathetically. 'You're never gonna see these people again in your life so you might as well make an arsehole of yourself and be bollocking done with it.'

The Weasel Man has swung it for me...besides I've got no choice. I'm doomed. I've got to perform. Like a condemned man on his way to the gallows, I begin the slow walk towards the stage. My fellow passengers are cheering me on from every angle. It seems like the eyes of the world are focussed on my every step. I'm walking in slow motion unsure of what lies ahead. I don't know why this is happening to me. Maybe it's fate.

In times of need, Dicky Cox usually flashes into my mind. Like a bad penny he's turned up again. 'My cousin once went on *Stars in Your Eyes* as Glenn Miller,' he used to brag at every available opportunity. 'He went into the mist and was never seen again!' To be honest, I don't know if Dicky Cox even had a cousin, but it's too late to start contemplating it now.

Before you can say 'What's New Pussycat?' the resident band have struck up. Then, out of the corner of my eye, I spot her. Daphne. I was right; she was here all along, hair blowing in the gentle breeze as she gazes down from Deck 13, her hands folded over the gleaming white railings. It's my big chance. I'm off. And there's only one song that's going to clinch the girl of my dreams. Tom's greatest: 'Delilah'! Within seconds I'm thrusting my pelvis like a madman.

'I saw the light on the night that I passed by her window.'

The crowd take over. 'La la la laa…' They're all with me. Everyone.

'I saw the flickering shadow of love on the blinds.'

Same again. This time louder. The place is going barmy.

'She was my woman. As she deceived me I watched and went out of my mind.'

I'm possessed by some Welsh devil. Of course! I've hit the jackpot. Daphne's half Welsh. If this doesn't get me inside the Port Enhancement Queen's pants nothing bloody will. As predicted, the ship goes into its second frenzy of the evening. I swear the bloody thing's about to take off and fly us to Italy.

'Why, why, why Delilah.'

Those that don't sing fill in with the middle bit. A sort of 'Diddle, diddle, diddle diddle, der'. I'm cheered to the rafters as I finish. On top of the world, I bow to Daphne's who's smiling and applauding. I'm probably having the best night of my life. I gulp down my drink, ready to charge up to Deck 13 to meet her. I'm flying high. The night is mine. For once, I'm going to grasp the opportunity, sweep Daphne off her feet and introduce her to my friends on table 69. I look again. She's gone. Like a ship in the night she's disappeared. There one moment…gone the next. I wonder if I've just had my Val Doonican moment – and muffed it.

11

The Pillsbury Dough Man is dead.

This morning, the good ship *Perfect* is in mourning. The pumped up passengers who were so high-spirited the night before, have come crashing back down to earth with a bang. I knew there was something wrong when Oh Danny Boy raced into my cabin with only a quick 'Good morning, sir', and no oatmeal biscuits on the tray. The girls on reception looked glum. Faces like mangled marshmallows the lot of them, but that was the norm with those three. Alfred calls them, 'See No Evil, Hear No Evil and Speak No Evil.' As I began to climb the stairs, Rosemary and Roger raced towards me. I knew they were in the vicinity because a faint smell of stale ferret was competing with the fragrance of lemon fresh polish.

'Trevor's passed on,' Rosemary said, barely able to get all three words out, such was her desperation to tell me the news. For a moment I'd thought they were talking about one of their ferrets.

'Oh, I'm sorry to hear that,' I said, with half my mind focussing on the warmth of this morning's baked beans.

'All that Chubby Checker nonsense on the Sunshine Deck last night,' explained Roger. 'He came on the boat with a heart condition and The Twist just about finished him off. Overdid it, see. Happened just outside the Golden Penny after the cocktail party. Alison tried her best with him, but they reckon he'd gone within seconds.'

I suddenly clicked. 'Oh,' I said with an element of shock in my voice. (Receiving sympathy I can manage, giving it is, unfortunately, another of my weak points.) I looked blankly at the two of them, and then bowed my shaking head. 'Terrible,' I mumbled into my shoes. It was the best I could do under the circumstances. I wasn't expecting death at this stage of the holiday.

Poor Mrs Cocktail Stick. It's going to hit her hard. First she finds the love of her life, it's shaping up to be her vintage vacation...and then the poor bugger goes and snuffs it. I wonder if they ever had sex. Maybe they were on their way to cement the start of a loving relationship. What a terrible way to begin a day in the Italian port of Livorno. It's a grim place as well by the looks of things. Weather overcast (as it should be after the news we've just had). On first impressions, it looks a bit like Grimsby, but without the haddock and chips. Mouthy Kev is going on his daily constitutional. He walks a mile every morning around the decks; says it gets his juices flowing. He's stopped to gaze out onto the bedraggled looking dockside.

'Have you heard about the Pillsbury Dough Man – I mean Trevor?' I correct myself quickly. 'Mrs Cocktail Stick's boyfriend. You know, "Come on let's twist again." '

Oh no, he's looking blank. I'm going to have to break the tragic news to him.

'Yes, he's dead,' blasts Mouthy Kev in his own inimitable way.

'Oh, so you knew.'

'Knew? It was all hell let loose outside the Golden Penny last night. Put me off. I was on a winning streak – a row of melons – then crash bang, he's on the ground like Humpty Dumpty falling off the sodding wall. Fat git. I cashed in my tokens and went to meet Kate.'

Heartless Yorkshire swine. He's turned on his heels to complete his walk. He turns again.

'See this,' he says, pointing to his *Les Misérables* T-shirt. 'It's the best musical of them all. I could watch the matinee, leave the theatre, walk around the block and go and see it again in the evening. *Les Mis*. The greatest.'

Don't tell me, you're a close personal friend of Jean Val Jean, I think as he marches off again, singing as he stomps proudly around the deck without so much as a second thought for poor old Trevor, the now deceased Pillsbury Dough Man. He thinks he's in the chorus of *Les* bloody *Misérables* when he should be feeling *Les Misérables* himself. I mean, nobody should have to encounter death on a once in a lifetime holiday.

Breakfast is a miserable affair. They're all talking about 'the fat man that kicked the bucket outside the Golden Penny'. No sign of Mrs Cocktail Stick though. What's she going to do? Fly home from Italy, holiday in ruins? Surely not, after only knowing him for two days. Funny. She was the closest person to him when he died, but she couldn't really have known him at all. And what about the funeral? Does she follow the coffin into the church, or slip quietly in at the back and slip away again almost unnoticed? I'm glad she's not around this morning. I wouldn't know where to put myself.

Anyway, all this business has taken the shine off my Tom Jones performance. I half expected a hero's welcome at breakfast. I thought about it in my rocking-chair before I turned in last night. 'That'll put the heat into the baked beans,' I mused as I smiled sweetly to myself. It would be like the birthday scene from *The Railway Children*, when Bobbie the eldest daughter, breezed around on a cloud of air while the whole village smiled and shook her hand in the mist filled front room. There wasn't a dry eye in the house. That's how it should have been for me this morning, not all this doom and gloom.

The Pillsbury Dough Man's a bastard. He's robbed me of my finest hour. (Sorry Lord, but this is me all over. I manoeuvre myself into a winning position only to have the bloody shag pile

159

pulled from under my feet.) Daphne should have been the first to stand and applaud as I'd headed for the sausage counter, although she's a mystery herself, appearing and disappearing like she does. I even briefly considered her to be an illusion, a figment of my imagination, a mirage. But that's silly. She's the Port Enhancement Talk Queen.

I'm more determined now. I'm going to do two things today if it kills me ('though not literally Lord. We've had enough of that for one voyage). One: I'm going to find Daphne and ask her out for a drink. Two: I'm going to the children's room to confront What's-her-name – Claire. We've only had a brief encounter in the Happy Days Diner since I discovered she was on board. Somehow that's not enough for me. I can't help thinking there's some unfinished business and it's beginning to unsettle me.

A row of coaches has pulled onto the quayside, waiting patiently to ferry the *Perfect* passengers to either Florence or Pisa. I'm not going to either and I'm beginning to think that's a mistake. Thankfully, there's a free courtesy bus to take us into the small town of Livorno, so I'll still be able to get off the ship. (No good hanging around here if the weather's turned nasty.) It's picture time before we head to shore. Today we're posing in front of a cardboard cut-out of the leaning tower, holding a fake pizza in one hand and a mini Italian flag in the other. Come back Cyril the Seal, all is forgiven. Rather embarrassingly, I take a small trip at the top of the gangplank. A stout uniformed officer is quick to take hold of my arm and prevent a rather nasty tumble. 'Steady,' he booms. Almost straight away, from behind me, there's another boom. Well, more of a shriek really. It's somebody calling my name.

'Malcolm!'

It's Daphne...with Claire. I ask you. What kind of a hand is that for fate to throw at me? Although my aim today was to confront these two women, I didn't expect to meet them both whilst stood in front of a cardboard Leaning Tower of Pisa with a fake pizza in one hand and a mini Italian Flag in the other, clutching on to some bloke's arm for dear life.

'Smile sir. That's lovely,' says the ship's official photographer without the faintest whiff of sincerity.

'Hello Daphne. I'm just having a picture done.'

She smiles. I curse my luck. It's another opening line from hell.

'I enjoyed your Tom Jones last night.'

Hang about! She's smitten, I can tell. It's written all over her face.

'Tom Jones?' says Claire. 'You never did Tom Jones for me.'

'Oh, have you two already met?' asks Daphne, looking at Claire confused.

'Met! We went out with each other for five months. He's Mr Potato Head.'

Sod it. What's-her-name, Claire, is making a mockery of me. She's Daphne's mate by the looks of things. Should have known. Both working on the same ship. Bloody obvious they'd know each other.

'Are you going to Florence or Pisa?' Daphne asks.

Hang about again! She still wants me.

'Neither. It's Livorno for me, I'm afraid.'

'Oh, what a shame. We're going to Florence. It's such a lovely city. I could've shown you some of the sights.'

Knockers, knickers, knackers, clackers. The only fucking trip I've missed out on all holiday and the girl of my dreams is itching to show me her sights. I shake my fist to the heavens as Daphne and Claire stride arm in arm towards 'Coach 5 – Florence'.

Bleeding marvellous. That's it then. My goose is well and truly cooked. Just think, we could have lost Claire and spent the afternoon supping white wine in one of the most romantic settings in the world. As it is I'm stuck in the arse end of Italy on my own, and by the time Claire's finished with her character assassination on the bus, I'll have been firmly kicked into touch. I bet they're discussing my pink maggot as I speak. Bastards.

Sure enough Livorno has nothing to offer. The Italian flag flutters over a small, yet scruffy square as I leave the courtesy bus thinking about my lost opportunity. If it weren't for bad luck, I'd have no luck at all. Now where do I go? Left towards the square, or right towards the sea? I'm bound to get this decision horribly wrong. Like the famous tower, I seem to have spent centuries doddering on the brink. Now I'm at it again. If I go left, I'll finish up in a no-go dead end alley. Within seconds I'll be pounced on by a group of muggers who take everything and leave me for dead in a pool of my own blood. After spending three days in intensive care, I'll wake to find that if I'd turned right, I'd have stumbled upon a stunning view of the city of Pisa. I go right.

There's nothing much to see. Except for Norman DeVine. He's wandering around the port looking for something to capture his imagination. Just like me. Maybe he's already been left and now he's come right to see if he's missed anything. I wonder if he's had a tiff with Claire, or maybe she's just gone off on a girly shopping trip – with my girl. ('My Girl.' A 1965 number one for The Temptations, the world's most successful R and B vocal group.) Whatever the case, I've got him down as an unknown quantity. You'd swear he was gay to look at, bi-sexual at the very least.

I walk past and nod. It's a simple form of recognition. He nods back. 'No wonder Judith flipping Chalmers never came here,' he says with a wry smile. It's another day of upsets. The Pillsbury Dough Man nearly makes me cry and the mysterious Norman DeVine has made me laugh. You wouldn't have put money on that twelve hours ago, but then, it's a funny old world. And the best thing about Livorno? A small shop selling chocolate biscuits and crisps. I buy a six-pack of Penguins, and four bags of Walkers Cheese and Onion crisps. Makes a change from oatmeal biscuits.

My rocking-chair has become my best friend on board the good ship *Perfect*. I'm onto my second Penguin, reading the *Nautical Newsletter* and dreaming of what might have been had the good Lord pointed me in the direction of 'Coach 5 – Florence' when I was booking my holiday tours. I'm surprised DeVine's got time for a ramble around Livorno. He's got another one of his musical spectaculars in the Hippodrome Theatre to think about. 'A Whistle-stop Tour through Royalty in the West End. From *The King and I* to Queen's *Bohemian Rhapsody*.'

I'm no stranger to royalty myself. I'm on first name terms with Jean – Jean the Tea Chest Queen! She's a lady who drinks at my local. Eighty-four years old and claims to be the oldest tea chest player in the world. (I must tell Kenneth about her; they could team up as a double act.) Jean Perkins is her name. Her husband Archie went to his grave convinced that man never landed on the moon. He got on the local television news, even made it onto the front page of *The Indicator* (our local paper). He used to say the Americans conned the world by filming the moon scenes at Aberystwyth in Wales. I can almost hear him now: 'It'll never be done again in my lifetime. Why? Because it was never done in the first place.' He died in 1988.

The day in Livorno had dragged. The sun never shone and, like a lovesick schoolboy, I spent an hour watching the coaches return from Pisa and Florence through my picture window, desperate for another glimpse of Daphne. In a desperate attempt to lift my spirits before dinner, I'm going to down a large scotch in Alexander's Bar (the posh one).

'Have you had a good day sir?' asks the waiter politely.

'Lovely, thank you.'

Why don't you tell him the truth? 'No, I've had a shit day actually. The Pillsbury Dough Man's dead, I dropped a clanger on the gangplank and by now Daphne knows all about my fumbling ways between the sheets. In love terms, I'm dead and buried and I've come here to drown my sorrows before entering the den of vice that is table 69. And how about you?'

Oh Lord. Table 69. So far the story reads like this. Alfred and Andy are a gay couple, although Alfred's far too old for Andy and looks like a well-pruned leprechaun. Andy's got three bollocks and likes cooking and extreme ironing. Alfred once had an affair with the man that read the shipping forecasts on Radio Four, and June and Tom are a pair of swingers. June's had it up the Knick Knack Paddy Wack from some lusty Latvian, as well as having a bit of 'how's your father' with Mouthy Kev, the uncaring Yorkshireman who looks like a character from Michael Bentine's *Potty Time*. Meanwhile, Tom's keen on tickling a lady's Ginger Rogers with his well-worn toothbrush (although he's got an electronic one now), and Kiss Me Kate (Mouthy Kev's wife) has tried to seduce me in my rocking-chair wearing a 'Luck be a Lady Tonight' blouse. I got scared and ushered her away when she started stroking my head and singing, 'Chick, chick, chick, chick chicken. Lay a little egg for me.' I'm desperately chasing Daphne in the shadow of my one and only ex-girlfriend who turns out to be the ship's resident Punch and Judy artist, and Kenneth the Weasel Man is a bit-part actor who once played a transvestite in *The Persuaders*, auditioned for *The Onedin Line*, sold cucumbers on *Albion Market* and now holds the world record for playing Wurzels tunes on his recorder, with his nose. He's currently trying to master the clarinet with his backside.

On the way to the Monte Carlo, I check out the action in the piano room. It's the same old story; a row of geriatrics slumped in their fake antique armchairs. They're all asleep as the resident pianist plods his way through 'Somewhere Over the Rainbow'. (My keyboard mentor, Colin 'Fingers' Gilbert wouldn't have stood for this – he'd have had them all going with his 'Little Stick of Blackpool Rock'. He was a big George Formby fan.) I wouldn't be surprised if we had at least another two kick the bucket before we arrive home. Already there have been rumours of an elderly lady who spent the first three days of her holiday in the lift! By all accounts – and the details are rather sketchy – she got herself totally lost on the way down from the breakfast buffet. By the time the ship's stewards found her, she was in a state of total confusion, no more than a jibbering wreck (although she still remembered to put in a verbal complaint about the cold beans).

Thankfully, there's still plenty of life on table 69.

'We're playing "Give us the next line",' says June as I reach the table. I'm the last one in because I had a second large whisky. Roger the Waiter and Downtrodden Donald are hovering. They're waiting to get going with the food orders. Marlene pours the wine and says 'Good evening' to each of us by name.

'We go round the table with a popular song,' says an already overexcited Andy explaining the rules. His hands are dangling loosely in mid-air. It gives him the appearance of a Thunderbird puppet. 'Everyone in turn has to remember the next line. First one to fail gets a forfeit.' I can't even begin to wonder what the forfeit is for the unlucky loser.

June starts. ' "Food, Glorious Food." ' I think I'll be all right with this one. It's *Oliver!*, and I've watched Mark Lester perform the song a million times. The question is what will I be like now the pressure is on? I'm useless under the spotlight.

'Hot sausage and mustard,' says Tom. It's the most I've ever heard him say. And he's smiling. Must have had a birthday treat from June. A complimentary laa-laa titivation with the electronic toothbrush. Probably needs new batteries already. Kate's next:

' "While we're in the mood." '

' "Cold jelly and custard," ' Kev blurts out the line in a matter of fact sort of way as if the game is just far too simple for a man of his musical knowledge. I'll show the swine. Kenneth's spot on, and it's a good call too:

' "Pease pudding and saveloys." '

I'm starting to panic.

' "What next is the question?" ' Andy's safe, and Alfred hardly waits for him to finish before he comes up with the next bit:

' "Rich gentlemen have it, boys." '

I told you. 'Rich gentlemen have it boys.' Alfred the leprechaun is Andy's sugar daddy. My theory has been confirmed with a line from *Oliver!* And it's true you know; rich gentlemen *can* have anything. Boys, girls, sugar baby loves, leprechauns, unicorns, weasels... The list is endless.

Now it's my line. I've gone blank. The spotlight has fallen on me and they're all waiting, but I can't get it out. Maybe the emotion of the day has taken hold. I'm dumbstruck and the table's started to count down from ten...nine...eight... I'm going to be the weakest link. It's one word, I know it. I go through the song again in my head but the clock's ticking away. Four...three...two...one. ' "In-di-gestion!" ' I'm correct – but I'm a fraction too late.

'Time's up,' shrieks Andy at the top of his voice. 'Oh Malcolm, love. You're such a twat.'

Sugar Daddy and Sugar Baby Love look round. They're sat on the sometimes vacant table 35, opposite table 69. I noticed them as soon as I came in. She was telling Donald the Downtrodden how he'd brought her a new pair of trainers from an exclusive shop in Florence. That's sure to keep the old man in blow-jobs for the rest of the trip.

I can't believe it. I've flopped big time. My head falls into my hands. I'm dejected. A growl of frustration bursts from my mouth. Andy and Alfred, in an amazing outburst of childish behaviour, start chanting, 'Forfeit, forfeit, forfeit' and Kev joins them with that smug look of 'a man that didn't have to try too hard'.

'Now, Malcolm,' says June asserting her authority in a 'listen hard because I'll tell you this only once' fashion. (I don't know why she's always the ringleader, but she has been since day one and I guess that's the way it will always be.) 'I've got a forfeit specially designed for you. Get me the camera, Thomas.'

I sit like a schoolboy outside the headmaster's study as Thomas passes the camera. It's one of those disposable affairs.

'We want you to take a picture of two potatoes sat on the wall of the Trevi Fountain when you're in Rome tomorrow.' She lets out a laugh. They know I'm employed by the British potato industry. I bet they've been secretly sniggering behind my back. 'Tom and I thought of forfeits for you all over coffee in Pisa today. Well, once you've seen one sodding leaning tower, you've seen them all. We brought the camera specially, didn't we love.'

Andy's protesting, 'It's too easy. Think of something harder.'

'It's not that easy,' I retort, desperate for things not to get too out of hand. A picture of two potatoes sat on the wall of the Trevi Fountain in Rome, I can handle quite nicely thank you very much; that's if I can find the potatoes.

'You've got to take the photos *and* bring a souvenir back to the table tomorrow night,' he continues. The request seems fair enough so I agree, but he's still not finished. He can smell blood and he's determined to make me suffer. He's a thrill seeker, you see. Irons his slacks halfway up Mount Everest. He's seen life in the extreme and he's going to make this difficult for me if it's the last thing he does. 'You've got to bring us a pope souvenir. A tacky one at that.'

'Yes,' says Alfred. They're like a pack of wolves going in for the kill now. 'Bring us back a "Pope on a Rope".'

The whole table falls about laughing. I'm doomed. How can I possibly go around the Vatican City asking for the Pope on a rope? I'd be the one on the end of a rope by the end of the day. Strung up by the knackers and hanging from a Roman lamppost. That's what they did to Mussolini. They don't take prisoners, these Italians. Still, the challenge has been set, and I'm ready to rise to it.

Before leaving for another scotch in the Paradise Ballroom, I have a sly word in Roger the Waiter's ear. Sure enough, within ten minutes he's beckoning me to the kitchen entrance where he produces two of the finest King Edwards I've seen in a long time. A real pair of beauties. I recognize them instantly. I was once part of a team of eight who spent four weeks on a new hard-hitting campaign: 'One hundred and one things to do with a King Edward.' Unfortunately, after four weeks we could only come up with fourteen, and one of those was to stick it up your arse. We'd lost heart by that stage. The campaign was dropped. So that's the camera and the potatoes sorted. I'll arrange my spuds neatly in front of the Trevi Fountain and I'm halfway there. Now all I've got to worry about is finding a bloody 'Pope on a Rope'.

I'm still lost in thought as I pass The Paradise Ballroom. It's filling up nicely. Stocky, Sweaty Linda the Boot Scooting Baby is putting her recruits through their paces with a couple of stomps followed by a sailor step. Kenneth's there, just in front of Miss Cruise Bore who's still battling her way through the heel switch with her mother and father either side. It's almost certainly the only entertainment she's going to get on this trip now Daphne's spurned her lesbian advances.

Mrs Hair Bear Bunch is getting ready for the line dancing to end, so the real dancing can begin. You can see it in her eyes. She's after a cha-cha, followed by a quick waltz, before ending the evening with a mambo. She's waiting patiently, sandwiched, as always, in between her two Muppet companions who are wearing matching sweatshirts. It's a nice touch. One reads 'If I were a...' while the other simply says 'Rich man'. Quite classy. But then, it's worth making an effort for Mrs Hair Bear Bunch. She's in the Salvation Army; the good Lord is on her side.

I may enquire about joining the Salvation Army when I get back. Me and Dicky Cox could go together. They might give me a free tambourine if I introduce a friend. After all, I'm more in need of saving than anyone. It's been another day full of drama and another night with no sign of Daphne. I'm ready to get a good night's sleep before embarking on my big Roman adventure. The Deck F corridor is deserted as I slip my key card into the lock and watch the little red light turn green. But suddenly I can feel a second presence. It's like a sixth sense. I turn to bid good night to Oh Danny Boy. It's got to be him. A faint waft of Charlie Girl fills my nostrils. I'm wrong. It's Kiss Me Kate, my hardy Perennial. She's returned. The woman's a human boomerang. Surely I haven't got to go through this shenanigan night after night?

'Hello chicken, can I have a quick word?'

Oh good. She's come to apologize for her wicked behaviour, and she's going to promise me she'll never try to seduce me again.

'Of course you can Kate, come on in. You can sit in the rocking-chair if you like.'

A silly mistake maybe, but it's my way of being extra kind. I'm so in love with that rocking-chair that I'm trying to figure out ways to nick it. I've enlisted the help of Andy and Alfred although I don't know what good they'll be. I perch on the edge of the bed.

'I'm sorry about the other night,' says Kate gently. I'm right – an apology. Thank heavens for that.

'Look,' I stand up and gently take hold of Kate's hand. 'It was a genuine mistake. I don't think any less of you for what happened. In fact I'm very fond of you. I like everyone on table 69. I'll remember you for a long time to come.'

I'm reassuring her. Playing it just right for once.

Kate stands. 'Well then take me now. Shag me in this rocking-chair. Rip my knickers off with your teeth and ram your Gin Gan Goolies into my Dorothy Squires.'

Oh God. Gin Gan Goolies! She's brought The Scaffold into it. Mind you I did like The Scaffold. A cheeky scouse pop group, if my memory serves me right. I think one of the members was Paul McCartney's stepbrother – him from The Beatles. Struck gold with the record 'Gin Gan Goolie' while also having hits with 'Thank U Very Much' and 'Lily the Pink'. As for 'Dorothy Squires'! Former wife of Roger 'The Saint' Moore, who rose to superstardom after being discovered by American Pianist Charlie Kunz. Imagine using the great lady's name to describe, well, your Kunz. It's enough to make the inimitable Ms Squires turn in her grave.

Help! I've given her the wrong signals. I've over-compensated on the compassion front and she's straddling my rocking-chair, hitching up her halter-neck frock in front of my very eyes. She thinks she's Mary Quant but she looks more like Mary Hopkins. Her legs are spread-eagled and I can see her virginal white pants. A couple of centimetres either way and I'd get a bird's eye view of *her* Lily the Pink.

'Can you smell my Charlie?' she asks. It's a catastrophe. I don't want to make love to this woman yet she's gyrating before me, begging for it. The devil half of me says give her a quick fumble and she'll get off your back. My angel side wins the day – just in time. She's leapt out of the rocking-chair and she's trying to pin me to my bed. I've given her an inch and she's taken a mile. Next she'll be swinging off the fake antique mahogany wardrobes.

'No, Kate. You're squashing my King Edwards.'

I'm starting to panic, but I have to protect my spuds at all costs. I've been carrying them around all night. I just haven't had the chance to put them in my oatmeal biscuit draw ready for tomorrow's challenge. Besides, Kate can't possibly feel like chicken tonight. She's already polished off a plump breast in white wine sauce at the dinner table.

'I appreciate you may be damp downstairs again...' Once more, I'm struggling to find the right words to fit the occasion. Suddenly I come good: 'I like you and I'm fond of your Charlie. But I don't want to make love to you knowing your husband is upstairs waiting for you.'

Kate rises quickly. Yet again, she knows she's on to a loser. I'm a damp squib in the 'help me make it through the night' stakes.

'For your information,' says Kate angrily, 'my husband has had sex with umpteen women since we've been married.'

She doesn't have to tell me. I've already seen her husband having it away with June. Imagine the scene if I let *that* cat out of the bag.

'Well, I'm sorry to hear that but I still don't want sex with you tonight. The death of the Pillsbury Dough Man has upset me and I'm feeling a little off colour.'

What am I saying? I need to end her obsession now, not have her feel sorry for me and come back for a repeat performance tomorrow night. Kate's mood changes.

'I'm sorry,' she says. Now we're back to where we began. 'I find you extremely good looking and, for a moment, I got completely carried away.'

I'm not going to be quite so kind this time. Otherwise we'll be going round in circles for the rest of the night. She turns on a sixpence this one. One moment she's sweet Dorothy from *The Wizard of Oz*, then she's the Wicked Witch of the West, demanding me to give her a Munchkin up the Dorothy Squires. There you are! Proof that I've become sucked in to their ways. I'm using all sorts of daft phrases to describe a plain and simple shag. Mind you, I'm beginning to think there is no such thing on board the SS *Perfect*. For the second time, I open the door so Kate can make her way back to Mouthy Kev.

'By the way,' I ask cautiously, 'did you pass the children's jacuzzi on your way down?'

'Yes,' says Kate a little bemused.

'Did you hear June singing "The Lonely Goatherd"?'

'No,' says Kate even more confused. Thank heavens for that. 'She was halfway through "Climb Every Mountain" when I went past. Between you and me, I think that woman's got a screw loose.'

Oh Danny Boy is on the prowl. He looks at Kate, looks at me, smiles, winks and says: 'Have a good night's sleep, sir.' He thinks I've shagged her. Maybe I should have. After all, her old man's up to all sorts of tricks with June. I hated him at first but now he's starting to grow on me, despite his ruthless two-timing. I reclaim my rocking-chair.

Malcolm's Log.

I've reinstated it in sheer exasperation.

It's Wednesday, June 25th. I'm exhausted. The Pillsbury Dough Man is dead.

12

Arrivederche Roma. The ancient city's got no chance now we've arrived.

There's no sign of any ruins on first glance, just another crane-dominated skyline shadowing another ugly port. The real stuff is an hour's bus ride away. I'm glad – I'm not in the mood for sights just yet. My mind's full, and bubbling over with unanswered questions.

One: what am I going to do about Kiss Me Kate? I've been talked into sharing a taxi with her and Mouthy Kev tomorrow. Viewing the bloody half built temple in Barcelona. What if I let the cat out of the bag as we explore Antonio Gaudi's greatest, yet still unfinished masterpiece:

'By the way Kev, your wife has been trying to have it away with me for the last three days. She truly is a smouldering bit of stuff under that prim and proper exterior. We're becoming close personal friends. Oh, and as a matter of interest Kate, June had her Knick Knack Paddy Wack wrapped firmly round your husband's bone when you heard her singing "Climb Every Mountain" near the children's jacuzzi. Now, shall we all move on to the museum?'

Two: I know we're on holiday and everyone's supposed to be having a laugh, but the death of the Pillsbury Dough Man has hardly been mentioned. A pair of his extra large trousers has been respectfully draped over the chair he once occupied in the Monte Carlo Dining-room (even though some thought it a bit off-putting for his fellow diners). But I think more effort should be made to commemorate his sudden passing. I'm willing to propose the idea of a memorial service for Trevor, the ex-Pillsbury Dough Man. Mrs Cocktail Stick could throw a wreath into the water while we all sing a couple of lines from that hymn: 'For those who perished on the sea.' It's a little overdramatic, I know, but we can't let the moment pass without so much as a bye or leave. I'll find Mrs Cocktail Stick and put it to her. I wonder how's she handling it? She's at that funny age for a woman. The shock could send her either way. It's worrying me blind.

Three (the big one): where do I stand with Daphne? I've been trying to track her down since that first port enhancement talk but something always seems to crop up. If it's not Claire, it's Kiss Me Kate. If it's not her, it's Mouthy Kev and June. Even the Tosser in the Blazer has tried to stick his oar in. It's so frustrating. It's almost driving me round the bend.

I thought I'd got her in my pocket at the cocktail karaoke party. Then she performed her incredible vanishing act only to turn up on the gangplank the following morning and practically ask me to give her one in Florence. As luck would have it, I was on the other bus. I may see her in Rome. Even if I don't, I'm going to leave no stone unturned tonight in my quest to hunt her down. If I'm not gazing into her beautiful blue eyes by the end of the evening, I'll eat my 'Pope on a Rope'.

And that brings me nicely to question four. My table 69 challenge. Where am I going to get my hands on a 'Pope on a Rope'? I wonder if they'll settle for a Virgin Mary? I've packed the camera and two King Edwards into my 'Spud-U-Like' satchel. I'm also taking two Penguin biscuits and my last remaining bag of cheese and onion crisps. I ate one bag before I went to sleep last night – comfort food. I was half expecting Kiss Me Kate to burst through the door and pin me to the rocking-chair again. Every time the fake antique mahogany wardrobes creaked, I jerked. Bolt upright. I was erect for a good ten minutes at quarter past three this morning.

Fancy having to complete a challenge on your holiday. I hate tasks at the best of times. Margaret Chandler's wayward son Maurice is currently tackling a mammoth one. He's been bet one thousand pounds that he and four mates can't break into the now derelict Wembley Stadium and score a goal at each end. They've been given a disposable camera as well. Imagine that. I've sunk to the depths of wayward Maurice Chandler. Mind you, he's on for a thousand big ones. What's my reward if I dangle a 'Pope on a Rope' in front of June's snout this evening? I dread to think. And what if I fail? My nerves are on edge again. I can hardly eat a mouthful of breakfast.

I had this feeling when I was seven years old. My mum entered me for a talent competition singing the Rolf Harris classic, 'Jake the Peg'. She was quite forward thinking for a woman in the early 1970s. Knocking me into shape for a possible *Stars in Your Eyes* appearance later on in life. She turned my cricket bat into the 'extra leg', covered it in trouser material and put a shoe on the end. Cleverly, I had a hole in my coat pocket so I could hold the cricket-bat-cum-extra-leg and the unsuspecting village hall audience would never know. 'Look at that kid,' they'd mumble as I entered stage right. 'He's got three legs.'

Waiting in the wings to stun the expectant crowd with my routine, I felt just like I'm feeling now. I didn't want to do it, and the suspense was killing me. When Mr Smallwood, who ran the Scouts and organized Bob-a-Job week (he was also a big knob in the Leo Sayer fan club) asked who wanted to go first, my hand shot into the air. Before I knew it, I was on – and then off. I can remember the words to this day: 'Wherever

I go through rain and snow, the people always let me know.
There's Jake the Peg. Diddle diddle diddle dum. With his extra
leg. Diddle diddle diddle dum.'

I came second to a boy who played a very small harmonica,
although my mother said it was a farce because he was almost
a professional. Got down to the last twelve in his regional
audition for Bobby Bennett's *Junior Showtime*. Today, I'm
going for broke. No more 'Jake the Peg'. Today, Matthew,
I'm going to be... Jack the Lad. I'll complete the challenge
and return triumphant to the SS *Perfect* before conquering
Daphne in front of the Bjorn Borg mural in the Champions
Bar. Stand aside, unflappable Swede. It's the summer of the
unstoppable spud.

The Hippodrome Theatre is already full of pensioners.
They've got their fluorescent badges, and soon they'll be
jostling for position as the race for the front seat of the tour
bus hots up. Look at them. Like greyhounds waiting for their
traps to open. One frolicking hare and they'll be halfway
down the home straight and into the first bend.

On the gangplank we're having our pictures taken in front
of a cardboard cut-out of the Coliseum. How apt. I'm the
gladiator going into battle. Before smiling, I look back to
make sure there's no sign of Daphne and Claire. It's a case of
once bitten twice shy after my shameful display on the
gangplank in Livorno.

I'm on Coach 14, where some half Italian bird is hogging
the mike and telling us to beware of the gypsies with their
outstretched newspapers waiting to pick a pocket or two in
front of the Spanish Steps. I've been a big fan of day trips
from a very early age. I remember taking the Banana Splits on
one jaunt to Blackpool! It was in the early days of the battery
powered portable 'take it anywhere' television. Well, I say
'take it anywhere'. Mine was the size of a suitcase, yet more
awkward to keep hold of, but the extendable aerial meant

you could tune into your favourite programme wherever you were in the country.

It was Saturday morning and I was determined not to miss out on an episode of *The Banana Splits* (Fleegle, Bingo, Drooper and Snorky; tra la la etc.). Not surprisingly, I barely got a flicker. I thought I caught a glimpse of *The Arabian Knights* on the M6 just north of Cannock, but apart from that, it wasn't worth the trouble. I was left lugging my television up the tower, along the golden mile and onto the pleasure beach where, to make matters worse, I got stranded on top of the Alice in Wonderland ride. Power cut. The 'take it anywhere' television experiment was an unmitigated disaster.

The half Italian bird gives us a final set of instructions as we disembark in a car park underneath St Peter's Basilica in the Vatican City. Her blue umbrella points skyward to a rendezvous point, to which everyone has to return by 3 p.m. Otherwise, the rest of the day is ours. We're free to explore the gems of Italy's most famous city.

The dome of St Peter's Basilica rises majestically from the square of the Vatican. Hundreds of Japanese tourists are racing around trying to get the best pictures. They don't do beach holidays these Japanese. They're far too busy discovering the world, scurrying from one tourist hot spot to another, desperate to cram it all in. They grab their pictures, then bog off.

Religion has never been my specialist subject, but I can't help wondering what Jesus would have made of all of this. If he was here with me now, I'd ask him straight out. 'We built this for you. It's yours. It's our way of saying thank you. What do you think?' I'm sure he'd have marvelled at the splendour of the place and appreciated the workmanship. Then, he'd have looked at me square on with those deep, worldly wise yet slightly humble eyes and said: 'You can pray just as well in a pit as you can in a palace, my son.' Obviously, he'd have thought of a better way of putting it, but I'm just trying to make a point.

I gaze in awe around the huge Vatican square. Breathtaking buildings surround it, reaching out to the roadside beyond, and then bending inward like the two outstretched arms of a mother ready, willing and desperate to embrace the whole world in her heaving bosom. But there'll be no Papal blessing for me today. He only comes out on a Wednesday and a Saturday. I've missed the boat again. I'm set to remain pope-less. Everybody is. Except, of course, for Mouthy Kev and Kiss Me Kate who are probably inside this very minute having their own personal audience (close personal friends I expect). I'll bet June's kissed his holy ring of fire on many occasions. I'll wait until the end of the afternoon before going inside the Basilica, but I will go and have a look. After all, it's free, and I'm not going to look a gift-horse in the mouth. For now, however, I've got work to do.

Rome's easy to explore. Cross the beautiful bridge, which is magnificently flanked on both sides by a host of angels, and you're halfway to paradise. (Billy Fury, number three in 1961.) Look left to see the Spanish Steps in the distance. A short walk and you're at the Piazza Navona, the city's most glamorous square. Well, it's more a giant oval really. In medieval times, the popes used to flood the piazza to stage mock naval encounters. Where's Lucille Bullock when you need her? She'd have had a field day with a couple of Monsignors and a pair of secateurs.

My mate Roland Rotherham, the food historian – you remember, he ate roasted arse of monkey in the Himalayas; he's also eaten goat, dormouse, zebra, swan, pelican and marinated beaver – reckons the Romans had the worst diet of them all. Didn't realize that while they were stirring away with their iron tools in their iron bowls, they were slowly poisoning themselves. That reminds me. Dr Rotherham also created a weasel casserole. He brought a saucepanful into work one day, but after my experience with his zebra curry, I decided not to touch it. Maybe I'll revisit it when I get home, in tribute to my mate Kenneth.

Out of the Piazza Navona, and the small brown signs soon have you at the Trevi Fountain (via the Pantheon). The place is swarming with visitors desperate to hang on to the coat-tails of their half Italian guides. There's dozens of different coloured umbrellas up as tourists cram into the rather confined space in front of the main attraction. It looks like Wimbledon during a break in play for rain. Down the steps, and coins are going in from all angles as people perch on the wall. Never mind three coins in the fountain, there must be three thousand – and it's still early. The Trevi Fountain was designed so you would hear the water before you stumbled across it. Today the hustle and bustle of tourists drowns out the cascading water. You're there before you know it, and what an atmosphere.

Mrs Hair Bear Bunch is sat on the wall between her two Muppet friends. She's got a face like a dropped pile as they all bunch up so a kindly Japanese lady can take their picture. I can tell she's itching to get back on board the ship for a quick Palais Glide at the afternoon tea-dance. My suspicions are confirmed almost immediately as Mrs Hair Bear turns to one of her elderly gentlemen, looks around distastefully at the gathered hoards, and grumbles, 'There's not much here!'

'There's not much here!' She's in bloody Rome. It's one of the most remarkable places on the planet. She's sat on the edge of the Trevi Fountain – one of the world's greatest landmarks – moaning that there's nothing to see. A mischievous thought crosses my mind. Wouldn't it be marvellous if Mrs Hair Bear lost her balance for a split second and toppled in backwards? Arse over tit, taking the two Muppets with her. Three old farts in a fountain. Marvellous to watch, but a disaster for Mrs Hair Bear. The unexpected dunking would almost certainly dislodge her wig, leaving

Neptune and his trusty Tritons looking on in disgust at the unfortunate scene developing under their very noses. She'd end up half drowned and hairless, at the mercy of thousands of sniggering Japanese tourists. I don't think the poor woman would ever get over it.

Anyway, I'm waiting for my moment, and here it comes – an empty segment of wall. Cunningly I delve into my holdall and produce a pair of King Edwards in one swift, yet elegant movement; like Zorro casting the sign of the Zee with his trusty sword. I carefully place my spuds neatly on the wall, trying to stay calm and not draw too much attention to myself. What's all the fuss anyway? I'm taking a picture of two potatoes on the wall of the Trevi Fountain surrounded by thousands of people in the heart of Rome. Happens every other day, I should think.

Within a few seconds I've done it. I couldn't get the whole fountain in; nobody can, it was designed that way. But I reckon I've got half of one of the wild sea horses, and plenty of water. What a picture! My Roman quest is halfway complete and the spuds are back inside the bag.

It's not a bad idea this. I'll recreate it for the *British Potato News*. Let's get the innocent spud to as many world landmarks as possible. I can see it now: 'Around the world with 80 Desirees.' Just imagine it. The Maris does a tour of Paris. A sack of Pentland Javelins outside the pyramids. A steaming bowl of mashed Marfonas perched on a barrel with Niagara Falls as the stunning backdrop. A Premiere sits proudly in front of Buckingham Palace (preferably on the outstretched gloved hand of one of the queen's guards), and a saucepanful of Saxons on the steps of the Sydney Opera House. Watch out Margaret Chandler, my little scrag-end. This holiday's revitalizing me. I'm coming back with a bang, once more to be crowned the golden boy of the British potato.

Just in front of the fountain a pair of newly-weds appear from the archway of a Roman church. The crowd cheer as the groom lifts his bride into the air. It's romantic. I think of Daphne. Then I think of Dicky Cox.

He once tried to organize the first ever World Wife Carrying Championships. The idea was that contestants had to race over a course of obstacles with their other half on their back. The winner got his wife's weight in potatoes. It never took off in this country, although in Finland it's become something of a national sport. Dicky and me decided we would check it out if we ever got on that holiday to find a unicorn in the Finnish forests. Personally, I think we've got more chance of winning the wife carrying championships than finding a unicorn, but that's another story.

Time's moving on and I'm still a 'Pope on a Rope' down. The euphoria of the picture has taken its toll and I'm almost mown down by a cute little Audrey Hepburn look-a-like who's straddled over a scooter. (They're very fond of scooters, the native Romans.) With my new-found, evergrowing spurt of confidence, I give her my, 'Fancy a bit of English?' glance. It's a sort of 'Come to bed with me, I'm interesting' glare mixed with an air of 'We've got a royal family, you haven't' cockiness. What a coup that would be if I pulled a proper Italian chick in Rome; the fashion centre of the world. It doesn't work. 'Twat!' she shouts back, headscarf blowing in the breeze. On second thoughts, she's more of an Elsie Tanner than an Audrey Hepburn. Probably born in Doncaster.

What do I care? I'm within spitting distance of the Spanish Steps, and that's where I'm going to open my crisps. After all, that's how my career took off. Well, not exactly with a bag of crisps in Rome. It was a bag of Potato Puffs from the school tuck-shop. Cost me two and a half pence in new money. Best two and a half pence I've spent in my life. I became a Potato Puff addict, and I told them so when I was being interviewed for my job at the British Potato Marketing Board. Couldn't fail.

Unfortunately, my tribute to the Potato Puff on the Spanish Steps in Rome is brought to an abrupt halt when some whistle-blowing Italian bobby races through the crowd. He's coming straight at me, waving his arms furiously. Surely I'm not going to be arrested for taking a picture of two potatoes at the Trevi Fountain. I'm too young to be locked away in some Mediterranean hell-hole of a prison. Oh. He wants me to stop eating. Eating is not allowed on the Spanish Steps. Amazed and embarrassed I scrunch up my half-eaten bag and scuttle away with my head hung low. The shame of it all. I've been reprimanded by a stiff-necked Keystone Kop. How was I supposed to know they operated a 'no food zone'? It's not fair. 'Sod the little bugger,' I say to myself, making sure the Italian officer is well out of range. Then, as a final tit-for-tat gesture of defiance, I blatantly lob the V-sign to a harmless old lady sat minding her own business on the bottom Spanish Step. I feel justified in my sudden ruthlessness. I decide to stick two fingers up to the Coliseum as well. My ill-fated sustenance break has turned me against the city altogether. On top of that, Rome's too hot and sticky to do any more dashing around, so I'm going back to the Vatican for my 'Pope on a Rope'.

It's difficult explaining the concept to Italian shopkeepers.

'*Hello, I'm Eng-er-lish. Have you got a 'Pope on a Rope',* s'il vous plaît?' Heaven only knows why I'm shouting. '*A pope. Carved in soap. Suspended on a rope.*' Now I'm making a strange swinging movement with my hand. She's never going to get it. '*Gracias,*' and onto the next.

I don't know why it's so difficult. There are pope pens, pope rubbers, pope coasters, pope pictures, pope ornaments, pope tea-towels, pope mugs, pope T-shirts, pope badges, pope hats, pope brolleys, pope videos, pope cassettes, pope blow up cushions, pope wine screws, pope key-rings, pope cuddly toys and even pope bible gum with each segment of candy tastefully wrapped in a verse out of the great book. It's like *The Generation Game* without the conveyor belt.

I'm losing heart. But it's worth one last try. I pick a grubby little store within the shadow of the dome. Inside the shopkeeper shuffles about nervously. He's probably heard of this English madman who took a picture of two spuds on the wall of the Trevi Fountain, tried to eat crisps on the Spanish Steps and is now running riot in the Vatican City asking for the Pope on a rope.

'Pope on a Rope?' I ask, almost certain of a blank look. The shopkeeper's an odd looking thing. Reminds me of a modern day Rumplestiltskin.

'Pope on a Rope,' says Rumplestiltskin in broken English. He puts his hand to his mouth and rubs his grubby chin. At least he's having a think about it. Suddenly his face lights up a little. He beckons me towards the front of the store and grabs a small pope fridge magnet. Fridge magnet? Blast, he's misunderstood me. It's no good, the game's up. He walks back to the counter and fishes around in a box underneath. 'A pope,' he says, showing me the small statue with a magnet glued to its back, 'and a rope.' The clever little bugger's cracked it. He's produced a small piece of string from out of nowhere and tied it tastefully around the pope's midriff. The pope's swinging in front of my very eyes. Rumplestiltskin, you're a genius. In fairy-tale terms, he's just spun my straw into gold. Look at me Rome; I'm the miller's daughter.

The trip back to the boat is a triumphant affair. I fall gently to sleep on the back seat of the bus, confident in the knowledge that my mission has been completed. It's a milestone in my life. In a strange way I've exorcised my tragic experience with *The Banana Splits* in Blackpool. Steadily, I'm beginning to rebuild my life on a more confident footing. I'm on a mini-roll, but my biggest challenge still lies ahead.

It's another formal night and I've planned it like a military exercise. One: put the camera film into the developing kiosk near the Golden Penny Arcade where the Pillsbury Dough Man met his maker (see, I'm still thinking about him). Two: wait for the moment, and thrill the whole of table 69 with my 'Pope on a Rope'. Three: flushed with success, make my way to the Woody Woodpecker Children's Club. This is the brilliant bit. I'm going to use Claire as a foil, just like she used me all those years ago. She's bound to know where Daphne hangs out after dinner. I'm going to callously extract the information from her unsuspecting lips. I'll pay her back for Terry 'T-Bone' Taylor once and for all. And four: with the necessary information on her whereabouts under my belt, I'll 'unexpectedly' bump into Daphne and we'll spend the night with an Orgasm or two. We could watch the sun come up over Barcelona. It's faultless.

There's a small hiccup on table 69. Mouthy Kev and Kiss Me Kate have gone for the more casual dining experience. They're having an Indian bistro in the conservatory so they're going to miss my moment of pope glory. Bastards. Fancy setting someone a challenge and ignoring them just when they're about to produce the results of a hard day's toil. It's a good job Andy's eager to talk.

'Have you ever been out with a circus performer?' he asks. Momentarily, his question throws me. Besides, I'm still trying to pinch the evening's menu for Dibble the Muffin Man back home.

'What? Er, no, I don't think so,' I reply.

Bloody marvellous. Has everyone forgotten my Roman quest? I've noticed at almost every other table you get greeted with a friendly 'Had a nice day?' or 'Did you manage to get to the Sistine Chapel?' What do I get? 'Have you ever been out with a circus performer?' I ask you.

'Well,' says Andy in full flow, 'Kenneth's first love was a tightrope walker – he was doing an advert for Toffee Crisp when they met – and Alfred once had an early dabble with a fire-eater.'

Alfred chips in: 'Angelo was his name. Unstable. Ended up having a nervous breakdown just before a show in Rhyl. He was a fire-eater. A twisted fire-eater.'

'I once fell for a daring young man on a flying trapeze,' says June. 'But that was only on the television. He went through the air with the greatest of ease. I thought, yes love, you can go through my big top without a safety net any day of the week. And then Tom had an encounter with an incredible bearded lady once in Southport. We just thought it would be an amazing coincidence if you'd gone out with a circus performer.'

'I had my money on you with a lion tamer,' Andy said. Alfred lets out a playful growl while Andy gives one of his little titters. I was wrong about these two. They're perfect for each other. It's a match made in heaven. As for me, I'm caught between two tales of the unexpected. On one hand, do I delve further into the story of Thomas the Electronic Toothbrush and his encounter with the incredible bearded lady in Southport, or do I press on with my incredible Roman adventure? I'm pressing on.

'Have you all forgotten?' I ask slightly bemused. 'My forfeit.'

A shriek comes from June. Alfred clasps his hands in anticipation. 'Let's see what you've got then, Martin,' says Kenneth the Weasel Man.

'My name's Malcolm, Kenneth.'

It's no good, he's oblivious, and anyway, I've got a mighty tale to tell. A round of applause greets my potato story. They gasp when I reveal how I was led away from the Spanish Steps by a burly Italian gun-toting Deputy Dog (I exaggerated slightly on that one). Look at me, the world's worst small-talker, holding court on table 69. This holiday is becoming a life-changing experience.

'And now, Ladies and Gentlemen...'

There's a momentous and collective whoop of delight from table 69 as I produce my four-inch pope, swinging merrily on

Rumplestiltskin's piece of string. It's a moment I'll remember all my life. Kenneth roars so loudly that his teeth lunge forward. Then, they kick back with such ferocity that he almost swallows his complete top deck. In a desperate attempt to compensate, the Weasel Man jerks his head down and cups his hand to his mouth as if to catch his wayward dentures. Fortunately, they don't drop out. Unfortunately, Andy, who thinks he's helping out in a crisis (remember, he was the last victim of the flying teeth), gives Kenneth's back a mighty whack which sends the Weasel Man sprawling back towards the table. He's on course for the condiments – and Alfred's dinner. With seconds to spare, however, Alfred calmly slides his plate to one side, Kenneth's head rams against the table with a dull thud...and the falsies have stayed put. I'm glad. I didn't want another 'tooth fiasco' spoiling my moment.

And what a moment it is. Alfred lifts his glass high into the air to toast my success. June leans over to plant a delicate peck on my left cheek. Now that is a surprise. First time I've seen her do anything delicately. I thought she'd have yanked my trousers down and gone for another one of her Ginger Rogers moments. Tom stays silent, but he gives a kindly nod. My achievement has been duly recognized, even in his funny old world. Kenneth, now fully recomposed, leads the applause while I sit there drinking in the adulation. It's the proudest I've been since I made the local newspapers after finishing third in a fancy-dress competition at the age of six. I was narrowly beaten by a tree and the Statue of Liberty.

The tide has turned. A rare feeling of victory is starting to creep in. Hello world, it's the new me, and I'm a *winner*! Next stop: Claire at Woody Woodpeckers. It's getting late and I'm full of pan-fried calf liver and creamed leeks. I've had a fair amount of Californian Red as well (Dutch courage). Usually, I'd give up the ghost at this point and retire to my rocking-chair. Head in towel. But not tonight. I'm determined. Just hope I'm not too late to corner Claire.

Superb. There are no children in the Woody Woodpecker room. But there *is* movement in the red and white Punch and Judy canopy. I stride onwards, certain that my luck has finally changed. Then suddenly, I stop in my tracks. I'm frozen stiff by the thought of years gone by. I've seen that canopy swaying like this before.

It's all coming back to me. The village fair. Terry Taylor with his shovel-like hands grasping my girlfriend's bosom while I was over the other side of the field, handling his well-hung goose. Maybe she's at it again. Norman DeVine could be in there at this very moment. He could have Claire's Mr Punch thrust firmly into his groin while he meddles with her Judy. I can just imagine it. What the hell. I've got nothing to lose.

I move closer. Muffled sounds. She's definitely in there. Having sex with Norman DeVine like she did all those years ago with the fifty-three-year-old vegetarian faggot man. I don't care. Tonight is my night. I've got bigger fish to fry and I'm half full of Californian Red wine. Anyway, tonight the boot's on the other foot. What do I care if Norman's got his pants down by his ankles giving her one up the Dorothy Squires? No. I'm going to give Claire the fright of her life, then leave them to it as I chase the woman of my dreams. I pull back the entrance to the Punch and Judy booth with one sharp tug. 'Hello Claire.'

I'm as cool as an iceberg lettuce. I'm enjoying the moment. I know she's in there and up to no good. I look. Then look again.

'*Daphne!*'

Oh fuck no. I've had too many disappointments in my life. Another might send me over the edge. I'm going to end up like Alfred's twisted fire-eater. But it's true. I stand for a second; it seems like a lifetime. Claire and Daphne are in the Punch and Judy booth. Snogging. Daphne turns to stare at me, her beautiful blonde hair ruffled, then looks to the ground as she quickly fastens the top three buttons of her blouse.

'Malcolm, you absolute twat,' screams Claire, as Daphne runs past me and out of the Woody Woodpecker Club. 'You're always, always spoiling my life. Why can't you just fuck off and die like that fat old bastard last night?'

Claire barges me out of the way with an ice hockey-like charge. She's after Daphne, stopping momentarily to hitch up her lace thongs. I'm standing alone, facing a deserted Punch and Judy booth and a broken wooden train at my feet. Mr Punch is hanging face down, his nose dangling into the open mouth of the crumpled up crocodile. It's a tragic scene. And it's the final knife in my holiday romance coffin. Claire's right. It might just as well have been me instead of the Pillsbury Dough Man.

Slowly and dejectedly I make my way back to cabin F153. I sit in my chair. Towel over my head. It's all gone wrong again, and I was having such a bloody good day. I should have known things were about to take a horrible downturn. I'm only allowed fleeting moments of happiness in my life; that's the way the good Lord wanted it to be. I should have worked it out. Daphne tells Cruise Bore she longs to be a fellow. Spiky Claire tells me her relationship with Norman DeVine is for 'business reasons only'. I had him down as gay from day one and I was bloody spot on. They leave for Florence hand in hand. Oh Malcolm. You little sodding prat.

Dicky Cox was right all along. Claire's a buffet bird, but now, it seems, she's letting both men and women help themselves. I'm that distressed, if Kiss Me Kate came knocking tonight I'd bite the bullet and give her one. After all, why should I be the only fair-minded, straight-thinking man left in the entire universe. And she has got a well-rounded pair of knockers. I'd shag her blind. In the name of the now deceased Mrs Lighthouse and her 'dingers' and 'dongers'.

What the heck, I should've thrown caution to the wind years ago. Instead of all this 'marriage or nothing' muck, I should've been chucking it about like a human seed drill. I've ballsed up for nearly thirty-eight years. I've got it all wrong with women and now I'm counting the cost. For the second time today, I wish Jesus was next to me. I'd ask, 'What did you do that to me for?' Foolishly, I look to the heavens. Predictably, I don't receive any revelations. Maybe he's waiting for me to join the Salvation Army before he answers my questions in full.

Very slowly, I fish my two King Edwards out of my holdall. Like Mr Benn in the cartoons, I've decided to keep them as a souvenir. Then I dip into the breast pocket of my dinner jacket. Excuse me for a minute. I'm just going to eat my 'Pope on a Rope'.

13

Malcolm's Log. It's Friday, June 27th. We're in Barcelona. Olympic City 1992. Daphne's a lesbian. Claire's a lesbian also. Dag nab it, the pair are an item. The Pillsbury Dough Man is dead. Mouthy Kev is shagging June on a regular basis by the children's jacuzzi, while Kev's wife Kiss Me Kate has tried to seduce me on two separate occasions in my cabin. Kenneth the Weasel Man is still having trouble with his teeth, the breakfast beans are cold, my hopes of a holiday romance are in tatters, and I've eaten the Pope! Hopefully, today things will get back to normal.

In a way I'm strangely satisfied with the events of last night. Getting a glimpse of Claire in a passionate clinch with Daphne might be some blokes' idea of titivation. For me, the shock was far too great to constitute the makings of a sexual fantasy. It's killed my two birds with one stone, and at least now I know where I stand. As for Claire's outburst... I'm beginning to hate that woman. Don't know what I saw in her in the first place. The girl's a complete out and out tart. It's obvious she's exhausted all available male options, so now she's getting her sexual kicks with a lady. The Port Enhancement Lady at that. The Port Enhancement Lady I've wasted more than a week trying to get off with. I realized last night, submerged in my own doom and gloom, that – apart from my mother, the Angel

– not one girl has ever told me she loved me. The day a female looks me straight in the eye and says 'I love you' is the day I pack up my clobber and head for the land of happy ever after.

I've never understood the ins and outs of true love. Especially when it comes to the nitty-gritty. However, today's a clean sheet. A new start. I've decided that a holiday romance is off the cards. I'm just going to enjoy myself and revel in the delights of my new-found weirdo friends, starting with Mouthy Kev and Kiss Me Kate. Don't forget, we're sharing a taxi en route to Barcelona's most famous landmark. In the words of Jessie Matthews, I'm about to toss all of my cares over my shoulder. Willy-nilly, if needs be.

After breakfast, I make a beeline for Mrs Cocktail Stick. She's sat with Roger and Rosemary, the ferret couple. She looks surprisingly jolly considering her boyfriend has just recently perished outside the Golden Penny Arcade. I'm going to be sympathetic to a fault.

'Hello Alison.' Good start. 'I was sorry to hear the news. How are you feeling?'

Not a bad attempt overall. She can see by my face that I'm concerned. I've tried to twist it up in a caring sort of way.

'Oh, I'm all right thank you Malcolm. They've been lovely on board the ship. Laid Trevor to rest in the mortuary yesterday. I was just telling Rosemary and Roger, it's too expensive to fly him back in a coffin, but they offered to let me go home – flight to England and everything. I told them to bollock off.' She lowers her voice. 'He wouldn't have wanted it, you know.'

Mrs Cocktail Stick seems to have taken the death of her lover very well.

'Anyway,' she continues, 'the Captain let me use his study to take a phone call from his sister. Lovely woman. She wants me at the funeral. Front row. He died a happy, happy man.'

At that point I decided to intervene. 'I was thinking, Alison. Maybe we should have a memorial service for him before we get home. What do you think?'

'Oh, Malcolm.'

She's taken aback by my thoughtfulness. She's going to jump at the chance and I'll make sure I organize it to perfection.

'Don't be such a miserable twat. I've already told you. He died a happy man. He wouldn't have wanted all that moping around and bouquet tossing. Anyway, I've already laid his trousers out in the dining-room!' She pauses for a second and then pokes the air as if she's suddenly stumbled on a master plan. 'We'll all do the twist at the *Perfect* Party on the last night. That'll be much more appropriate, don't you think?'

Mrs Cocktail Stick's just called me a miserable twat. Why does everybody end up calling me a twat? It's a conspiracy; the whole world's ganging up on me, I'm convinced of it. And Mrs Cocktail Stick of all people. I was only trying to show some compassion. But I understand. A mass twist on leaving night she wants, and a mass twist she'll get. We'll be twisting the night away in honour of the Pillsbury Dough Man. I think she's got it just right. And she's made me think. We've got just three nights left on *Perfect*. Although, according to today's *Nautical Newsletter*, there's action all the way home. Norman DeVine and Perfection have their big show tonight in the Hippodrome Theatre. It's a whistle-stop tour around *West Side Story*, 'The musical that changed musicals forever.'

The newsletter says: 'Norman and his team have been building up to this big climax all holiday.' I think I know how he feels. It's probably the only climax he gets with his other half chasing the Port Enhancement Queen in Woody Woodpecker's. I wonder if I should ask June if she's ever had it up the Woody Woodpecker. The answer's almost certainly 'yes'. Porky Pig probably showed her his Pixie and Dixie by the children's jacuzzi, while Tom was polishing some poor woman's Daffy Duck with his Mickey Mouse toothbrush. That woman has definitely affected my thinking. I doubt I'll ever be the same again. A Wild West BBQ is planned for tomorrow's 'Day at Sea'. Then the last night is *Perfect* Party Night. The newsletter tries to sum up the emotion of the occasion by describing it as 'a chance to say a final farewell to those unforgettable friends you've met on board. Who knows, you may all meet again some sunny day.' Cheating gits. They've pinched that line off Dame Vera Lynn. Still, it gives me a chance to drink myself half stupid before we hit the white cliffs of Southampton.

I hope the Spaniards are ready for me. I'm at my very best when I'm three parts pissed. Just give me a bar and the sunshine; it's like waving a red rag at a bull. I don't really fancy having my photograph taken on the gangplank with a plate of paella and the Olympic flag behind me. The snap of me with Cyril the Seal has been up outside the Golden Penny for over a week. Don't they understand I'm not interested in their bloody pictures?

Kiss Me Kate is waving me towards the courtesy bus. Apparently, it drops us off at the Ramblas which, according to Daphne, is a bustling promenade full of street artists. Supposed to be the nearest thing they've got in Spain to Blackpool's Golden Mile. (I should have brought the Banana Splits in tribute.) From Ramblas it's a short taxi ride to our unfinished temple. After that, I'm finding some quiet little bar on the sea front to get as pissed as arseholes. Kev's first to greet me.

'I've been farting all night,' he says.

It's his way of saying, 'Good morning Malcolm and how are you today? Are you ready to take in one of the classic sights of this cultural Spanish city?'

'Bloody chicken vindaloo at the Indian bistro night. It was that hot I had to get the cabin boy to put the sodding toilet rolls in the fridge. Kate's arse is on fire as well, isn't it petal?'

193

Interesting. She's gone from a flower to a petal since we've been on board. His bluebell would certainly turn into a bouquet of withered flowers if I blew the gaff on her and her sordid goings on.

No sooner are we off the bus than Kev's burst into his Freddie Mercury. 'Barcelona! La, la, la, la, la, la, la, la.' You've got to give it to him for bravado. He loads his wife and me into a waiting cab and before you can say, 'Blue Spanish Eyes' (Al Martino), the three of us are off again through the busy streets of the Olympic City. It looks clean enough, but the architecture's a bit on the wild side. It's all twisted. Should suit the passengers on the SS *Perfect* a treat. It's this Antoni Gaudi fellow. They treat him like a god here. Almost made him a saint before he got run over and killed by a runaway tram. The world's first ever 'hit and run' accident. Now his name is used to describe anything that lacks taste. Ironic, I muse.

Margaret Chandler had a thing about gaudiness. 'Neat but not gaudy, my little scrag-ends!' she used to squeal after one of her monthly office clearouts. She was a stickler for keeping on top of things, and 'casting out the clutter' – said it kept us all on the ball. In a way, I've taken a leaf out of her book this morning. I'm clutter-free. I've brought nothing off the ship except for my cruise card (you need it to get back on deck; it's like a clocking in card), and enough Spanish pesetas to get me well and truly blotto. I've left the crisps in my oatmeal biscuit draw. I'm not going to risk a repeat of yesterday's nasty incident on the Spanish Steps.

In the taxi, there's an awkward silence for a short while. I'm struggling for space, wedged like a sardine between Kiss Me Kate and her weighty other half. It's not pleasant. Kate's gone way over the top with the Charlie Girl, Kev's squashing me and it's beginning to get a little uncomfortable. In fact, I think the blood's stopped flowing to my lower right leg. Kate shuffles one stiletto nervously, before her husband breaks the ice.

'So then Malcolm. My wife's not good enough for you, eh?' Kev's looking at me strangely.

'What do you mean?' I ask him fearfully. I'm not sure I want to hear the reply.

'Well I ask you. She's practically thrown herself at you for two nights and she's not had so much as a sniff in return. What's wrong with you? Don't you think she's attractive in her own sort of way?'

I can't believe this. I'm cornered in a taxi with Kevin asking me why I'm not shagging his wife. She's just sat there with a quizzical look on her Thelma Ferris-type face. Kevin doesn't wait for my considered response.

'It's all right pal. We have an open marriage. We meet up with Tom and June every year. Same trip. But the golden rule is that we treat each other as total strangers. It adds a bit of *je ne sais quoits*.'

I think he means *Je ne sais quoi* but I've got to let it ride on this occasion. His dramatic confession is not over – not by a long way.

'We all love the musicals, and we like to dabble with a bit on the side. It's the perfect scenario. Everyone goes home happy and fulfilled. Nothing ventured, nothing gained.'

Oh Lord. They're all in on it. I was right all along. I've innocently hit upon a table of swingers. The Tits Out for the *Titanic* Club. I clocked it the first time I set eyes on them and it's been bloody true. From the moment Captain Fletcher dropped the gangplank, this gang have been dropping their drawers. They're the gangplank gang-bang gang.

'And the lads love it too,' says Kate.

'Andy and Alfred?'

I'm keen to know more now. I've nothing to lose. I thought I knew Kevin and Kate's darkest secrets. It turns out I knew nothing.

'Oh yes,' continues Kate quite unashamedly. 'Kevin likes a bit of the other occasionally.'

'So does Andy. Doesn't he, Katherine?' adds Kevin.

She looks down in a shy, schoolgirl sort of way. 'Well, he is good with an iron, and he can stiffen anything with a tin of spray starch. It's like watching an artist at work. Marvellous. You should see the way he handles my underwear. Goes through my knickers like a steam train. And I always let him loose on my dicky dirts when we're on holiday.' (I think she means shirts, but I can't be sure at this stage.) She turns to whisper in my ear. 'He's got three balls you know. Got a knacker bag that looks like a pawnbroker's sign. It's quite fascinating from the back.'

So, she's having it away with Andy, who's shagging Alfred, who's bonking Kevin, who's knobbing June, who's probably having her Ginger Rogers tickled by Tom, who's almost certainly got his toothbrush to Kate, who's tried to shag me twice.

'Now, let me get this clear. June, Tom, you two, Andy and Alfred. You're all swingers, right?'

'Correct,' says Kevin. Fancy *him* swinging both ways. Must come with the territory when you're a big knob in manure management. 'We thought when Nancy and Bernard were forced to pull out at the last minute after that bit of bother with the soap star and his barmy boyfriend, we'd have the chance to try a bit of "Lonnie Donegan" with a brand new couple. What were we given? You and that skinny little fucker with the false teeth.'

'Lonnie Donegan?' I'm lost.

'It's one of June's phrases,' says Kate. 'She once had sex with another woman's old man who was a dustman. She told him to give it to her up the Cumberland Gap. It still makes her titter to this day.'

I'm too deep in thought to titter. Lonnie Donegan. Had a pair of hits with 'My Old Man's a Dustman' and 'Cumberland

Gap'. It never ends. I'd love to get a glimpse into June's brain. I think it would be a major breakthrough for modern medical science.

'Kate had high hopes for you at first,' Kevin's racing on now, 'but I knew you were a limp lettuce the moment I set eyes on you. He's a cowardly lion, I said. Never had his wicked witch of the west up the yellow brick road in his life. I said it first night, didn't I Kate, love?'

'June thinks you're asexual,' adds Kate. I sit there taking it all in. 'According to her, you don't like women and you don't like men; you just like potatoes.'

'Yes,' Kevin agrees, starting to viciously poke my arm. It hurts. He's got a powerful index finger by anybody's standards. 'And,' he continues with another prod, 'you can't' (prod) 'shag' (prod) 'a spud' (big prod).

'Oww!' I protest. Anyway, he's wrong. Claire did. But she's a lesbian now. It's the most remarkable taxi journey of all time.

All too soon the magnificent Temple Expiatori de la Sagrada Familia lies before our very eyes. It's a spiky affair. Could almost be a monument to Mrs Cocktail Stick. The Japanese are out in force. Apart from that, it's all SS *Perfect* passengers done out with their fluorescent pink stickers, following some Spanish bird who has her red umbrella pointing firmly towards the cloudless continental sky. I'm not overimpressed with the thing. It's loved by some but loathed by others. I'm not even passionate enough to loathe it. St Michael's Cave in Gibraltar had a bigger impact on me. Why they labelled Gaudi a genius, I shall never know. He's not fit to wipe Jack Russell's backside in the genius department. Even Des O'Connor is higher in Malc's Marvellous Men Hit Parade than this Gaudi geezer. Anyway, I'm ready for the return journey to the Ramblas. Nothing could better the drama of the taxi trip on the way here. Now I'm ready for the second instalment.

197

'So Kate. Have you encountered Tom's electronic tooth-brush yet?' I ask mischievously as we leave the stone temple behind.

'Toothbrush? Oh, I see. No. I haven't had the toothbrush, but I've had the toilet brush, the feather duster and the Dyson vacuum cleaner. He's very non-contact you know.'

A Dyson? Whatever has Tom done to Kiss Me Kate with a Dyson? It's almost too dreadful to contemplate.

'And what about Nancy and Bernard? Were they a nice pair?'

'Oh yes,' says Kate. 'The bees knees. Nancy's very big in Little Hampton. Organizes some very exclusive parties. June had a soft spot for Bernard. Used to call him "Bernie the Bolt". You know, him off *The Golden Shot*. Used to load the crossbow for Bob Monkhouse and little Annie Aston.'

'Is there anyone June hasn't got a soft spot for?' I ask tentatively.

'Kenneth,' booms Mouthy Kev. 'Drop us just here, gringo,' he adds.

The taxi driver looks puzzled. I don't think he fully under-stands. Kev has another blast at trying to get us involved in a full-scale international incident.

'Just by the market Manuel, if you please. Greasy-arse!' He roars with laughter and gives Kate a hefty nudge. He's very unwieldy. How he's won trophies for his badminton I shall never know. Must be something to do with that special shuttlecock he keeps hidden away in his drawers.

'Are you coming up the Ramblas, Malcolm?' asks Kate.

'No thanks. I'm going to find a nice little bar by the waterfront.' I think they've gathered by now that I won't be joining them for a gang-bang, but even so, I'll keep my distance and go my own way.

Of course, Dicky Cox would have been straight in like a ferret down a hole. He once claimed to have bedded two ladies representing Copenhagen when he visited the International

Potato Fair 2000 in Luxembourg. He gloated for a fortnight. I can almost hear him now: 'If anyone tries to tell you a bird in the hand is worth two in the bush, don't listen. They're talking total shit.' He made quite a splash on the British stand that year. Had his picture taken for the Global Potato Journal. Not because he bonked two women, you understand. It was for his work on promoting our spuds. They called him 'The cutting edge of the UK potato'.

Manuel has dropped us off by a quaint little market at the bottom of the parade. I should have set up a stall selling my excess oatmeal biscuits. I've got enough to feed most of the city. To my left is the sea; there are more cruise ships in dock here than anywhere else. To my right is the city, and beyond that, the mountains. That's Barcelona for you. Squashed between the mountains and the sea, but the place simply oozes class.

The song says it all: 'You've either got, or you haven't got, style.' Barcelona has it by the bucketful and if *you*'ve got it, it stands out a mile. A cable-car straddles the harbour while clowns, street artists, traders and human statues bid for a pitch on both sides of the Ramblas. It's a splendiferous array. Full of delicious colours and exotic aromas. For me, it's the continent at its best. The place is buzzing, and I can't resist a quick wander, but only when Kev and Kate have firmly disappeared out of sight. For my return, I've chosen a bar near the water's edge. Not too far from where the courtesy bus picks up and drops off. I don't like to stray too far when I'm on my own. (I could never have been a backpacker. The mere thought of it puts me on edge.) The sun's shining, the water's glistening, the cruise boats are waiting and I've no love worries to weigh me down. This is a lad's moment. A large beer and me. In times of crisis, it's the perfect double act.

My mind wanders. If you ask me, it's all got a bit too raucous on board the SS *Perfect*. First I innocently stumble on a table full of sex maniacs. On top of that, I know for a fact there was a heated argument at the Horlicks Bar last night. There have even been reports of a full-scale scuffle in the laundrette when two ladies clashed over a vacant spin-drier! It's enough to make the ex-*Canberra* cruisers turn in their graves, and by the looks of one or two of them, they're about ready. It's a good job I've decided to distance myself from it all today. I'm making time for me, and for once, I think I've made the right decision. They've got Eric Clapton on inside. I can hear it perfectly. I let 'I Shot the Sheriff' wash over me. I'm at peace with the world. I'm content. I lie back in my plastic chair and tilt my face towards the sun.

I begin to sing. Stoop and Droop scuttle past me on their way to catch the courtesy bus. I think Stoop's a bit tiddily. She's singing too. I'm blowed if I can make out the tune, but the words are plain enough. 'Valencia. Stick your head between your knees and whistle up your Barcelona.' Droop joins in. 'Valencia. Stick your head between your knees and whistle up your hacienda.' In pigeon fancying terms, the two old birds have turned into a pair of squeakers.

Again I tilt my face sunwards. Again I'm interrupted.

'Hello Martin.'

That can only be one person. Kenneth the Weasel Man and his Magnificent Dancing Dentures. I've told him time and time again that my name's Malcolm. I think he finds the whole thing amusing.

'Can I have a beer with you while I wait for the courtesy bus?'

'Feel free. Here, have one on me.'

Kenneth's been on a tour to the Olympic Stadium.

'How are you getting on with Linda the Boot Scooting Baby? Have you pulled her yet? Or has she given you the side step?'

This is the new me see. Content and happy to engage in small talk. My world isn't spinning as quickly. I'm not as confused.

'Well, she does like older men. I know that for a fact,' he says, 'but I can't see her falling for me. It's these bastard teeth. They'll be the death of me, the buggers. And I can't have them changed. They're a family tradition – been passed down through the generations. I can't throw tradition out of the window, can I?'

'Well, teeth aren't everything,' I say sympathetically.

I feel for Kenneth. I can see he's had a rough ride in life (despite his brief flirtation with fame on *The Persuaders* and *Albion Market*). Only one sniff of romance, from what I can make out, when he dabbled with the tightrope walker while filming for the Toffee Crisp advert. I'll bet he hasn't lost his glass slipper yet.

'*Teeth aren't everything!*' says Kenneth in astonishment. 'These fuckers are.' I think I've hit a raw nerve. 'They're that precious I soak them in whisky every night. Do you know, Martin, it's my greatest wish to have a son to pass my teeth on to when I take my final bow and face my final curtain. I'd die a happy man.' Just like the Pillsbury Dough Man. 'But time's running out. And it worries me to death. If I don't have a son, what's going to happen to the bloody teeth?'

Kenneth shakes his head; he's almost in despair. He's worried sick about the family false teeth.

'I could've pulled anything in my heyday – that's the disappointing thing. I should've struck while my iron was hot. They once tipped me to be the new James Bond, but I couldn't go to the audition because I had a small part in *Charlie's Aunt*. Missed my chance.'

James Bond! In some ways, Kenneth and I have developed a James Bond on table 69. Thrown together in the face of adversity, we've become bosom buddies. In desperation, I try to boost his flagging spirits in my own special way.

'Look Kenneth.' It's a firm start. 'You've got to stop being a *Doctor No*. Try becoming more of a *Thunderball*. Turn yourself into *The Man with the Golden Gun*. That way,

Linda the Boot Scooting Baby will be all over you like an *Octopussy. Never Say Never Again.* Linda's bound to be at the Wild West BBQ on the Sunshine Deck tomorrow. I'll help you pull her. We'll give her the *Golden Eye* and before long she'll be *For Your Eyes Only.* With me behind you, you'll be *Licenced to Kill.* She'll be gagging for a good Moonraking. After all, You Only Live Once.

'It's twice, Martin,' says Kenneth. '*You Only Live Twice.*'

Fuck it. And I was doing so well. Anyway, who am I to offer advice? The man who's spent the whole holiday trying to shag a lesbian. And my only sexual conquest to date remains *her* lesbian lover. Apart from that I've fancied the Masked Lady who went crazy with a pair of secateurs, and I had a quick fondle with the girl who fantasized about having oral sex with a giraffe. Now I'm helping Kenneth on his no-hope mission to pull a line-dancing instructor at a Wild West BBQ. Still, he seems to have cheered up. And if all else fails, he could go for Mrs Hair Bear Bunch. She's fond of bit-part actors. If Kenneth's capable of getting a small part in *Charlie's Aunt*, the possibilities with Mrs Hair could be endless.

With a warm handshake, Kenneth's off to catch the afternoon prize bingo session. I admire him for the way he's stuck to his teeth. It's just a shame his teeth don't stick to him. Still, he's a man of honour, and on table 69, that's a unique achievement. And we only met because Nancy and Bernie the Bolt pulled out of the swingers annual tour. Now that's fate for you.

I'm on my own and into another large one. Peace returns. Contentment takes over. Gently I close my eyes and snuggle down into a comfortable, sort of diagonal position in my chair. Almost without realizing it, I begin to smirk quietly to myself. Eric Clapton's still singing: 'I'm knock, knock knocking on heaven's door.'

'Excuse me,' a soft voice from out of nowhere nicely compliments the feel of the moment. 'Are you the bloke on table 69 with three bollocks?'

Alarmed, I drag myself back into an upright position in one sudden movement. In a flash my eyes are wide open. I'm face to face with Miss Cruise Bore. She's leaning towards me with an inquisitive stare. Panic-stricken, I say the first thing that comes into my head. 'No, I'm sorry. I've only got two.' It's a ridiculous response, but how else could I reply?

Miss Cruise Bore stands before me wearing a gleaming white, 'I've splashed out on *The Mermaid*' T-shirt. I squint and put my hand to my eyes. I've slagged her off all holiday, once had her down as Daphne's lesbian lover before I discovered the horrible truth. Now she's part blocking my sunlight, just inches from my face – and she's talking bollocks. She's clearly got more to her than I first thought. In hindsight, I've done Miss Cruise Bore a disservice. I'll be kind to her.

'Andy's the one with the three balls,' I explain in a 'being kind' sort of way. Now, what next? Should I politely tell her to piss off. After all, I'm having a bit of private tender love and care, and I'm not prepared to talk testicles. But then, I'm intrigued. Point one: how did she know there was a man on table 69 with three balls? Point two: I quite like the way she's broken the ice. She's amused me. Miss Cruise Bore hovers for a second; she's waiting for me to speak but I'm just staring at her blankly. I don't know which way to turn.

'Can I sit with you for a while until the courtesy bus comes?' she asks, helping to ease the dilemma.

Well, here's a turn up for the books. This is the tomboy I met on my very first day. I thought she was anchored to her mother and father. I gave her a shagability rating of just two and a half. (Mind you, I *did* only have a back-end glance and a side on semi-stare.) Now she wants to sit by me.

'I liked your Tom Jones very much,' she says, flicking her unstyled shoulder-length strawberry-brown hair back in a nice girly sort of way. (I remember I was impressed with that when I spotted her line dancing with her mother and father.) Talking of which, where are they now? I've not seen her on her own before. I ask her.

'Mum and dad? Oh Lord. I've escaped from them at last. But not before they made me put on this.' She points to her breasts. I think she means the T-shirt. 'This is their fifteenth cruise. They've brought me a T-shirt back from every one, and on this holiday they've made me wear them all. Still, they mean well.'

Heavens. I seem to have got it all arse about face. Miss Cruise Bore's quite sexy when you've got the sun in your eyes, and you've downed two pints of lager on the sea front in Barcelona. I'm beginning to see her in a different light. Her blue eyes seem to sparkle. Never noticed before. And she's got knockers. They were obviously hidden from view under her baggy sweatshirt on day one. She's slim too; the trousers did nothing for her backside as she climbed the stairs for the life-jacket rehearsal. She should've come to me for a few handy fashion hints and tips. Still, I'm not interested. 'Too late!' cried the king as he shook his wooden leg. My courting days are over. She's missed the boat...and the bus. It's gone without her. Shame.

'Let me get you a drink,' I say reassuringly. After all, there's nothing wrong with being friends. She orders white wine. Large. I can feel Miss Cruise Bore getting into her stride.

'I tried to get your attention at the cocktail karaoke but I kept getting pestered by some tosser in a blazer.'

Now she's made me laugh.

'I've spotted him too. Here's your drink. I'm sorry, what's your name?'

'Maria.'

'I'm Malcolm.'

Awkward silence for a second. Funny that. I experienced an awkward silence earlier when I was sandwiched between Kevin and Kate in the taxi. That's my second one of the day – it's not an encouraging sign. I decide to pick up the baton and run with it.

'It's my first cruise. Is it yours?'

There you are. Look at me. I'm suddenly the king of small talk.

'Oh God, yes. I was engaged to a fellow for three years. He left me. Nasty business. Rocked me a bit and I started to let myself go.' (That would explain the bad hair, then.) 'Mum and dad decided to take me away for a break so I could relax and get back on my feet. I think it's working. I feel more content with myself. It's like the world's turning a little less quickly and I'm becoming a real person again.'

Now I'm going for the big one. 'But how did you know about the man with the, you know…' I'm now pointing at my groin, '…balls?' I'm trying hard not to appear too rude.

'I overheard two old ladies by the side of the pool. You can't help but tune in to other people's titbits. I've been eavesdropping for the best part of two weeks. They're an odd pair. One walks with a stoop and the other has a droopy face.' She stops to giggle. 'Stoop said she once courted a fella with only one ball. Then, Droop told her she'd heard there was a bloke on table 69 with three. I whittled down the options and thought it must be you.'

Double bloody hell. Maria is a female version of me. Can such things happen? Do I fancy her? I don't know; it's all quite different. I feel easy in her company, I'm not scared and she's already made me laugh. I like her, but my days with the ladies are over. I've decided to settle for a tongue sandwich on a Saturday, a pint with Jean, Jean the Tea Chest Queen, and, of course, my potatoes.

The second courtesy bus flies past. I'm on the wine with Maria now. We're laughing. She's noticed Stoop and Droop, and she's keen to know about my mate: 'You know, the thin man who always seems to be losing his teeth.' She too was sad to hear that the Pillsbury Dough Man had collapsed and died just hours after he'd made us all twist, although, unlike me, she'd made a point of finding the mortuary. She was intrigued that there should be one on board at all.

'Apparently, they go down like ninepins on a cruise,' she informed me. I could have told her that. I predicted it myself after the story of the woman stranded in the lift. Maria continues: 'The record is six. Happened on a Christmas tour of the Caribbean. Two went almost simultaneously in the Paradise Ballroom. Bliss were in full swing at the time with "Knees up Mother Brown".'

Told you again! I always said the Paradise Ballroom was cursed, and I should know – I've been spread-eagled on the shag pile myself. Still, her talk of death has sparked me into life.

'We could always twist together at the *Perfect* Party night,' I suggest, not even thinking that I was actually asking Maria on a date.

'No thanks,' she says. I realize I might have overstepped the mark. 'If we don't see each other until we twist at the *Perfect* Party on the last night, it means we won't meet up until we're almost home, and quite frankly, I'm fed up of chasing you round the sodding ship. Anyway. There's a 1950s tribute in the Happy Days Diner tonight. It's wild in there. Would you like to treat me to an Orgasm?'

What a line. I've never been chased by a woman in my life. It's a deal. Maria and I are off to the Happy Days Diner. Together. Tonight. At the Happy Days Diner. Me... And Maria. The girl fancies the pants off me and I never knew. In some ways her admission has given me the upper hand. I'm beginning to feel quite cock-sure of myself. I'll string her along for a while. No! It's not me. I'm far too old in the tooth to suddenly turn into Dicky Cox. Besides, I'm almost through my second bottle of house white. The mixture of sun, Chardonnay, and the prospect of sex could land me in hot water. I'll play it safe for an hour or so. It's a lovely moment though; Eric Clapton's singing to us, and we're singing along to 'Let it grow'.

'Clapton's finest in my opinion,' I say.

'Get lost,' says Maria. ' "Tears in Heaven" after his little son died. How can you top that?'

Hattie Jacques walks past with her husband, Clive. Looks like they've made friends with Mrs Jigsaw Puzzle. Hattie's moaning. 'I think I overdid it at the midnight buffet last night,' she says, gently caressing her enormous midriff. 'Either that or I stumbled upon a rancid prawn among the vol-au-vents.'

Clive and the jigsaw woman are sympathetically hanging on Hattie's every word. I tend to feel more sorry for the rancid prawn. In fact, I'm on the side of the vol-au-vents as a whole; they wouldn't have stood a chance when she moved in. Like lambs to the slaughter (or, in this case, lightly raised puff pastries). If some women see their body as a temple, Hattie must treat hers like a warehouse.

The jigsaw woman is struggling to keep up as Hattie and Clive stride onwards towards the courtesy bus stop. 'I wonder if she's finished yet,' says Maria with a quizzical glance. Amazing. She's looking at Mrs Jigsaw Puzzle.

I thought these moments only happened in the movies. It looks like we've been wandering around the decks of the SS *Perfect* thinking almost the same things at the same time. Only I was chasing Daphne while Daphne was chasing Claire, who I'd already chased many years ago. Meanwhile Kev was chasing June, Kenneth was chasing his teeth, and all the time, Maria was chasing me, although she was under the impression that I had three balls. I hope the fact that I've only got a pair won't put her off. (Kiss Me Kate was chasing me too, but that doesn't count. Anyway, she was also chasing Andy, who was chasing Alfred, who was chasing Kev.)

I sing to the sunshine: ' "And I say yes, you look wonderful tonight." ' We laugh some more and catch the last courtesy bus home. Who would have thought it? Me and Miss Cruise Bore sitting together. On the front seat of the coach. And she's quite a decent creature. In fact, she has the makings of a bloody masterpiece. It's on for tonight as well. Happy Days Diner. 7 p.m.

The ship pulls away from Barcelona as the waiters serve their canapés on silver platters. A middle-aged clever dick with the build of a beanpole is dangling over the railings, peering through his binoculars. Getting out of Barcelona harbour is a tricky business but Mr Know-it-all is doing his best to keep his largely uninterested passengers fully informed. 'It's all right,' he announces in his irksome drone. 'They can turn these things on a sixpence nowadays. Power steering you see.' Personally, I think he's talking through his arse, but I'm not prepared to take issue with him. Anyway, I'm too chuffed with the day's events to let anything myther me. Bliss strike up with 'Yellow Bird, Up High in Banana Tree.' I'm not drinking a cocktail. I'm already part pissed, and I'm as high as a kite. It must be Barcelona. It's possibly the sunshine. Or the class. Or the style. Whatever the case, I've suddenly bounced back – just like a 'Rubber Ball'. (A big hit for Bobby Vee in 1961.)

Bravo Barcelona.
If you were a football team, I'd chant your name until I
    could roar no more.
If you were a musical, I'd stand and applaud.
If you were a singer, I'd shout 'Encore'.
If you were a chef, I'd send my compliments.
If you were a bride, I'd sling my confetti over your
    bright white veil.

I could salute you with the greatest prize of all. A place in my heart.

But I'm about to hang the 'No Vacancies' sign there. I know it. In one afternoon, my heart has been conquered. I think I'm falling in love. With Maria. Miss Cruise Bore, of all bloody folk.

But wait. I should be holding my horses for a while. After all, I don't know if I'm ready to tumble in at the deep end so soon after writing off my hopes of true love. No. Maybe a gentle paddle tonight to test the water. Even so, I'm still feeling good, which is odd for me. As a rule, I would be as nervous as a kitten getting ready to meet a girl. I was sick for three hours before my first date with Claire at the Plough the Fields and Scatter Pub. This is different. Taking a final glance in my bathroom mirror, I spare a second to congratulate myself.

'Have a good night, sir,' says Oh Danny Boy as I leave Cabin F153. I turn and smile. If it wasn't for Dicky Cox, I reckon Oh Danny Boy would be my best friend in the world, even though he probably still thinks I'm a fully paid up member of the Table 69 Tits Out for the *Titanic* Club.

Before long, I'm ready...and Maria's waiting! There's not a Cruise Bore T-shirt in sight. Instead, she's wearing a sexy little crop top exposing her belly button. She's really started to come into her own since she met me. I'm obviously doing her the world of good. To prove my point, the words 'Glamour Pussy' are emblazoned in blue glitter across her dingers. See, she's my pussy and I'm her owl. It's finally happening just as I predicted it would. Best of all, it looks like she's had a swift blow-dry at the beauty parlour. It's quite a transformation, I can tell you.

The Happy Days Diner, as usual, is on fire. Row upon row of fake gold discs are splattered over the blue-and-white-striped walls, while a massive mock jukebox dominates the corner of the room. Maria is stood beneath an oil painting of Ricky Nelson. (I don't think it's an original.)

'You've missed Guy Mitchell,' says Maria, handing me my first Orgasm of the night.

'Oh, what was it. "Singing the Blues"?'

'No. "She wears Red Feathers and a Huly Huly Skirt." Number one in 1953. Oh, I'm sorry. My mind is full of daft facts and useless information.'

Sugar Baby Love and Sugar Daddy are dancing to 'Rock Around the Clock'. Maria's noticed them before. Asks me if I think she's a relative or a lover. I'm certain she's his lover, especially after the 'new trainers from Florence' conversation on the table next to ours. Two more Orgasms and the talk turns to Lonnie Donegan and his Cumberland Gap. (I wonder how June is this evening.)

I spend the next half-hour letting Maria into the dark secrets of table 69. She thought that three-ball Andy was a revelation but he's only the tip of the iceberg. She's laughing like a drain when I explain that June likes it up her Ginger Rogers, but Tom's more likely to tickle your laa-laa with a Dyson.

'How does that work?' she cries in amazement.

'Maria. I've no idea.'

They're playing Danny and the Juniors as we leave. 'At the Hop.' (Should be my theme tune following my legendary antics as king of the hedge-hoppers when I was at school. At the very least, it's a good omen for what may be about to follow.) It's late. But it seems like no time has passed at all. It's a beautiful night, so I agree to take Maria past the children's jacuzzi, just in case. The cooling breeze is welcome relief from the clustered atmosphere of the Happy Days Diner.

'If you hear a couple of verses of "Climb every Mountain", you know they're at it.'

There's nothing. I don't know whether I'm relieved or disappointed.

'I'll let you into a secret,' says Maria. 'I first liked the look of you when I saw you hovering around the doorway during the line dancing in the Paradise Ballroom.'

Blimey. I pulled when I was least expecting it. My work colleagues told me it would happen like that. I can almost hear Margaret Chandler now. 'Loves lurks in the most unlikely doorway, my little scrag-end,' she used to say. It was her well-worn catch-phrase. Dicky Cox and I used to poke fun at her for saying it, and now it's coming true. Mrs Chandler was right all along.

Maria goes on. 'Then I fell for you big style at the Captain's Ball. That woman who does the port enhancement talks was trying to make a pass at me when you stumbled over to tell us you were going to Gibraltar. I thought how gentle you looked... Then you fell onto the shag pile. I knew it straight away. I said to myself, that man's got a good heart. And a good heart these days is hard to find.' (Fergal Sharkey.) 'So I searched for you. Even turned up to a port enhancement talk but you were too busy looking at that girl, Daphne isn't it? I was going to barge over and tell you, "She's a lesbian you great wazzak." I'd given up on you by the time we'd got to Barcelona and suddenly there you were, waiting for me on the sea front.'

It's a lovely story, but I wish she'd tipped me off about Daphne. It would have saved a lot of time and trouble.

'So, what happened with your fiancé?' I'm keen to find out more.

'Oh... What's-his-name. We met at university. We both studied the French Revolution. Then he set up his own internet firm for women who wanted a sex change. *IWantaWilly.com*. They said he'd make a fortune. Giving women advice on the most important decision of their lives, in an entertaining, yet frank and informal sort of way. Got me on board as a partner.

Couldn't fail, he said. The only place where women could go for advice without the whole world knowing. A sort of "suck it and see" operation. He was about to create a similar set up for men when the crash came. He went doolally. Ran off with a girl called Ruth. She's Ronald now. Hurt like hell. The doctor put me on sleeping tablets for a month.'

'What was the male version of the business called?' I ask attempting to lighten the tone. '*IDon'tWantaWilly.com*. Or maybe *IWantaFanny.com*.'

She laughs again. I'm pleased. I let her in on my story. She's amazed that What's-her-name – Claire – is on board the SS *Perfect*. Even more amazed when I tell her she pulled Daphne.

'Let's not waste any more time.'

Maria's going to launch into a speech, but I'm not sure what's coming. I hope she's not looking for sex this early in the day. It would spoil the whole night as far as I'm concerned. I'd much rather a steady run-up than a dramatic first night poke. It's not my style. As it is, I'm off the hook – it's a relatively tame suggestion.

'Let's meet up tomorrow for the Wild West BBQ. You could buy me a burger if you fancy it. And I'd love to meet your friends on table 69. They sound wonderful.'

There's a slight pause. Maria looks down at her feet. She's waiting patiently for an answer. And it's good news for her. I fancy it. In fact, I fancy it more than I've ever fancied anything else before in my life.

'You're on. As long as you don't try and get me into their club.'

She laughs. It's up to me now. The ball's in my court.

'Well, good night then.' It's that terrible moment. Do I go to snog her? Is that too forward? Will she feel disappointed if I don't? I've never had a girl chase me. I feel like I've just been cornered by Duncan Norvelle. (You know, 'Chase me'. What on earth became of him?) I'll go for broke. We kiss, but in a nice, friendly, 'It's not going to kick off tonight, but it will in time' sort of way. It's more romantic than a snog, yet far more sexual than a peck. It's a sneck.

She tastes beautiful. I reckon I'm slowly sending her into ecstasy. She's crazy about me. Her nipples are on stalks. You can't miss the things poking through her crop top like a pair of guided missiles. I did that – amazing. Leapy Lee was right when he sang about those 'Little Arrows' that hit you when you're in love. I've just felt a major prick in the bull's-eye. Maybe she *is* going to turn out to be Mrs Right, Mrs Potato Head. Maria makes off into the evening. From the Hippodrome I can just hear Norman DeVine's tribute to *West Side Story*; the musical that changed musicals forever. They're singing about Maria. I can't help thinking there's an element of fate here.

'Maria,' I think to myself. 'How's that for a coincidence – I've just met a girl called Maria!'

This can't be happening to me. Soon a freak tidal wave will sweep me off the deck of the SS *Perfect* and out to sea. Just when I thought I was winning, the forces of nature will intervene to put paid to my one hope of happiness. Or maybe not. Maybe this is my Val Doonican moment, my Jessie Matthews-type big break. After the blood, sweat and tears of thirty-seven years, I've become an overnight sensation. I'm a Pop Idol. This is the feeling Jack Russell must have had when he walked out onto the field at Lords, all those years after wishing on a chicken bone at his council house in Stroud.

I gently float back to cabin F153. I wouldn't mind if Oh Danny Boy was waiting, bent over my rocking-chair, trousers round his ankles, begging me to give him one up his Moulin Rouge. I'd send him packing, of course. Just like Kiss Me Kate. But it wouldn't bother me. It's Malcolm's moment at last. Tonight belongs to me.

14

It's party time on the *Perfect*. And I'm ready for the biggest blow out of them all.

I can't wait to meet Maria at the Wild West BBQ. I've hardly stopped mulling over her all night. But I'm not going to forget my pledge to Kenneth. I'll be on hand to help him with Linda the Boot Scooting Baby, who's driving him crazy. Strangely, I'm still full of confidence. On a high. It's the same sort of feeling you must get when you're scoffing Ferrero Rocher chocolates at the Ambassador's house. I've semi-snogged Maria and I'm ready and raring to go. I think I've finally met my soul mate, but I'm not tempting fate. That's what the last few days have taught me. Take it all in your stride. By the end of the holiday, I could've ditched Maria and become involved in a passionate three-way clinch with Stoop and Droop.

Malcolm's Log. It's Saturday, June 28th. (Saturday – tongue sandwich day.)

What do I know about Maria so far? Point one: she's no cruise bore. Studied the French Revolution at university before falling for the fateful charms of What's-his-name. Point two: tragically dumped by What's-his-name after he made her a partner in his *IWantaWilly.com* company. He later ran off with a girl called Ruth who, true to his company's word, finally got a willy and became Ronald. I don't know if they're still an item. Thought it best to leave the story at that point.

An internet site for transsexuals hell bent on a sex change. Funny business, although I can see the attraction. Worldwide appeal. It must be tough for anyone trapped in a body of the opposite sex. Why *not* approach the subject in a relaxed and jokey way, while explaining in a forthright yet informal manner the swings and roundabouts of introducing a willy into one's already complex world. He still sounds like a total shit though, this What's-his-name. I'm glad his internet bubble burst. I hope him and Ruth (or Ronald) live happily ever after in sex change land.

Point three: I know Maria's surname, although like me, she's not very keen on it. What could be worse than Malcolm Williams? The kids teased me something chronic at school. I was labelled 'Little Willy' in the school playground. Mind you, I was going through my organ music phase so I suppose they had a point. While they were out tasting booze for the first time on a Friday night, I was at home, tucked up in bed listening to 'The Organist Entertains' on Radio Two. It was just a phase.

Maria thinks she's fared even worse in the surname stakes. But I don't agree. What's wrong with Maria Doolittle?
'It's because everyone thinks I'm related to Doctor Doolittle,' she told me. 'I get people asking me if I can speak rhinoceros!'
'Well, you should tell them,' I replied. 'Can I speak Rhinoceros? Of coserous!'
It made her laugh. Anyway, I'm reminded more of Eliza Doolittle. The simple flower girl who became a lady, thanks to the work of Professor Henry Higgins. I told her so last

night. I made her say: 'The rain in Spain falls mainly on the plain.' And when she did, I expertly executed a sharp little stab into her exposed midriff and told her: 'You've got it. I think you've got it.' The feeling of my bare flesh meeting hers for the first time very near turned me on. For the second time that night I felt a slight prick in the nether regions (it was those little love arrows again). In Eliza Doolittle terms, I could have danced all night.

> Point four: Maria fell for me the night I stumbled on her and Daphne at the Captain's Ball, although I'd already tickled her fancy when she clocked me lurking around the Paradise Ballroom. Originally she had me down as having three balls, although maybe she used that to weave her way into my little world. Finally, and most importantly, I think she loves me – and you know that can't be bad. (The Beatles, of course.) I'm logging off.

The rest of the day is a blank page and I'm excited. There's the Wild West BBQ on the Sunshine Deck this afternoon, followed by the *Perfect* Party Night tomorrow. Our final fling before the emotional farewells. I think I'll do another Tom Jones. It's worked in the past and there's no point in changing a winning formula. You ask any successful football manager.

Then there's the official tribute to the Pillsbury Dough Man. We've got to twist again to celebrate his life and commemorate his rather sudden and unexpected passing. I'm warming to that concept. It makes you think. What dance would you get the assembled mourners to do at your funeral? The hokey-cokey springs to mind. Although you wouldn't want that on the SS *Perfect*. They'd be putting it in, when they should have been taking it out and shaking it all about. This lot are more suited to the Shag (I think it's got some-thing to do with Northern Soul), although I wouldn't mind watching Mrs Cocktail Stick attempt a Pogo. If she achieved any great height bouncing away to a Sex Pistols number, she'd look just like a javelin. I'll make sure this dancing thing takes place at my funeral. When I'm dead and gone, I'll have them all doing the Mash Potato in honour of a life given over to the humble spud.

Once again I feel the need to give myself a hefty pat on the back in front of my bathroom mirror. It's an awkward manoeuvre and I can't help thinking that all this self-gratification is becoming something of a ritual. Still, it seems to be doing me no harm. Finally, I step out into the small, narrow world of the ship's corridor.

Oh world at sea.
Oh world at sea.
What's next in store for me?

Stoop and Droop are in their usual pale blue easy chairs in front of the picture board. The thought of getting involved in a complicated love triangle with them before we get back to Southampton is pushing it a bit. It was just my imagination, running away with me. (A hit for The Temptations, I think.)

I've got to call in to the photo booth for my 'two potatoes perched on a wall by the Trevi Fountain' snaps. On my way in, I see they've finally taken my pictures out of the gallery. All of them. Me with Cyril the Seal. Me in front of the Leaning Tower of Pisa looking startled because I've noticed Daphne and Claire following me in hot pursuit down the gangplank. Me in front of the cardboard Coliseum has gone too. And there's no sign of me with the Olympic flag and plastic plate of Paella. They're all gone. Binned I expect. No takers. Still, the King Edwards look splendid in front of the cascading waters of the fountain.

I'm going to make a splash myself when they see these on table 69. I'm beginning to regret the fact that I ate my 'Pope on a Rope'. Mouthy Kev and Miss Me Kate never saw it (although they never even mentioned it in Barcelona). I tried to retrieve it this morning while I was sat on the toilet. I looked briefly at the contents in the loo bowl but couldn't make a pope out in amongst the poo. (For a moment, I felt guilty about their blockages law. But I decided it was alright to flush the Pope down the loo – because he *had* been through me!)

I've decided to ask Maria to dinner. Roger the Waiter and Donald the Downtrodden are sure to set me up an extra place if I ask. The only problem is, I don't want the swingers getting the wrong idea. We're not going to be cannon-fodder for their sordid party tricks. At least I'm not. And I'm sure Maria isn't that type of lady either. That's the point. She's once, twice, three times a lady. (Definitely The Commodores.)

I'm going to miss this boat terribly. The ladies at reception have now become the *Perfect* Disembarkation Help desk. Help, my arse. They're still looking as miserable as sin. I've not dared to tackle them all holiday and I'm not going to start now. Elsewhere though, things are livening up a treat. The grand shuffleboard final is taking place on the top deck, while the last 'Travelling Alone Get-together' is underway in the Ritz Bar. There's a whist drive morning at Champions, while Barbara tackles duplicate bridge. I think Nicola's finally given up on her *découpage*, but the jigsaw lady is in her usual place, scurrying around like a hamster trying to put the last 500 pieces into place. She's done well. I would have put money on her not getting beyond the outside frame. I know for a fact she didn't do anything yesterday. She was walking around Barcelona with Hattie Jacques and her husband; I saw her with my own eyes. It was just after Maria had made her way gently into my life.

That's it. I've had more than I can take. It's no good hanging around waiting for the BBQ to start. I may only have two full days left with Maria. I may never see her again for the rest of my life. I'm going to find her. Now. And it's not long before I do.

'Malcolm!'

She's happy to see me. I can tell. She's near the Woody Woodpecker Club. (I hope she hasn't been anywhere near the Punch and Judy tent.)

'Where the hell have you been, Mr Elusive? I've been looking for you everywhere. They ought to call you the Scarlet Pimpernel.' She stalls for a second to gather her thoughts. 'How are you this morning?'

'I'm all the better for seeing you,' I answer honestly, while taking a discreet little look to see if there's any activity in her nipple department. Nothing yet. But then, I haven't touched her.

'You always manage to say the right things,' she says. 'You're lovely.'

Wrong Maria. I've spent my whole life saying the wrong thing. Maybe you've made the difference. But you're right. I am lovely – in my own sweet way.

I tell Maria about tongue sandwiches, cheese and onion crisps and penguin biscuits. She can't stand tongue, but she has got an unlikely passion for brown sauce and sweetcorn doorsteps. It looks like snack times will be a never-ending thrill if we tie the knot. (I could even introduce her to Dibble the Muffin Man and his marinated beaver rolls.) She tells me about her mum and dad, and their friend who plays the piano in the Ritz Bar. (I remember overhearing her conversation on day one. The pianist in the Ritz Bar. Had him down as some sort of trumped up Liberace. I swore I'd never go in on a matter of principle. How wrong I was.) Maria's father is a retired merchant banker. She's an only child. Just like me. Although my father died, and my mother, the Angel, gets by on turning people's trousers up. Good job Wonderweb was a diabolical flop or she'd have been out of business a long time ago.

Soon it's BBQ time. I ask her to help me with Kenneth and Linda. She agrees, and within seconds we can hear Bliss playing 'Yellow Bird' on the Sunshine Deck.

'What's 'Yellow Bird' got to do with the Wild West?' I ask Maria, slightly confused.

'I expect they don't know any Tammy Wynette or Dolly Parton,' she replies.

I'm not having that. ' "Stand By Your Man!" ' I protest. 'How can anyone *not* know how to play Stand By Your bloody Man?'

We sing together, desperately trying to keep in tune. ' "Stand by your man. And show the world you love him." ' We're fighting against the 'Yellow Bird, Up High in Banana Tree' tide. And it's not easy.

'Hello, Malcolm. Someone's enjoying themselves all of a sudden.'

It's June, Tom, Mouthy Kev and Kiss Me Kate. With Andy trailing not far behind.

'Grab a table, Kevin,' says June, chief swinger. 'Tom, Screaming Orgasms for everybody please.'

Screaming Orgasms. They're the same as Orgasms but you take out the amaretto and replace it with vodka. Deadly. I think Maria's going to get a full-scale insight into life on table 69 whether she likes it or not. They've only just met her and already it's Orgasms all round.

'So, who's a dark horse then?' June asks me, smirking like the cat that's got the cream. I try to shrug off the question, but I suppose she's got a point. In fact, on current form, I'd say I was the darkest horse since Black Beauty.

Meanwhile, on the makeshift Sunshine Deck stage, Linda the Boot Scooting Baby is getting ready to parade her skills with the Paradise Ballroom prancers.

Sugar Daddy's in the line-dancing line-up. He's getting on famously well with Linda. They're in fits of laughter when he gets his sailor step mixed up with her slide. He's grabbed her waist when he should've been slapping his leather. Kenneth did say she liked the older men. But surely not Sugar Daddy. He looks like Benny Hill's old sparring partner. But thicker set and with a small amount of grey hair to the sides of his balding bonce.

Oddly enough, Kenneth's conspicuous by his absence. Still, I introduce Maria to what's left of the table 69 team. She looks Tom up and down. I know what she's thinking... Electronic toothbrushes.

Andy's looking nervously around the Sunshine Deck. 'What are you doing love?' asks June. 'Sit down. You're making me feel uncomfortable,' she adds, looking a little uncomfortable.

'He's scanning the joint to see if there's any spare sausage,' laughs Mouthy Kev. He rams his elbow into Maria's side. She smiles but I know she's winded. Anyway, he's got no right to talk. If I've read the situation right, he's not averse to a spare bit of sausage himself.

'I'm looking for Alfie,' says Andy. 'He went for a spot of quoits with some tosser in a blazer, and I haven't seen him since. He doesn't even know how to play. Don't know where the bloody hell he could've got to.'

I can just imagine it. Alfred and the Tosser in a Blazer. They're not trying to get their hoops over the rod at all. They're having a bit of slap and tickle in the shower and sauna hut. I told you it was a shagging den. Alfred's probably got his rod halfway up blazer-man's hoop as we speak. Table 69? I love them to bits, but if you ask me, it's all a sham. Sham 69. (Punk band. Had hits with 'Borstal Breakout' and 'Angels with Dirty Faces' – the latter being quite apt for this mob.) Anyway, the point is, they're sex-crazed sods the lot of them. Except me. And, who knows, I might be set to give my Sonny Bono an outing at any moment.

Andy stands on his seat. Tom returns with the Orgasms. The smell of freshly cooked sizzling chicken wafts across the

Sunshine Deck. Bliss strike up with 'Coward of the County'. (Kenny Rogers.)

'I preferred that one,' says June. ' "You picked a fine time to leave me, Louise." '

' "Lucille!" ' we all cry in unison. Except for Tom who sits quietly and smiles shyly. He's the one man on this boat I haven't been able to work out at all. Suddenly Andy, still perched on his chair, bursts into life.

'Bloody hell,' he gasps.

'Have you seen him?' I ask. He's probably caught a glimpse of his gay partner, pants around his ankles, being force-fed lamb kebab while the band plays Kenny Rogers. Frightening. But no, it's not Alfred who's come into view. It's far more exciting.

'There's a fight!' Andy's getting excited. He's started to colour up. 'Quick everyone, on your chairs.'

For a second, there's a mad panic as the table 69 regulars, plus Maria, scramble to stand tiptoe on their white plastic sun-loungers. And he's right, there's yet another full scale tussle taking place on the SS *Perfect*, hot on the heels of the Horlicks Bar brawl and the dust up in the laundry room. This time, though, it's a real sodding showdown.

For a second, I lose concentration as, out of the corner of my eye, I spot Alfred making his way onto the Sunshine Deck (no sign of the Tosser though. Alf must have done a Dicky Cox – 'Find 'em, fuck 'em and forget 'em.') But the reappearance of Andy's partner will have to play second fiddle to the unfolding drama at the Wild West BBQ. I quickly summon Alfred; I don't want him to miss his fair slice of the action. I know how he likes a bit of a nip and tuck. 'Alfred. Quick. Fight.' And what a kerfuffle! Sugar Baby Love's trying to drag Linda the Boot Scooting Queen off the dance floor by her hair. Sugar Daddy's looking on amazed as Linda screams in agony. This'll put an end to her rolling grapevines for a while. The fearsome Lancashire Lassie is frantic. 'You keep your sodding hands away from him,' she squeals to the now hapless Linda. It's going to develop into a bar-room brawl, I just know it. Before long there'll be chairs flying though the air.

We'll be in the newspapers for sure this time. First, a fat bloke dies while doing the Twist. Then a quiet man gets arrested for eating cheese and onion crisps on the Spanish Steps, and an even quieter man is detained on charges of indecent assault when he tries to tickle the first mate's laa-laa with his electronic toothbrush. His wife gets carted off for seducing Everard the cabin-boy; a gay man is found in the sauna and shower room on Deck 13 with a quoit stuffed halfway up his arse; there are fisticuffs at the Horlicks Bar; pushing and shoving in the laundrette; cold beans at breakfast; an old lady stranded in a lift; and now this – sea rage. It really will go down as the cruise from hell.

The brawl continues. From out of the crowd, little Kenneth the Weasel Man rushes to Linda's aid. But he's struggling to keep upright. For a start, the Bay of Biscay's started to swell up; the ship is rocking more than usual. What with that and his overbaggy shorts flapping like an elephant's ears around his all too skinny legs, Kenneth's in danger of going tits up.

'Keep out of it, you little fart. Unless you want your teeth rammed down your gob,' roars Sugar Baby Love.

'That wouldn't be difficult,' says Alfred with one of his vicious little side swipes.

It's over in a flash as two uniformed crew members step in to quieten things down. But in the commotion, Kenneth has been knocked to the floor. His love hopes are in tatters as Linda storms off to the safety of her cabin. He's scrambling around for his dentures. They had no chance in the mêlée. Poor bugger. He's spent the whole holiday getting pushed from pillar to post. He'll very likely go back to Somerset covered in bruises.

Sugar Baby Love is taken away, but you can see she's itching for a bust-up. 'Come and have a go if you think you're hard enough,' she growls at Hattie Jacques who is just returning from the bar when she's innocently caught up in the crossfire. She's quite taken aback by the whole affair. Bliss resume with an up-tempo rendition of 'Catch a Falling Star and Put it in Your Pocket'.

A wave of sympathy washes over me as I watch Kenneth's desperation grow by the minute. 'I'm going to rescue him. Unfortunate little bleeder.' Maria comes too and we see him safely back to the table.

'Thanks, Martin,' he says dusting himself off. 'Bloody muffed it this time, haven't I?'

Normality returns, but the atmosphere has been well and truly dampened by Sugar Baby Love's violent outburst. She obviously thought Linda the Line Dancing Queen was trying to pull Sugar Daddy – and by all accounts, she was. Been after him all cruise according to the still crestfallen Kenneth.

'His real name is Sam, and he's made a fortune out of pickles,' Kenneth explains. 'She's been trying to get her hands on Sam the Pickle Man and his considerable wad since we left Southampton. They were all over each other at the prize bingo yesterday. I wouldn't mind, but he won a bottle of champagne for a full house. I only wanted one number myself. Jammy git.'

Interesting. Those who thought there was a 'lustful undertone' to line dancing have been proved right. I shall never look at a line dancer in the same way again. Indeed, the Weasel Man himself had got his finger firmly on the pulse. 'Line-dancing classes,' he told me at the start of the holiday. 'The best place for a bit of spare on these things.'

Kenneth's decided to spend the rest of the day watching the grand shuffleboard final, while Maria and I head off to find a quiet corner of the good ship *Perfect*. Cue *Love Story* theme again. It's game on. We walk hand in hand on the poop deck, stopping for half a lager on the outside patio in front of Alexander's Bar. I tell her about the small vases that contain the peanuts. 'They're because men don't wash their hands after having a wee.' She's impressed with my knowledge. I've pulled her, make no mistake.

She wants me to meet her mum and dad in the Ritz Piano Bar before we go to eat on table 69. The shenanigans of the day haven't put her off. She can't understand how such a nice bunch, on the face of it, get up to all sorts of sordid things when push comes to shove. Shocking, I agree. But I'm used to it. I've had it rammed down my throat all week. Before we leave each other to get ready for the evening session, Maria gives cabin F153 the once over. For a moment I wonder if this is going to lead to our first shag. I'd quite like to get it out of the way because it's beginning to worry me.

She's in here. Alone. With me. Do I start subtly taking my trousers down? Shall I go for the more direct smash and grab? Do I throw her onto the rocking-chair before thrusting my hand up her sarong or shall we kiss and let nature take its course? Is it right, at this stage, to mention my banana-flavoured condoms? Would she prefer to see my King Edwards?

I'm starting to shake, and my state of trembling uncertainty isn't helped by an instant flashback. It's Brenda Burston on the Witch's Hat all those years ago. My stuttering sexual past has decided to come to the fore. Luckily, Maria breaks the ice.

'I suppose you're thinking about sex,' she says.

'No,' I reply in haste. I'm a bloody liar, and she knows it. I must have sex written all over my face. 'We've got the rest of our lives to think about sex.'

I'm saying the first thing that comes into my head. But I've hit the jackpot yet again. Suddenly I've turned from a stumble-bum into a smooth talking wordsmith. She's delighted:

'You're right. The rest of our lives.'

I think in an indirect sort of way, I've just proposed to Maria.

She leaves the cabin. I see her out. Oh Danny Boy's there. 'Good evening, sir. Would you like a stiff one?' He must think I've shagged the whole boat with all the comings and goings.

Before I know it, I'm dressed and showered. For some unknown reason, I'm feeling well in control of my destiny. I'm surprised that I'm still standing straight after the bollocking I'm giving the alcohol. But then I've always been able to hold my liquor. It's one of my plus points. (That and the fact that I very rarely suffer from hiccups.) Drink helps me. It spurs me on. In the words of the great philosopher: 'I drink, therefore I am.' They even say at work: 'He's a twat, but he can't half take his booze.' It's been my saving grace.

I've even been forward thinking enough to spray aftershave on my tackle, just in case the need should arise later on. I've decided to leave the Sea Breeze well alone this time. Instead my boxer shorts are soaked with Brut 33. Dicky Cox says it's coming back into fashion, so I brought three bottles from the market lady before I left.

In my bathroom cabinet, the banana condoms are lined up like an army on red alert. They're poised for action, and I'm taking one with me just in case. I'm thinking ahead. Maybe a little too far ahead! All sorts of things are buzzing around in my brain. For instance, what will happen when the holiday is over? Maria still lives with her parents in Brighton. (She thinks she lives quite close to Andy and Alfred – small world.) I live in the 'genuinely civilized city' of Lichfield, Staffordshire: quite possibly the potato capital of the world and home of Samuel Johnson (the man who wrote the English Dictionary). Our cathedral has three spires. Come to think of it, that's probably why I didn't find Gaudi's temple all that inspiring. Seen three spires, seen them all. When will we meet? How will we feel when we're on dry land? Forget it for now. Let's live for tonight. In the words of the song: 'We've got tonight. Who needs tomorrow?' (Can't think who did it for the moment. I've got my mind on other things.)

Maria's father is a welcoming chap. Very posh, keen to meet me. And her mother's not the battleaxe I had her down for on the first day either. Only she's a bit more standoffish. I think she's carefully weighing me up before making a final decision. It's her dad who gets the ball rolling:

'We know the pianist in here old chum.' (Chum? It's a dog food. He thinks I'm a dog.) 'Bill Bailey. Brilliant with his fingers. Puts that Richard Clayderman to shame. And he's notorious in cruising circles you know,' continues Maria's dad with a glint in his eye. I know he's going to tell a story and I know I'm going to have to laugh at the end of it.

'One afternoon he was playing a magnificent grand piano on the Sunshine Deck when suddenly, the ship was hit by a freak wave and the bloody thing rolled overboard. There was Bill Bailey sitting on his stool tinkling into thin air, his piano in the sodding sea,' he laughs heartily. I snigger too, mostly out of politeness.

Maria's father gives me an intense two-second glare. I can read his mind. 'Come on then you little twat,' he's thinking. 'It's your turn to speak – and you'd better have an impressive line in patter or else you're out on your arse.' (It may be a lot to think in two seconds but I'm convinced that's the size of it.) My future happiness as a surrogate Doolittle has boiled down to a single joke. Sometimes, I wish I was Bob Monkhouse. I feel the dread of a first time comedian stepping out for an open mike slot. But if I duck the challenge at this stage, I'm well and truly knackered.

'Bill Bailey. As in, "Won't you come home Bill Bailey, won't you come home?" ' I reply in haste.

It's a poor gag compared to the grand piano overboard tale. Daddy Doolittle holds his glare while sipping a gin and tonic. But I've got her mother smiling, and Maria seems quite pleased with my opening gambit too. The old saying may be true.

Loves sees no faults. Anyway, as I've already observed, Bill Bailey isn't a patch on my old keyboard instructor. Colin 'Fingers' Gilbert would eat him for breakfast.

It seems my timely interjection has won the old man over. Soon he's happy to take control again. I might just have passed his acid test. 'Why don't you take your mother to the toilet, Maria.' Oh shit. I'm in for one of those father and son chats. Either that or Maria's mother suffers from some terrible disease that means she has to have her bottom wiped. That means if she ends up living with us, I might end up scrubbing her backside with Andrex every five minutes.

'I'm glad she's found someone at last,' says Maria's dad (Alan, 'but you can call me Al'). 'I expect she's told you about that bastard and the *Willy.com* incident. Very nasty. The wife – Betty – never liked him. Called him Willy Wonka. Then blow me down, if the blaghard doesn't go off with some woman who turns into a chap. I said: "You're better off out of it. Leave old Willie Wonka to have fun in the chocolate factory." ' He winks. 'Know what I mean?'

I do. Since Margaret Chandler went out with an original Umpa Lumpa man, there's nothing you can tell me about the chocolate factory that I don't know. I've seen an original golden ticket! Anyway, I'm half thinking of Paul Simon from Simon and Garfunkel. Didn't he record a song about Al and Betty? I wonder if he wrote it for Maria's mum and dad.

'Come on then, we'd better be off.'

It's Maria. She's back. And within a flash we're on our way to table 69. But it's been a fruitful first meeting with Betty and Al. I'm convinced I've just taken my first tentative steps along the long and winding road to love and marriage. (I'm told it goes together like a horse and carriage.)

Maria laughs when I ask her about Paul Simon, even though she's probably heard it a million times before. And she's looking lovely. Hair and everything! It's the last time we'll be wearing our formal gear. Tomorrow, at the *Perfect*

Party, it's a casual night. (Andy and Alfred fought tooth and nail to make it fancy dress, but Captain Fletcher was having none of it.)

Look at the two of us, strolling towards the Monte Carlo Restaurant as the sun casts a shimmering line across the sea. I feel like a three-year-old in the children's jacuzzi. It's as if I've got the whole world in my hands. (A 1950s hit for Laurie London – but you don't hear much about him these days.) Soon, these very hands will house Maria's tits. I can almost feel them now. A 'dinger' in one hand and a 'donger' in the other. She'll have nipples like thimbles.

Captain Fletcher's at dinner tonight, doing the rounds and trying his best to shake off Hattie Jacques. She's clinging onto him like an overweight limpet. She wants to get her hands on his compass again by the looks of things. Roger the Waiter is keen to sit Maria at her newly laid place at the table. For my money, she's got the best seat in the house. Between Kenneth and me. At least they've kept her away from June, the king of the swingers.

I'm straight in with my pictures of the King Edwards, while Maria asks how Kenneth's feeling after that unfortunate affair on the Sunshine Deck earlier. He is looking a little down, come to think of it. But then he has every right to be. He's just seen his last chance of having a son to inherit the family dentures slide slowly away. What will happen to the family falsies now, when Kenneth kicks the bucket? The whole sorry affair could signal the end of a long family teeth tradition. When the Weasel Man conks out, so will the gnashers. Of course, there may still be time to rescue his sagging love interests. In my opinion, it's boiled down to Mrs Hair Bear Bunch or bust. I'll try to slip a word in for him. I can't help feeling I owe him one after failing to help in his quest to get hitched to the line-dancing beauty. (But then, I didn't know she was hot on the trail of Sugar Daddy, who we now know as Sam the Pickle Man.)

'Your new lady's very charming,' says June whispering into my ear. 'Have you given her one yet?'

'No June, but in your tried and tested opinion, is she a goer?'

June hesitates for a minute and takes one last discreet look.

'Once you get her warmed up she'll shag your arse off. What's her name again?'

'Maria.'

'Oh lovely!' She bursts into song. I might have guessed she'd bring *The Sound of Music* into it somehow. It's the one about Maria climbing a tree, ripping her skirt and having curlers underneath her wimple. June asks me to find a word that sums up Maria.

'Oh, that's easy June. In a word, perfect. ' I'm getting to be quite a dab hand at this instant quip lark.

'Ahhhh, listen to this everybody. Malcolm and Maria are in love. He's just told me.'

I never told her any such thing, but Maria doesn't seem too unhappy with the notion, so I'll second her emotion. (Smokey Robinson and the Miracles.)

Mouthy Kev calls for champagne from Donald the Downtrodden, and within seconds, Marlene the Wine Girl has charged over with a bottle of Château des Grandes Noelles – vintage. The toast is to Malcolm and Maria.

I turn to June. 'You're not trying to get us into the club are you?'

She's not. She's more intent on pumping Maria for a bit more information.

'What's your surname love? Oh... Doolittle. Where do I know that name from?'

I'm bracing myself for a 'push-me-pull-ya' gag. It doesn't come. June thinks hard, then squeals.

'*IWantaWilly.com*. Tom was enquiring into *IWanta-Willy.com* and Maria Doolittle was the name that came up on the internet. I sang to you, didn't I love. "All I want is a willy somewhere." You know; Eliza Doolittle.'

'It's *room*, June. "All I want is a *room* somewhere." '

I'm always putting her right. It's a good job she's had me this holiday – if you see what I mean. Kenneth's quick to pick up the 'sing-song' baton and run with it. Before long, the whole table's at it again. ' "With one enormous chair." ' (Well, I've got my rocking-chair.) ' "Oh, wouldn't it be lovely." '

I've gone all passionate, thinking of red-hot sex in *my* chair with Maria. It only lasts five seconds. (The thought, not the sex.)

It seems the table is unshockable. Any subject can be discussed freely and openly, so there's no need to cover up Maria's past. Anyway, what was Tom doing looking into *IWantaWilly.com*?

'Tom's already got a willy, hasn't he?' I ask politely.

It's more of an inquiry than a statement. You never know.

'Not a very good one.' June giggles for a while. Tom's in a world of his own, as usual. 'We thought it was some sort of penis enlargement agency but it turned out to be for women on the verge of a sex change.'

The thyme-scented beef soup has gone down a treat. The wine's flowing and Maria is quite content to be sat on the swinger's table. All's well, for a change.

I choose the lobster while she goes for a breast of pheasant. It turns out that Andy and Alfred only live about two miles from Maria's family. 'It's very posh,' says Andy. 'All fur coat and no knickers if you ask me,' Alfred adds.

Captain Fletcher arrives at table 69. It's the first time he's strayed up our end. No wonder. He's as straight as a gun barrel in every sense of the word. Done out to a turn, all prim and proper and oozing authority, as you might expect from a man in his position. June's sure to fancy him. But it's Maria who captures his attention.

231

'There's something very important I want to ask you in front of the whole table,' she says.

Everyone stops. Alfred's in mid-gulp. He's poised with a spoonful of exotic fruit pavlova. He puts the spoon down and waits for the question. Even Tom's pricked up his ears.

'Malcolm and I want to get married on board the SS *Perfect* tomorrow, before we get home. You're an able seaman. Will you tie our knot?'

There's a stunned three-second silence...then, the whole table erupts as one.

It's a Mount Vesuvius moment. Mouthy Kev hugs Alfred, Andy hugs Kenneth who's trying to kiss Maria at the same time, but his teeth won't quite make the journey. Tom turns and looks. June and Kiss Me Kate are squawking like a pair of demented peacocks. Like ripples in a duck pond, the news spreads quickly to table 35, then table 15. Within seconds everyone's stopped eating. They're all beginning to applaud. Mouthy Kev finally releases Alfred from his bear-like clinch. Good job too, the colour's begun to drain from the poor bloke's cheeks. He stands on his chair and shouts at the top of his voice: '*We're going to have a wedding!*' Soon the whole place is cheering. Captain Fletcher holds his hands in the air as if to put a halt to the hullabaloo.

'I'm very sorry. That won't be possible.'

'Ohhh,' says June, lurching towards Kiss Me Kate. 'He's very firm, isn't he?'

Kate doesn't have time to answer. Kevin stands on his chair again. '*The bloody wedding's off!*' he booms dejectedly. A groan echoes around the table, and then the whole room lets out a communal 'ahhh'. It's like being at a high-pressure, winner-takes-all football match. The crowd rises as one, ready to salute the winning goal as the ball heads for the top corner of the net. Then, from out of nowhere, the goalkeeper springs off his line and gets a hand to the ball, deflecting it just past the post for a corner. The delight, within a fraction of a second, has turned to despair.

'I'm afraid that sort of thing only happens in the movies and on television,' says Captain Fletcher.

I'm bemused by the whole thing; in a total state of shock and awe. A few seconds ago I was set to become a married man. I hadn't asked anyone. I hadn't even been asked. But I was happy to go along with the euphoria of the moment, especially when Kenneth took hold of my right arm and thrust it into the air like a boxer who's just been handed the world crown on a split points decision. Now it's all over before it even started. The skipper explains some more.

'The ship isn't licensed, and even if it was, there's nobody on board that would have the right to marry you off the cuff, so to speak, at such short notice. I'm so sorry to let you down.'

There's another three seconds of silence. And more silence still. The usual hustle and bustle of the dining emporium has died down to a mere muffle. I don't know what to do with myself. Nobody does. Everyone's waiting for the next move; the whole bloody room's on tenterhooks, desperate for Mouthy Kev to broadcast the next instalment. Momentarily, the silence is shattered by the simple sound of a spoon falling innocently into an empty dessert bowl. The noise is deafening against the backdrop of a now completely hushed Monte Carlo Restaurant. Then out of the blue, an unfamiliar voice.

'I'll do it.'

It's Tom. He's turned round and uttered his first half sentence of the holiday.

'Yes,' shouts June, punching a clenched fist into the air. 'Tom can do it. He's a celebrant.'

'You mean he can't have sex? What's that got to do with my wedding?'

I'm confused. Anyway, listen to me all of a sudden. *My* wedding!

'No. Not *celibate*. He's a *celebrant* with the British Humanist Association. You must have heard of the humanists. They're all at it these days with humanist weddings – everyone.'

Blank looks. Nobody knows who they are.

Tom rises to his feet. It's amazing. Like a phoenix rising from the ashes. His face, for the first time, illuminated. He's found life; a second wind; a new coming. The table's on a knife-edge as Tom begins to explain. Captain Fletcher's listening intently.

'I'm a humanist.' He's firm, yet gentle in his delivery. 'We believe this world and this life is all we have. We therefore try to live full and happy lives ourselves, making it easier for others to do the same.' We're all mesmerized. He speaks beautifully. It's quite touching. 'Humanist weddings can take place wherever the couple wish and take whatever form they choose. Often, they're written especially for the couple – sometimes by the couple themselves. It's a non-religious affair between two people who genuinely want to share their lives, whatever their beliefs or backgrounds.'

Spontaneously, the diners on table 69 applaud. Tom is turning into an unexpected saviour. Tom explains that the role of a humanist celebrant is the same as that of a clergyperson. It's not a legally recognized affair, but as long as we have our marriage registered when we arrive home, it's all above board and proper.

'With your permission, my good man,' Tom's addressing the bloody Captain now, 'I'd be honoured to marry my good friends Maria and Malcolm – the humanist way.'

Tom elegantly sits back in his seat. Job done. All of a sudden, the man's become a marvel. Now, it's all eyes on Captain Fletcher. Mouthy Kev's back on his chair in a flash, but he's jumping the gun.

'*The wedding's back on!*'

The place erupts for a second time.

'Sit down, you loud-mouthed bleeding arsehole. We don't know yet,' yells Kiss Me Kate in an angry and quite unexpected broadside. Under different circumstances, the table would be in shock. With the pressure of the moment, we let it pass. Kev sits down like a naughty schoolboy.

'The Captain's still thinking about it,' says Kate. She's come off the boil and she's down to a simmer. The hushed silence turns to eager anticipation as everyone waits for the skipper's considered opinion. Has he bought the idea or not?

'I'm aware of humanists,' he says. Good start. He thinks for a moment. 'Yes. I'll happily let you use the ship.' He's bought it. 'I'll get Bliss to play for you. How does midday, just after the message from the bridge sound?' He pauses. 'How exciting. I've never arranged anything like this before.' He pauses again. 'Hooray for the humanists, then.'

Before you can say 'something old, something new, something borrowed, something blue', Captain Fletcher's off...and Kev's back up. *The wedding is definitely on, and that's that!* He's trying to regain his authority.

June intervenes. 'You'd better ask her, Malcolm.' She turns to the table. 'He hasn't asked her yet.'

'Kevin!' June's now in command. 'Tell them he hasn't asked her yet.' She beckons Kev back up onto the chair. He's becoming quite frustrated, torn between two lovers. One of them's telling him to get up, and the other wants him to stay down. It's quite a circus. Mouthy Kev's become the inter-round summarizer. He gets back on his feet. *He's asking her!*

The head chef has brought his workers out of the kitchens. The waiters are all poised. The place has ground to a halt.

'No,' says Maria.

She's said no! announces Kevin, throwing his head into his hands with a walloping thud. It's beginning to get too much for him.

'No!' says Maria again, only this time there's a hint of urgency about her. 'Not no, as in *no*! No as in, it was my idea. I'll ask him.' She gets down on one knee.

'*No, she's asking him!*' roars Kev.

I swear it's pure theatre. Well, at least it's better than anything Norman DeVine's produced so far.

'Kevin, you're pissing me off with your bawling and shouting,' says Kate. She's snapped again. 'Now sit down and shut the bollocking fuck up for a change.' She lands a meaty right hook into Mouthy Kev's unprotected groin. 'Oooooh!' The whole of table 69 felt that, but there's no time for sympathy. Not now. It's been another astonishing Kiss Me Kate outburst. Kevin's amazed by the sudden front of the woman. The tulip has turned into a triffid. He sits down. There's a nervous shuffle about the place.

Maria speaks softly. 'I know this has come as a bit of a shock to you. It has to me as well. But I feel so right with you. I mean, so comfortable, so happy. So, would it be all right with you if we got married? I mean... Would it make you happy?'

It's a stuttering performance. Her small-talk skills need work. The spotlight's turned to me. A thousand eyes are fixed on my mouth. I've almost seized up. For a split second, I'm dumbstruck.

'No,' I reply almost apologetically.

Kev jumps in. '*The twat's refused! The wedding's off!*'

Again a disappointed sigh embraces the dining-room. The diners, waiters, and chefs all turn to discuss the sad turn of events. Quickly, the mumble dies down. I've still got an ace up my sleeve.

'No Maria, it wouldn't make me happy to marry you. It would make me bleeding delirious.'

'*The twat's said yes!*' Kev raises his arms high into the air. '*It's back on!*' Kate looks daggers drawn at her other half. He shuffles quickly back into his chair. 'Yes, flower, I'm sitting down,' he says. 'Quite right petal, quite right.'

The cheer has turned into a roar. The roar turns into near delirium. June hugs Tom. It's the first time I've seen them touch, but he deserves a clinch. Suddenly, out of nowhere and without warning, Tom has turned into the hero of the day with three short yet so important words: 'I'll do it.' They could be the three most important words of my life, and they were spoken by Tom. Almost as important to me as 'I love you'. I still haven't heard them from Maria yet, but the night's young. Besides, I don't think I've said it to her. It's all been such a whirlwind.

The pandemonium continues. The Monte Carlo Restaurant is on fire. The Captain's back. He wants to be the first to congratulate us. Mrs Cocktail Stick flies over to kiss me, followed by June, Kate, Alfred, Andy and finally Mouthy Kev. Kenneth is jumping up and down like a lunatic, throwing his arms around like a madman, punching the air. Roger the Waiter brings over a bottle of champagne. 'It's from the gentleman in the blazer,' he says. Mouthy Kev looks at Kate. She nods a gentle nod of approval. He climbs back onto his chair.

'The wedding's on! That's his final answer! Sunshine Deck, noon tomorrow and you're all invited!'

Another cheer, another bottle of champagne – this time from Maria's mum and dad. They bring it themselves.

'Well this is a turn up, old pal,' says Maria's father. (Pal. It's a dog food again. He's obsessed). He turns to have a quiet word in my ear. 'I'm rather glad though. The old girl and I were beginning to think she was one of these lesbians. Know what I mean.' He winks.

I know what he means all right. I can't even begin to tell him what *I* had her down as. Anyway, the time's not quite right for a deep and meaningful chat with my father-in-law-to-be. After all, it's a turn up and a half for me too, almost too much for a simple man to take in. But how could I have wished for any better? It's a dream come true. Marriage has always been a huge fear of mine. I told Margaret Chandler I would never have the guts to propose, let alone go through the hell of organizing a wedding. This way, it's all laid on. I've done nothing. It's beautiful. Absolutely beautiful. And it's all thanks to the British Humanist Association and the do-it-yourself 'New wedding for a new millennium'. Table 69 is the celebrating capital of the world. It goes on for hours. People I've never even recognized on the boat are shaking my hand as if they're my brother.

Two things I must do before the night is over. One: phone my mum. The Angel will be delighted. Two: find my best man. I turn to Kenneth.

'Kenneth, it would give me great pleasure if you would do me the honour of being my best man. What do you think?'

Kenneth can't speak. He looks for a second. Then bursts into tears. I'm usually very uncomfortable when people start blarting in front of me. But this time I can handle it. Besides, I think he's trying to say yes. Alfred's crying too. It's all too much for him to take. Kev puts a reassuring arm around his waist. Andy asks if he and Alfred can be the matrons of honour. It's worked out perfectly for them; they always wanted a fancy dress theme on the last day. The way things are turning out I believe it's going to be the wedding of the century. Midday, tomorrow. On the Sunshine Deck.

Maria and I finally walk back to Cabin F153.

'Look at the time. It's nearly three o'clock and I'm getting married in the morning,' I say. I knew it must be getting on because I was starting to feel a little unsteady on my feet.

Maria sings, ' "Ding dong, the bells are going to chime." ' (*My Fair Lady*.)

'Will you be stopping over in my cabin tonight?' I ask, still slightly confused by the sex issue.

'Certainly not,' she replies. 'I can't see you on the morning of the wedding. It's bad luck.'

I'm confused. Point one: three a.m. means it already is the morning of the wedding. Point two: who in this day and age goes down the aisle without a poke? It's like going to the supermarket without your special offers pamphlet. I'm going to bite the bullet and have it out with her here and now.

'But we haven't made love yet,' I say. (Sometimes I can be a little old fashioned in my terminology but this time it's a calculated move. I don't want to put the woman off with crudity.)

'Of course not,' she insists. 'We're not married.'

Maria laughs, and pecks me on the cheek. It's a loving 'we've had a great day, now let's not spoil it with a quick wham bam, thank you mam; anyway, you're probably too pissed to get it up' sort of peck. She really cares for me. She disappears down the corridor and off into the night. Tomorrow I'm going to marry her. Quite shocking when you think about it.

'Hello, sir,' says Oh Danny Boy. 'I've heard the news. Many congratulations. I've brought you a stiff one. Have it on me. It'll help you sleep.'

He goes to turn away. Then he stops and looks back. He's uncertain, but he's going to do it anyway. He's going to engage me in a proper conversation. For one lovely moment, the servant and master scenario is totally forgotten. He really is my mate. He comes to pat me on the shoulder, but it turns into a very gentle hug.

'I hope you'll be very happy together, sir,' he says. He means every word.

Oh bloody hell. So do I, Danny. So do I.

15

It's Sunday, June 29th. My wedding day.

My tackle's shrivelled up like a prune – it's nerves. All sorts of funny thoughts ran round my head last night. It's been the most remarkable forty-eight hours on record. One minute I'm eating a pope fridge magnet in disgust at my lack of luck on the lust front. The next, I'm marrying Maria on the Sunshine Deck. And it's a humanist wedding at that. Plenty of pomp and circumstance and the boring bit at the registrar's office when we get home. Then there's *that* part of it. What happens when we get home? Does she come to my house? Will she like it? Will she still like me? Will she turn up? Was she just pissed? Was I just pissed? Was it all a dream? Then, I had a nasty thought while I was trying to drop off to sleep. What if it was all a prank. A cruel hoax. She'd had a wager with the Tosser in the Blazer that she'd get me to marry her before we got home. The bet was a bottle of champagne. After all, he did send one to the table last night. And her name: Maria Doolittle. It's not her name at all. It's the Eliza Doolittle story all over again. This time, I'm the fool that's fallen for it. Knockers, knickers, knackers clackers. No. That can't happen. She's too nice and this is the SS *Perfect*. I'm tying the knot this afternoon on the Sunshine Deck and it's going to be the wedding of the century. That's the end of it.

There's a knock at the door. It's Oh Danny Boy; I'd know that knock anywhere. He's arrived with a small bottle of Famous Grouse.

'It's a gift from Captain Fletcher, just in case you need a bit of Dutch courage today. I'll pour you a drop in your morning tea.'

Thank heavens for Danny. I must remember to tip him well before we get off tomorrow afternoon. That's the other thing. I've got my tips to sort out. Oh Danny Boy, Roger the Waiter, Donald the Downtrodden, Marlene the Wine Girl, they've all got to have a bit. *And* I've got to pack, ready for tomorrow's disembarkation. I'm beginning to panic.

'The Captain wants to see you both at 10 a.m. And Mr Underhill says he's on his way down. You know – Tom.'

Strangely, Danny's put me at ease. And he's emptied a good two thirds of the bottle of Grouse into my early morning tea. He's a fine gentleman. We'll be friends for life.

It's 7 a.m. Five hours to go. Another knock. It's Andy waving his travel iron in the air.

'Do you want anything done?' he asks. 'I don't mind going over your dickie, if you like. I've brought the spray starch.'

Not a bad idea considering the shrivelled up state of my dickie at the moment. Kate did say he could stiffen anything with that tin of spray starch. Tom's next to arrive. It's like Piccadilly Circus down here this morning. Well, I say it's Tom, but it's a different Tom to the bloke who's been sat on table 69 for the best part of a fortnight. I was wrong about him; he could talk all along. He was just waiting for his moment. Maybe there's a lesson there for us all.

'Dignified, caring and totally personal,' he says, describing a humanist wedding. 'It can take place anywhere. From your front room to a mountain top. But the rites I perform have no legal status at all. That has to be done at the registry office.'

'But what do I say? Is it a quick, "Will you have this woman as your wedded wife?" Do you need my middle name? When do I say "I do"?'

241

'You don't say "I do".' Tom's well in control. 'Well, not if you don't want to. The structure of the day is entirely up to you. You might want to make a promise to each other, words that will bind you together in love. You might want a special piece of music or a reading that means something to you both. Let's bring out what you both have in common.'

But I don't know. We've only known each other for one full day. If Tom had sat here forty-eight hours ago, I'd still be calling Maria Miss Cruise Bore, having just chucked Kiss Me Kate out of my room for a second time, while cursing my luck over the Port Enhancement Queen's lesbian love marathon in the Punch and Judy tent with my old flame. It's come up all at once, this wedding business.

'Well, just write down a few things that mean something to you and I'll soon knock it into shape.' Tom's very reassuring. He's going to see Maria. And if we can't think of a suitable ceremony, he says he's got the very thing. 'I did it for a lovely Latvian couple June and I knew. Beautiful service.'

I can't help admiring these humanists. Wouldn't everyone have their own customized wedding service if only they knew? After all, the wedding business is totally off the rails. Cars, receptions, horse and cart, honeymoon, white doves, thrones, uncles and aunties you'll never see again in a dozen years having a free nosh-up in some expensive hotel. I'm positive some youngsters fall in love with the idea of getting married, rather than fall in love with each other. Surely, the only people that matter on the day are the bride and groom. And the only *thing* that matters on the day is their love for each other. It's a wonder the whole world's not doing it the humanist way.

It's 8.30 a.m. Three and a half hours to go. There's a buzz at breakfast. Everyone's talking about it. They're all going to be there. Kenneth's waiting for me. He's my best man.

'Martin,' he says, 'this is the biggest honour I've ever had.'

We sit down to a full English but I'm not really hungry. Kenneth's noticed. He glances down distastefully as I play around with my sausage. He goes to tell me off, but then thinks better of it. He's got something more important on his mind.

'I'm so proud of you and I want to mark the day by giving you something that's very special to me. Call it a mark of my respect. My way of sending best wishes to you and Maria for the rest of your lives.'

I'm bemused. There's no sign of a present. What's he going to give me? I don't have to wait long to find out. Kenneth smiles, swiftly places his four spindly fingers inside his mouth, and scoops out his top dentures.

'They're all yours now Martin,' says Kenneth, handing me his top set.

Kenneth has given me his teeth. The family teeth that mean so much to him. The dentures he's stuck with through thick and thin in the name of tradition. They're mine now.

'If your first-born has to have them all out after a nasty dose of gum disease at an early age, don't worry. The teeth will take care of it. They'll protect him or her. I'd be proud to know your offspring were wearing my family teeth. I wouldn't give them to just anyone. But with you, I know they'll be looked after. Anyway, it's like you said. Teeth aren't everything.'

What a gesture. What a way to kick off my wedding day. He's given me his prized possession; the thing he cares about most in the whole wide world. Carefully I wrap them in my paper serviette and place them in my pocket.

'You're a great man, Kenneth. I'll treasure them.'

'Yes, you better fucking had. They're antique,' splutters Kenneth trying to get used to a world with no teeth. 'Remember, soak them in scotch every night. Put them by your bed with a drop of "Whisky in the Jar-o".' (It's a Thin Lizzy classic from the 1970s. Kenneth's a bit of a headbanger on the quiet.)

It's 9.45 a.m. Leaving breakfast, I wander around on the newly scrubbed decks. It looks like I'm the centre of attention. Everyone wants to say 'hello' or 'good luck'. The more restrained simply point and whisper. Even when I enter the lift, there's a ripple of applause. This is going too smoothly for its own good. Even the weather's fine; a few puffy clouds, but lots of blue. I'm starting to enjoy myself. When's the bombshell going to drop?

It's 10 a.m. Two hours left. Time I went and had a chat with the skipper. And met Maria. Remarkably, she's already there, in the Captain's quarters, having a small white wine. So this is what a Statesman Suite looks like. Magnificent. And the Captain's a fine man too. As well as my scotch, he made sure a bouquet of flowers was sent to Maria, and instead of a lecture on how marriage is an important step not to be entered into lightly, etc., he leaves us alone.

'I thought you'd want a few moments together before you go off and get ready. Feel free to use my room. If you need anything, just call.'

Maria's relieved to see I haven't chickened out. I'm relieved to see Maria's not using me as a bet. And she's delighted when I show her Kenneth's teeth.

'They were his pride and joy! We must keep them safe. Mind you, he might score with Mrs Hair Bear Bunch now he's got rid of them,' she says.

Good point. I hadn't thought of that. I'm still aiming to line the two of them up for a last gasp drop of holiday romance, even though I've got more than enough on my own plate. Maria said he could even go all the way and have one of those 'teeth implants'. She knew a girl who had it done. Every tooth in her body was taken out and replaced, until she had a brand spanking new full set. (By all accounts, there was actually nothing wrong with the old ones, but she insisted on having it done so she would look like her all-time heroine, Maureen Lipman. She chose what she considered to be a direct replica of Maureen's gnashers. Strange lot if you ask me.) Anyway, we're soon back to the business in hand.

Like me, Maria has given Tom carte blanche on the service. Looks as if we're going to get the Latvian version. I just hope he knows what he's doing, celebrant or no celebrant.

I'm helping myself to another whisky at the Captain's table. Maria says there's something we must do. She takes me by the hand and leads me into the Captain's bedroom. Great bed. It hangs from the ceiling like some oversized hammock. Maria's got a strange look in her eye. I've seen it before. It wasn't Lucille Bullock just before she produced her secateurs in Colchester. Nor was it on the riverbank after I'd gently tossed a pink maggot into the lap of What's-her-name – Claire, the lesbian. No. It was Dicky Cox when he used to stroll over and boast about his 'big ball at beaver castle', when he was on the verge of having it away with slippery knickers Sandra on reception.

Fucking hell. She's going to shag me. I can tell she's aroused, her overactive nipples are on the move again. I can't believe the effect I have on the woman. I never knew I was such a huge turn-on. But shag me in the Captain's hammock? No, she wouldn't. I'll ask her, just to be on the safe side.

'Maria! We're not going to have sex in the Captain's bed, are we?'

She grins a half-sweet, half-wicked grin, then puts her index finger to her lips. 'Ssshh.'

We *are* going to have sex in the Captain's bed. It's *my* 'big ball at Beaver Castle'. I'm a little hesitant.

'But if he finds out it'll all be off,' I protest in a half-hearted sort of way as Maria begins peeling off her 'Take me on the *Neptune*' blouse. I realize that at this stage there's no point in beating about the 'Old Bull and Bush'. Besides, I've still got that banana-flavoured condom on hand from the night before.

Sadly, it's not one of my finest moments. Firstly, I try to explain that I'm a 'chalk jockey'. She gets the wrong end of the stick and calls me a pervert. Secondly, when I finally put the cat among the pigeons, in the words of the great Nat King Cole, love ends before it begins. She can't be happy with that half-soaked, fumbling display. I'm no good away from home as it is, so I had no chance lolloping on the Captain's hammock. Couldn't get a firm grip. I decide to make a joke of it to ease the tension.

'Well, I'm glad I got that out of my system,' I say in a half-whisper, not knowing whether to laugh or cry. She laughs. I laugh too. The crisis has been averted. We've had sex in the Captain's bed just before our humanist DIY wedding service on the Sunshine Deck. It's going to be a great day. I'm convinced.

I'm halfway towards the Captain's en-suite, when Maria attempts to leap off the hammock. It's a difficult task to negotiate and she ends up in a bit of a tangle. There's something on her mind – and it's urgent. I can sense it.

'Don't forget, if it hasn't been through you, don't put it down the loo!' she shouts, finally untangling her toe.

Oh hell. She's referring to the condom, and she's right. But what can I do? I can't leave a used banana-flavoured johnny on the skipper's coffee table, not after he's been so nice to us. Equally, I can't block the ship's drains on my wedding day. I decide to hide the evidence in my jeans pocket. It's a bit of a mess, and I feel more than a little exposed, stood there in the Captain's suite stark bollock naked, trying to wrestle with a banana condom.

Between the sheets, it's not been the most romantic start by a long way – but at least it's got us laughing again. In fact, I'm starting to feel quite pleased with myself. You wait till I see Mouthy Kev. Let him try telling me now that you can't shag a spud. Maria just has. Well, sort of. I know I can perform much better than that when I'm into my stride. In sex terms, I'm like the little girl that had a little curl in the nursery rhyme. When I'm good, I'm very, very good. But when I'm bad, I'm horrid.

It's 11.45 a.m. There's an enormous crowd waiting in eager anticipation on the Sunshine Deck. I'm in my formal outfit and Kenneth's waiting on the stage; our informal altar. There's a real sense of occasion about the place. The lads from Bliss are playing 'Empty Chairs at Empty Tables' from *Les Misérables*. They're not very good at capturing the moment, this lot. Maria's father, Al, rushes out from the crowd. Betty's not far behind. I've just shagged your daughter in the Captain's hammock; that's the first wicked thought that comes into my head, but I'm not about to spill the beans. Al's waving one of his shoes around.

'I want you to have this Malcolm.'

Well. It's like Christmas all over again. First I get Kenneth's teeth. Now Maria's dad is thrusting a size nine into my palm, moments after Maria lost her glass slipper to me in the Captain's quarters. What next?

'It's lovely. Thank you very much Al.'

'It's tradition,' he says. 'It's my way of passing Maria over to you. She's all yours now my little cocker spaniel.'

(I was right. He thinks I'm a dog. Always has. I'm his little cocker spaniel.)

Maria's my responsibility. I hardly know the girl. He's right. I must be barking.

'How is Maria?' I ask, knowing I've seen her just an hour or so ago. Well, I say seen. Shagged to be more precise.

'She's very well. Sluggish start but she's perked up no end in this last hour. Never seen her so happy.'

Yes! It's goodbye Brenda Burston. In love terms, I've finally come of age. In fact, not to put too fine a point on it, I'm probably the sex king of the world. I have been all along and I never knew it. Bloody marvellous. I've given her one up the Ginger Rogers and bingo, she's leaping around like a Jumping Jack Flash. This wedding business, it's a gas, gas, gas! (The Rolling Stones.)

June appears with Alfred on one arm and Andy on the other. They're dressed in women's clothes. I forgot I said they could be the matrons of honour. And what a sight.

'Do you like my frock?' asks Alfred.

He's done out in one of Kiss Me Kate's formal dresses. The one with the halter-neck top that made her look like a Mary Quant cast-off. The same dress she had on when she tried to take me over the rocking-chair in cabin F153. When she parted her legs so I could see her white panties and smell her Charlie. It's all flooding back to me. Not a nice memory on my wedding day. Andy's decked out in a well-pressed June two-piece. Blouse and skirt. The three of them stand there for a moment. They look like the Beverley Sisters.

'You've forgotten something, haven't you Malcolm?' says June.

'What?'

'The bastard ring, you twat.'

'That's a bit strong June. You can't call me a twat on my wedding day.' I'm quite put out by her unprovoked attack. 'Anyway, I didn't think you had rings at these humanist affairs.'

'Tom said it's up to the couple,' insists June. 'You *can* have rings if you want. So…' She stops to produce a small box from her handbag. 'This is a present from your friends on table 69.' It's a ladies golden ring. 'Not quite a wedding ring but it's all we could do at the on-board jewellers in the time we had. Kevin went to see Maria's mum to ask about the size of her fingers. I think we've got it right, but they'll fix it for you tonight if you need an alteration.'

It's quite an overwhelming gesture. 'Thank you so much,' I mumble into my boots. It's a totally inappropriate Tom-like response (the Tom we used to know before he blossomed into the humanist preacher). But it's all I can do. I can't quite find the words.

Kevin and Kate arrive. Kevin's looking pleased with himself.

'Good luck lad,' he says. Then, with a crafty whisper into my right ear, he declares, 'And remember, if you want any shit shifted, I'm your man!'

It's a kind offer. After all, there's nobody bigger in manure management than Mouthy Kev.

Kate butts in. 'And may all your dreams and wishes come true when you say "I do".'

'They're not saying "I do", you twisted wanker,' says Kenneth. 'It's a humanist wedding. They've picked their own ceremony.'

It's hardly our own ceremony but I'll leave it. I think everyone's a little tense – that would explain the colourful language. Anyway, I've got Kate down as more of a twisted willow than a twisted wanker. Captain Fletcher comes next.

'Hello Malcolm. Your bride is ready, if you'd like to start.'

Tom shuffles into place on the makeshift stage. A kind of hush (Herman's Hermits) falls on the gathered hundreds on the Sunshine Deck. The new look, toothless Kenneth starts to rummage. He's looking for something in his pocket. He produces his recorder and places it delicately to his nose. On Tom's nod he starts up with 'Here Comes the Bride'. There's a mass 'ahhhh' from the growing crowd of passengers who are now jostling to get the best glimpse of what's becoming a glittering occasion. By anybody's standards, the wedding's off to a flying start.

Maria walks slowly towards the stage. She's wearing a beautiful long flowing cream 'off the shoulder' dress, and holding a potato blossom bouquet. Her hair has been stacked up (I like it when a bride has it up on her big day), and it looks like she's had a makeover at the beautician's. She looks stunning. Malcolm, I think to myself, you're a very lucky man.

Al's smiling, Betty's crying. Alfred gets out a tissue just in case – he's very Carol Vorderman when he's dressed as a woman. Andy hitches up his skirt and awkwardly hauls his underwear from out of his backside. He's uncomfortable, but then, it must be quite hard getting three balls into a pair of ladies panties. June's trying to catch the attention of the Tosser in the Blazer. The woman's a lush. Her lust knows no bounds. The Beverley Sisters have turned into the Ugly Sisters.

The scene is set. Tom stands facing the two of us. Maria's dad is to her side. Captain Fletcher stands next to Kenneth who's next to me. We're all lined up waiting for the service to begin. Behind us there's Maria's mum Betty, and the rest of table 69. And behind them, almost a thousand passengers. Mrs Cocktail Stick's there with Rosemary and Roger. The Tosser in the Blazer is next to Hattie Jacques and her husband Clive. This'll be a story for them to tell on their next trip. Mrs Hair Bear Bunch is accompanied, as usual, by her two Muppets (I think she's waiting for the ballroom dancing to begin). Last time she witnessed a wedding, her Russian acting friend was dancing at it. Even Mrs Jigsaw Puzzle has been prised away from the library. Daphne and Claire have made it too. They look good together.

The whole boat has ground to a halt. On the far side of the deck, Roger the Waiter looks on beside Donald the Downtrodden, Marlene the Wine Girl, Oh Danny Boy, Everard, Jerry Lee Lewis and the Indian Buddy Holly. The matching couple catch my eye. They're wearing identical white open-neck shirts with co-ordinated cream slacks and off-white shoes. And the biggest shock of them all. Sugar Daddy standing there as bold as brass, Sugar Baby Love on one arm and Linda the Boot Scooting Baby on the other. Now if he's shagged them both it'll be a miracle of modern science. Still, at least they seem to have called a truce. (Probably agreed to split the cash when he conks out.) Stoop and Droop are shuffling towards the front to get a better view. Arm-in-arm they appear to be holding each other upright.

'I remember my wedding day as if it were tomorrow,' says Droop struggling to keep her voice down.

I think she means yesterday but I'll forgive her. Anyway, it looks as if she's already downed three parts of a bottle of sherry. She's determined to finish her sentence even though everyone's eagerly waiting for proceedings to begin and, on this occasion, there's no need to put my finely tuned, well-oiled eavesdropping skills to the test. She doesn't care who's listening; we're going to have her 'wedding from hell' story whether we like it or not.

'Stunk to high heaven the old man did. Been mucking out his pigeons all morning. I took one sniff and fetched the lot up, all over the vicar's velvet cloak. Mind you, I was four months gone with Horace at the time… Used to think more of them bleeding birds than he ever did of me.'

Tom's had enough. He stands upright and bold before his congregation. Peering over his thick-rimmed Robin Day-like glasses, he delivers a short introduction.

'It gives me great pleasure to welcome you all on this happy occasion, to celebrate and witness the union of Malcolm and Maria, who wish to make their vows in the presence of their friends.'

He nods to the band leader and Bliss strike up with 'Nessun Dorma'.

It's unbelievable. Tom, the celebrant with the British Humanist Association; the swinger from just outside Luton who once tickled Suzanna the Chef's laa-laa with his toothbrush because he's very non-contact; the man who hero worships Jessie Matthews, and Sonny and Cher; the bloke who's said nothing all holiday other than 'I'll do it', is giving the most remarkable singing performance you've ever heard. He's singing 'Nessun Dorma' and there's not a dry eye in the house. It could almost be Pavarotti, except that Tom's much smaller in stature, he's not Italian, and to the best of my knowledge, Pavarotti has never titivated a woman's laa-laa. Still, Tom the Tenor has got the Sunshine Deck in seventh heaven. He's lost in a new world, hitting note after note with stunning perfection. The final crescendo is enough to send a shiver up your spine. The audience burst into an enthusiastic round of applause. I look at Maria with astonishment, and then at June who has a contented smile on her face. It's the look of a mother whose son has just won the egg and spoon race at sports day. (I was more suited to the sack as Maria recently found out.)

Next, Tom produces two sheets of handwritten paper. My bit is highlighted. The humanist service is about to begin.

Me: 'They say we're young and we don't know.'
Maria: 'We won't find out until we grow.'

It's Sonny and bloody Cher! I might have guessed it.

Me: 'Well I don't know, if all that's true. 'Cause you got me and baby I got you.'
Me, Maria, Tom, June, Alfred, Andy, Kenneth, Mouthy Kev and Kiss Me Kate: 'Babe, I got you babe, I got you babe.'
Maria: 'I got flowers, in the spring.'
Me: 'I got you, to wear my ring.'

'Show her the ring, you twat,' whispers June. I'm getting a bit fed up with this 'twat' business. That's twice in the space of ten minutes from the mouth of June. I show her the ring. She's delighted. I slip it over her wedding finger and Captain Fletcher starts to clap. 'Bravo' says Maria's dad. Her mum's still crying. The crowd know it's their turn to cheer. A nervy mumble of appreciation comes from the Sunshine Deck, the waiters, cooks, cleaners, first mates, pursers, they're all there. But the mumble dies down. The show goes on.

Maria: 'And when I'm sad, you're a clown.'
Me: 'And when I get scared, you're always around.'

Maria nods. 'Of course I will be.' Good job too, I've often got the willies up!
'It's your turn Malcolm,' says Tom. I've been thrown by Maria's interjection.

Me: 'Then put your little hand in mine. There ain't no
hill or mountain we can't climb.'

Maria holds my hand. Tom lifts his hands like a preacher. 'Everyone!' he demands, as Bliss begins to play and the gathered masses on the Sunshine Deck sing and sway. Even Captain Fletcher's at it.

'Hey, I got you babe, I got you babe.'

Tom lifts his hands again as if to ask for silence. He gets it. The man's turned into a revelation overnight.

Me: 'I got you to hold my hand.'
Maria: 'I got you to understand.'
Me: 'I got you to walk with me.'
Maria: 'I got you to talk with me.'
Me: 'I got you to kiss good night.'
Maria: 'I got you to hold me tight.'

It's lovely. We're both starting to fill up. Alison – Mrs Cocktail Stick – has broken down. She's kneeling at the feet of Rosemary the Ferret Woman, head in hands. It's probably the emotion of the week coming out of her. She's had a death and a marriage, all she needs now is a birth and she's got the whole set. Even Daphne and Claire are smiling. 'Ahh,' says

Claire. 'I'm glad he's happy after all.' Norman DeVine looks at his watch.

Me: 'I got you, I won't let go.'
Maria: 'I got you to love me so.'

Tom raises his hands again. 'Everyone!' We all know exactly what to do.

'I got... You babe.'

The cheering begins. Kenneth's practically on the floor, in almost exactly the same place where he fell yesterday after trying to rescue Linda the Boot Scooting Queen from a left-hander off the Lassie from Lancashire. I swear the throngs of 'dearly beloveds' are going down like dominoes in a wave of emotion. It's been the most touching wedding service of all time. Thanks in no small part to the humanists – and Sonny and Cher.

Tom continues. He gets out the scrap of paper I'd hastily written on earlier on in my cabin. The things that mean something to me.

'In the name of: Brenda Burston, Mrs Lighthouse, hedge-hopping, Barcelona, tongue sandwiches, Oh Danny Boy, the Pipes, the Pipes are Calling, The Angel, Czechoslovakian lashing sticks, Jake the Peg with his extra leg, Dicky Cox, Ginger Rogers, the legendary Jack Russell (Gloucestershire and England), "Knockers, Knickers, Knackers, Clackers" and Sir Thomas Harriot, I'm proud to announce you man and wife. You may kiss your wife now Malcolm. Congratulations. You're a married couple.'

Blimey. I'm married.

Maria looks at me quizzically. 'Who's Brenda Burston?' she mouths.

I forgot to tell her the story of Brenda being tongued on the Witch's Hat by Denis McGowan. I should've really, it was the moment when my biological clock started to tick. Still, it doesn't seem to matter any more. I don't think I'll ever bring up Brenda Burston again. I've somehow left her behind.

'And what about Sir Thomas Harriot?'

Maria's still confused. That was my masterpiece of the day. He was the man that brought the first ever potato into Britain from Colombia in 1786. God bless him. I don't think I did too badly with my hastily arranged 'things that mean the world to me' list. Anyway, Maria's got no time to dwell on it. She's soon surrounded. Embraced by her mother and father. I'm next to get a group hug from table 69.

'Thank the Lord that's over. These bloody suspenders are playing havoc with my varicose veins,' says Alfred.

'You can talk,' says Andy. 'June's leather thong is cutting into my piles something awful. I'll be red raw by the end of the day. You'll have to work overtime tonight with the preparation.'

'Would you like the band to play your first song?' asks the Captain, eager to get the party into full swing.

'Do you know any Fergal Sharkey?' I ask, expecting a nice slow version of 'A Good Heart These Days is Hard to Find'.

They don't know any Fergal Sharkey. Maria's quick to the rescue.

'Just give us "Yellow Bird, Up High in Banana Tree".'

Within seconds the Sunshine Deck dance floor is full. Yet another bottle of champagne is uncorked by Mouthy Kev. Then another, courtesy of Al and Betty, followed by a third from the Captain.

Soon it's my turn on the mike. The groom's speech. I'm ready for this moment. I've been preparing a love poem in my head all day. I was always very good at poetry. My greatest work, 'The Death of Mrs Lighthouse', still hangs above the receptionist's window at my old school. Just hope I can remember all the bloody words in amongst all the excitement.

'Dear Maria.'

It's a confident start (even the first two words rhyme, if you say them right).

'I'll be your owl if you'll be my pussy. We'll have children galore – or a rabbit. I'm not fussy.
If you'll be my Doonican, I'll be your Val.
I'll be your Pedigree Chum, if you'll be my Pal.'

That line was inspired by her father – he's looking pleased.

'You'll be the lady and I'll be the tramp.
I'll always be waiting if downstairs you get damp.'

Tribute to Kiss Me Kate.

'You'll be my Penguin biscuit. The spuds in my stew.
You're my West End sensation. I've got a Bobby Crush on you.'

The musicals link – I've thought of everything.

'If you're ever waiting on life's Witch's Hat,
I'll be there with my tongue – no doubt about that.'

She'll have to forgive me. I hadn't completely got the Brenda Burston saga out of my system when I dreamed up the rhyme last night.

'You're the apple of my eye. And you've got a nice pair!
You've made my days Sonny. My heart you can Cher.'

There are one or two blank faces in the crowd. Some are more than a little confused. But on the whole, my poem has gone down well. In fact, it's worked a treat. And now a toast:

'Ladies and Gentlemen, will you raise your glasses please to Maria, the British Humanist Society, and Jack Russell – Gloucestershire and England.'

The crowd give a disjointed yet hearty reply. I'm pleased with myself. I'm not one to hog the limelight, but today I'm well and truly centre stage. And I'm making a real go of it. In the words of the song, if they could see me now! I wonder what they'd make of it all back at the British Potato Marketing Board, if they could hear me holding court on the Sunshine Deck after the wedding of the century. Wait till they find out. It'll be the biggest thing since... Potato Pete.

Kate's well pissed. She's ditched the larger and lime in favour of gin and tonic. Bad move.

'I'm sorry about our couple of misunderstandings, chicken,' she says barely able to stand. 'No hard feelings?' she asks with a cheeky smile.

'Certainly not,' I reply abruptly. 'But, I must be honest, one thing's been bothering me all week.' Here goes... I'm bracing myself for a rather spectacular moment. 'What did Tom do to you with a Dyson vacuum cleaner?' I think it's time we had it all out in the open once and for all. (It would certainly put my mind at rest.)

Kate smiles. 'Nothing. He gets his sexual kicks by stripping stark bollock naked and cleaning the house from top to bottom. It's not very interesting for me but we do like to make sure everyone's fulfilled.'

'But what about Suzanna, the chef from Bishop's Cleeve? He spent all afternoon titivating her laa-laa with his toothbrush?'

'Oh her! Laa-laa's her West Highland terrier. Named after one of the Teletubbies. He needed a toothbrush to get into the cracks.'

'*What?*'

'She had this statue thing carved in his honour. It was one of the highlights of Tom's naked cleaning career scrubbing away at that statue. Mind you, it did come up a treat. It's his passion, cleaning in the buff. Well, that and Jessie Matthews. And Sonny and Cher. He could have been on stage you know. A professional. He was one of Britain's finest tenors in his day, then he got turned down for RADA when he was twenty-three. It was a huge slap in the face. Tragic really. June says he's never quite been the same since.'

'And he doesn't mind June having it away with every Tom, Dick and Harry?'

'Don't be ridiculous – he's a humanist,' says Kate, quite taken back by the question.

A humanist, of course. He's a never-say-die, real life humanist. In fact, I'd say he was the rising hope of the humanist movement after the events of today.

It's 3 p.m. I've been married for two hours. We've had our ups and downs but so far, on the whole, everything's going well. The Captain's said we can use his cabin for the rest of the day – sort of like a honeymoon suite. He's even arranged to have my bags packed and waiting for me when we get off tomorrow so I can enjoy the rest of the day.

Maria and I take a stroll to cabin F153. It's my last visit to the rocking-chair. She's coming back home with me tomorrow (Maria, not the rocking-chair). Al and Betty are coming down to bring her belongings later in the week. We're suddenly beginning to feel like a married couple. I hope they don't bring her collection of Cruise Bore T-shirts. Maybe they'll print up a new one to mark the occasion. (Although, I don't think they'd do very good business trying to peddle the 'I've been shagged in the Captain's hammock on the SS *Perfect*' version.)

'Thank you for the best day ever,' she says as I hastily arrange my tips into envelopes.

I've got to admit, it's been fantastic. Beyond my wildest dreams. And we've still got the *Perfect* Party Night to come.

Stroking the top of the rocking-chair, I say a final farewell to cabin number F153. You can hear June in the distance, leading the party with the hokey-cokey. Now if there's one woman who is sure to be putting it in when she should have been taking it out and shaking it all about, it's her. I say goodbye to my rocking-chair, my picture window and, the saddest bit of all, Oh Danny Boy, who is waiting patiently for me outside the door.

'Goodbye sir, I'll try and see you tomorrow. It's been a pleasure getting to know you.'

I slip a few measly quid into his hand by way of a tip. It's hardly right for what he has done.

'Oh shit.' I stop mid-corridor.

'What now?' asks Maria, almost desperate to yank me back into the Captain's hammock.

My banana-flavoured condoms. I'm determined to go into this mission fully armed, so I'm taking the lot. In this day and age you've got to have everything covered. I'm poised for passion. I'm ready to be tossed around on the high seas. Maria's my yellow bird, and I'm going to be up high…in banana tree. Roger and Rosemary the friendly ferret folk are waiting at my door with a bag full of home-made confetti. Within moments I'm covered in tiny bits of tissue paper. Condoms in hand, I kiss them both.

'Oh,' says Jolly Roger. 'Banana. We always preferred kiwi fruit, didn't we love?'

'Yes,' agrees Rosemary. 'But then dear, you were always very big down under.'

They both laugh hysterically for a few seconds. It's their little gag. They're both as sweet as sugar candy, but I've no time for idle tittle-tattle. Maria's already marched halfway up the corridor. I've got a Jolly Roger of my own to think about.

16

Hours married: six. Shags in the Captain's hammock: two and a half. (The half was a bit of a fumbled affair. First I struggled to prise her frock off, and then I thought I heard someone coming.) Stiff-uns consumed: innumerable. Lover's tiffs: nil. It's a piece of cake this marriage business. Why so many couples fall by the wayside I shall never know. It's all a question of give and take. And since exchanging our humanist vows, our bonds have grown even stronger.

The similarities between us are really quite remarkable. For example, when Maria was eight and a half, she wrote to *Jim'll Fix It* asking to go and visit the set of *Daktari* (children's show about an African doctor living in the jungle). I could hardly believe my ears. I had a model *Daktari* jeep with all the characters: Doctor Marsh Tracey, Judy the chimp and Clarence the cross-eyed lion. It was one of my most treasured possessions along with my Evel Knievel wind-up jump motorcycle (best used in the kitchen to fly off a home-made ramp over dad's slipper... Didn't run too well on carpeting). Anyway, I *also* wrote to *Jim'll Fix It* in an attempt to visit Robinson Crusoe on his island. (I wanted to meet Scottish footballer Willie Johnston, but my mother said the more unusual the request, the more chance I'd got of getting on.) Like Maria, I never received a reply. We're both *Jim'll Fix It* failures. How's that for coincidence! To my mind, it's proved that we have more than enough in common to make this marriage stand the test of time.

And now we're both eagerly stepping out for the *Perfect Party Night*. Our last night knees-up. Anything could happen in the next three hours and, knowing this lot, it probably will. The buffet is laid out on the Sunshine Deck, and the Bliss boys are belting their way through a series of sing-along favourites. They've moved from 'Who Were You With Last Night?' to 'Ma! He's Making Eyes at Me' to 'Hello, Hello Who's Your Lady Friend?' in just over two minutes; class act.

To one side of the Sunshine Deck there's a top table laid out for Maria, our friends and me. The centrepiece is a glorious penguin carved out of ice. On closer inspection, it's fake ice; but it's still splendid! (And a penguin of all things. I wonder how they knew.) As for the food, well, what a spread. The last time I saw anything remotely like this was at my thirty-fifth birthday bash. I'd got Dibble the Muffin Man to lay on one of his 'exotic finger buffets'. To tell the truth, it was a bit of a let down. Apart from the odd prawn parcel, it was all chicken drumsticks and cheese straws! Nothing exotic at all, despite the dried-up pineapple chunks scattered randomly among the pork pies. This is different, and everybody on board wants a piece of the action. They're all taking our picture or video-taping our every move. I've been asked dozens of times to write my home address on a crumpled piece of paper so the photographer can send me a copy.

'We're going to have the biggest wedding album of all time,' I tell Maria as we join our guests on the wedding table.

'I've got some to start it off,' she says, dipping into her shorts pocket. (We've gone from formal to casual – via the Captain's hammock.)

Maria produces a picture of me with Cyril the Seal, then me with the cardboard cut-out of the Leaning Tower of Pisa, me in front of the Olympic flag; it goes on. She's brought the flipping lot. That's why they'd disappeared from the picture board. If I add the one of my King Edwards in front of the Trevi Fountain, we've got the makings of a real work of art.

Roger the Waiter appears with his constant companion, Donald the Downtrodden. Odd sort, Donald. He doesn't say a lot, just has this knack for always looking awkward. I don't know anything about him, could be a mad axe murderer for all I know. Today, as usual, he's wearing his downtrodden-type permanent smile. I don't understand it. How dare he not have the full-on glow of a happy man on my wedding day. After all, he's got every reason to be content with his lot; he's been given the task of carrying the most wonderful wedding cake. It's got a horseshoe on top, covered beautifully in white lace. There's more champagne, a feast fit for a king, and then it's down to the serious business. The karaoke.

Andy and Alfred have kept their dresses on. They've gone the whole hog tonight with lipstick, powder and paint. (Shakin' Stevens if I remember correctly. Another class act, and a classic line: 'Is you is, or is you ain't?')

'Who are you this time, Marilyn Monroe and Jane Russell?' I ask.

'More like Muffin the Mule and Jack Russell,' says Kenneth.

I'm disappointed in him. I tell him never to take the name of my all-time hero in vain, even if he is referring to the dog breed. Kenneth apologizes. 'Sorry Martin – it's your day.'

Hattie Jacques is halfway through a rendition of, 'Hold me by the ankles but don't drop me till I've kissed the Blarney Stone', when from out of nowhere Mrs Cocktail Stick approaches the table. She's got a determined look on her face. She's a cocktail stick with a mission.

'I think I'm ready now,' she says.

How could we forget? It's time to pay a twisting tribute to our old pal the Pillsbury Dough Man. (It seems he's been dead for years what with all the other goings on.)

'I'll sort it,' says Mouthy Kev, striding up to the microphone.

He's soon up there asking people to remember one of our fellow passengers in the way that he'd love to be remembered. Bit hypocritical in my view. He was moaning blind the morning after it had happened. The mild and meek Mrs Cocktail Stick takes the mike. She's holding a pair of the Pillsbury Dough Man's extra large trousers tightly to her small bosom. (Rumour has it that Andy smuggled them out of the dining-room to give them the once over with his travel iron. They certainly looked well pressed to me.) She turns and looks at the assembled band behind her. It's fifty-fifty as to whether she's going to go through with it.

Suddenly she turns and with all the courage in the world, she screws up her tiny face and orders: 'Hit it boys.' Then, with a high-pitched squeal, she yells, ' "Come on everybody, clap your hands. Now you're looking good. I'm gonna sing my song and it won't take long. We gotta do the twist and it goes like this." '

Mrs Cocktail Stick is shaking her spike-like head from side to side furiously. Her well-groomed, blow-dried bob is beginning to take on a life of its own.

The band 'hits it' while Mrs Cocktail Stick twists with all her might. I'm up in a flash with Maria. Kenneth grabs Kiss Me Kate. (If he sticks with her he could be on for a last-minute snog. After all, she might have a thing for toothless weasels.) Slowly but steadily, the whole of the Sunshine Deck gets up to twist in tribute to the Pillsbury Dough Man. The mass movement of twisting bodies is enough to capsize the ship into the swirling waters below. Even Hattie Jacques is having a go, but she can only get a third of the way down before grasping the arm of her new mate, Mrs Jigsaw Puzzle. Sam the Pickle Man looks like he abandoned the twist a long time ago. He's decided to do 'the bump' with Sugar Baby Love on one side, and Linda the Line Dancing Queen on the other. I reckon the pair of them are trying to bump him off to get their sticky paws on his pickling profits. Still the gyrating goes on. It's a marvellous send off. The Pillsbury Dough Man would have been very pleased.

June begins to chant, 'Tom Jones, Tom Jones, Tom Jones.' It's my turn. And this time, I feel like the winning contestant on *Stars in Your Eyes*. When you return from the smoke-filled doors, misty eyed and on a high, you know you've got to perform again, but it doesn't really matter. The job's been done. You're flying as high as a Peter Powell stunt kite (Christmas best-seller in the 1970s).

My fellow passengers on the good ship *Perfect* are about to get the greatest 'Green, Green Grass of Home' they've ever heard in their lives. I'm going to give it a real tug. Mind you, the last time I gave anything a good tug I was stood at the opening to the Punch and Judy booth. Twice I tugged. Twice I got the shock of my life. Fingers burnt. Twice.

Those days are gone. Locked up in the file marked 'Dim and Distant Past' and shoved well underneath my Pans People paperweight. Do you know, the way I'm feeling, I might buy an SS *Perfect* paperweight to replace it. That's the sort of mood I'm in. It's a new era for Mr Potato Head. Before you can say 'It's not unusual' – and let's face it, on this boat, nothing is – I've peeled off my jacket and I'm going for gold. Sure enough there's a crescendo before I've even got to the first line.

'The old home town still looks the same. As I step down from the plane.'

I don't even have to continue; they're with me all the way. I began this cruise as Malcolm Williams. Suddenly, I'm Robbie Williams.

'And there to meet me is my mama and papa.'

I've subtly adapted the next bit to fit in with the occasion.

'Down the road I look and there stands Maria. Hair of brown, just like a pint of beer.'

Maria giggles. I think she appreciated my efforts.

'It's good to touch the green, green grass of home.'

The crowd sway like The Kop at a Liverpool football match. If they had a candle apiece it would resemble the end of a Barry Manilow concert. I really don't want the moment to end.

'Yes, they'll all come to see me. In the shade of that old oak tree as they lay me 'neath, the Green, Green Grass of Home.'

I swear my voice is bouncing off the back wall of the Sunshine Deck and wrapping itself around the ship's funnel. They can probably hear me back in Southampton (we can't be that far away now). True to my new-found form, I receive a standing ovation. I hold out both hands. I'm determined to bask in the adulation. I'm drinking in every last drop. I'm Malcolm 'Platinum Balls' Williams.

The bastard Norman DeVine is next up. The night is getting on. It's been a long day. I'm almost ready to hit the hammock.

'Okee dokee, ladies and gentlemen,' he says. 'Please take your partners for the conga.'

I don't know why I dislike the man so much, but it seems I'm not alone.

'How can you take a partner for the conga? It's done in a line, you perverted little puff!' booms Mouthy Kev.

DeVine slinks off, eyes to the floor, and the band begins. It's our last blowout of the vintage vacation. And everybody's at it. June the Loon is leading from the front. She has done all holiday. The Tosser in the Blazer is so close behind that he's almost halfway up her arse. (I'm sure she must have had his bone up her Knick Knack Paddy Wack by now. She doesn't usually hang about, and I've always said he was gagging for it.) Kenneth's clinging on to Kiss Me Kate for all of his worth, but Mrs Hair Bear Bunch has got her hands gripped around his waist. I said he should have gone for her all along. The two Muppets are a mile behind. They're forming a line of their own, which includes Hattie Jacques and her squirrel of a husband. Jigsaw Puzzle is not far off the pace, while Stoop and Droop have opted out of it altogether. They're sat chatting up a waiter. Judging by the way Droop's frantically fanning her hand in front of her face, it looks as if Stoop has dropped one.

'Pooh,' says Droop. 'They should stick that one in the *Nautical Newsletter*! Still dear, nobody ever died of a bad smell.'

The conga continues. Alfred, Andy and Kevin are behind Mrs Jigsaw Puzzle. I've got hold of Andy, so I glance down to see if I can witness anything remarkable between his legs. Kiss Me Kate said it was fascinating to watch his three balls swinging from the back. Nothing strikes me as out of the ordinary. Maria's holding me and she takes a firm grip as the line turns sharp left to do one final circuit of the Sunshine Deck. She's determined we're going straight on and up to the Captain's quarters. Good move, it would be silly to overegg the pudding at this stage. With one swift yank, we've broken clear of the conga, and soon we're on our own.

'Why did you carry potato blossom today?' I ask Maria as we make our way back to the Captain's suite, exhausted.

'Roger the Waiter sent it me. He thought it would make you happy. Anyway, Marie Antoinette used to wear it. You remember; "Let them eat cake." The French Revolution? I studied it.' She looks at the ring. The wonderful present from table 69. 'Why is that finger the wedding finger?' she asks, waving her left hand third finger into the air.

'Ancient Egyptians,' I reply. I'm coming into my own. 'According to them, the ring finger contains the vein of love which travels directly to your heart.'

It's a lovely note on which to end the day. The Captain's hammock is waiting. I'll take a stiff-un to bed. And when I wake up, I'll wake up a happily married man. You wouldn't have put money on it would you? Just over a week ago, I stumbled up the *Perfect* gangplank unaware of what was to become of me. Tonight I'm lying in the Captain's hammock with my beautiful new wife. It's a funny old game, life.

Malcolm's Log. It's Monday, June 30th. My holiday of a lifetime is over. I've met the girl of my dreams and married her. We're off to start a new life together. We're about to sail into the sunset, leaving the ship behind us. But we're going to take the memories to our graves.

I haven't slept well. What with all the sex and the hammock swaying, I've been all over the place like a pair of mad woman's drawers. Maria, on the other hand, went out like a light, woke up for sex, slept again like a log, woke up for sex, then dropped off again. A remarkable display. Looks like I've got quite a goer on my hands, but then, June did forecast it. I'm quite glad to hear the knock at the door. It's Danny's knock. My old mate's brought a pot of tea and a packet of Jaffa Cakes. Jaffa Cakes! They live like blooming lords these Captains.

Maria goes to pour the tea, but I'm having none of it.

'Stop!' I yell. (I'm quite firm when I want to be.) 'You've got to let the person who made the tea pour it. Otherwise, we'll have ginger twins.'

267

Maria looks at me gone out for a second, but I thought it was a well-known fact – it was always a very popular saying in our house. Oh Danny Boy smiles, and pours the tea.

At breakfast, there are a lot of sad goodbyes. Maria and I, Betty and Al look out on a grim, cloudy, wet Southampton. The Sunshine Deck, scene of all the action just hours before is now cold, damp and uninviting. The SS *Perfect* is home and hundreds of bags are being unloaded by dozens of workers. For the record, it's hours married: twenty. Shags: four and three-quarters. I doubt the Captain's hammock has ever witnessed such action. And the icing on the cake? Maria's had an orgasm. It was me! I gave it to her. I've never given a girl an orgasm before – not a real one. Well, I think it was an orgasm at any rate. Either that or she suffered some form of mild stroke. To tell the truth I'm not 100 per cent sure either way. But I do know that I was the cause of it – and it's made my holiday, I can tell you.

June and Tom are first to come over and wish us luck. June's a little flustered.

'You'll have to forgive me. I've just been playing Blind Man's Buff with Everard in the cabin. Quite a session, I don't mind telling you. Anyway my little bag of pork scratchings,' she says quickly regaining her composure, 'we'll all be on board next year. Same trip. Why don't you join us? You might have a baby potato by then.'

She's counting them up on her fingers: 'One potato, two potato, three potato, four. Five potato, six potato, seven potato, more.' Then she turns to me. 'Malcolm, you're like the son I never had.'

I think I'm the *only* one on board the SS *Perfect* she hasn't had – but that's not what she means. Anyway, I think she's right. We'll have to reconvene. There's so much unfinished business as far as I'm concerned. Kenneth the Weasel Man must return to make a determined effort to bed Mrs Hair Bear Bunch. I know she's a bit older than him, but I'm convinced he could snatch her from underneath the noses of the two Muppets. It had all the makings of romance last night when she was hanging onto his jacket as if her life depended upon it during the conga. They're so well suited. Consider the facts. She's got a wayward wig. He's spent half of his life trying to get to grips with a set of wayward dancing dentures. He played a transvestite in *The Persuaders*, auditioned for *The Onedin Line*, sold cucumbers on *Albion Market* and could've been the next James Bond if it wouldn't have been for his small part in *Charlie's Aunt*. She once knocked around with a pretend Russian who danced in the ale-house during the film version of *Fiddler on the Roof*. And she's such a kind-hearted old thing. Sells the Salvation Army newspaper at Cradley Heath market when she's not fiddling on the roof. Believe me. It's a marriage made in heaven. He could be her toy boy.

Then there's Tom and Andy. I've matched them up as well. Did it last night while I was hanging off the edge of the Captain's hammock, trying to get some shut-eye. I've worked out their perfect date. Andy could get his ironing-board out on top of Nelson's Column while Tom cleans the pigeon poo off Lord Horatio's hat with his electronic toothbrush – stark bollock naked. It's the ultimate adventure for the pair of them. What a partnership. Tom's electronic toothbrush and Andy's tin of spray starch. It would almost certainly bring the capital to a standstill.

Talking of Tom, I must thank him for his glorious service yesterday. He's gone back to his normal, shy self. His moment of glory came, and he seized it with both hands. Like a flower, he blossomed for one afternoon. It was his spring, and now, under the gathering dark clouds and spitting rain, he's started to wither.

He nods gently. 'You're very welcome,' he says hesitantly.

'By the way, where are Kevin and Kate this morning?' I ask, eager to say goodbye to everyone.

'Quoits!' says June, winking as she and Tom make their way into one of the newly polished lifts.

They don't give up these cleaners, not even on the last morning. The smell of Pledge is everywhere. For a split second I'm transported back to the office. Dibble the Muffin Man – our mobile sandwich seller – has a wife called Debra (the Muffin Mistress), who was once addicted to the smell of polish. In the end she had to go for treatment. I remember the day when Dibble was forced to turn her over to the quacks. He was devastated, but had no choice. He'd found her trying to use Mr Sheen as an underarm deodorant. It was the final straw.

They're a funny family. Dibble, being a big fan of the Bee Gees, named his only daughter Tragedy. At first I thought Tragedy Muffin had a nice ring to it, but Pimple the office new boy said I was being a twat because she'd never get a boyfriend with a name like that.

Maria hauls me back to the land of the living.

'Did June say quoits?' she asks.

I must admit, I found that rather peculiar as well. Imagine Kevin and Kate going for a game of quoits just moments before disembarkation. I never had them down as the sporty type. Well, not in that way.

'We're going to have to find them to say goodbye,' Maria insists.

I'm sure it's more for my benefit than her own. (She's like that, always putting me first.) Anyway, Maria's always had this theory about the quoits deck. She's convinced the Tosser in the Blazer murdered the Pillsbury Dough Man in the sauna and shower hut. She thinks he was desperate to get his hands on Mrs Cocktail Stick's millions. She had her down as one of these lonely eccentric millionaires looking for love. I'm not convinced and I tell her straight:

'Don't talk shit. The sauna and shower hut is a shagging den.'

I can only blame my forcefulness on the fact that my fresh dawn has started to kick in.

'Anyway, how did the tosser carry the Pillsbury Dough Man down the stairs to the Golden Penny Arcade without being noticed? He'd have needed a pick-up truck. Besides, Sugar Daddy is the only eccentric millionaire on board. Mrs Cocktail Stick is only interested in doll's houses.'

All the same, her theory has got me spooked. It's like going into a haunted house climbing up the stairs to Deck 13. We're hanging onto each other like Scooby Doo and Shaggy.

We're soon there though, and sure enough, within seconds of our arrival, Kevin emerges from the sauna room pulling his trousers up. He appears to be flustered. Maria said he must have had a good workout on the quoits court.

'Workout my arse. Shagging den. I told you all along it was a shagging den. This is where they all do it.'

I'm triumphant. Maria's disappointed, but she's keen to know who's going to appear next. We both are. You could run a book on it. It can't be June and Tom because we've just seen them downstairs. Otherwise, you pays your money and takes your choice. We wait with bated breath. Kevin hasn't seen us. We're cowering near the stairwell.

Well, blow me down. It's Kiss Me Kate. For once, he's given his wife one; in the shagging den; on Deck 13. They've definitely been at it. She's got her knickers in a right twist, and she reeks of Charlie Girl. I thought I recognized the smell as soon as I got up here. Wait a minute. There's more action. Bollock me raw. Sugar Baby Love is next to appear, desperately doing up her blouse and hitching up her skirt. It's like the charge of the light brigade, and it's not over yet. How they've all squeezed into a room no bigger than the soundproof booth of the popular 1970s game show *Mr and Mrs*, I shall never know. Maria's words once again echo my thoughts.

'It must be like Mary Poppins' sodding bag in there,' she says delicately.

Marlene the Wine Girl is out next, followed by Sugar Daddy who's struggling to do up his flies. He's got to be almost one hundred years old, and so far on this trip he's had it away Sugar Baby Love, Linda the Boot Scooting Baby that drove 'em all crazy, Kiss Me Kate, possibly Mouthy Kev and even Marlene the Wine Girl. They can't all be trying to get their hands on his money.

Kate's seen us, hiding near the stairwell.

'Here they are, the happy couple,' she says as if nothing's happened. 'I wished we'd have known. You could have joined us for a swift knock-up. We thought we'd have a quick one before we got off.'

Captain Fletcher emerges from the sauna and shower room. His face has coloured up like a beetroot. In fact, it's worse than that – he's suddenly turned into Captain Scarlet.

'Good morning to the happy couple,' he declares in a regal captain-like manner.

Dumbstruck, Maria and I look at each other with a mixture of bewilderment and amazement. We're so speechless that we can't even begin to search for an explanation. Even so, Maria is unable to hold on to the few words that come tumbling out of her wide-open mouth before she has time to snatch them back. (Our jaws dropped simultaneously, we have a lot in common that way.)

'Captain Fletcher! Well, bugger me,' she says. Again, she's captured the moment perfectly. For a second, Captain Fletcher looks awkward. He's noticed our joint look of horror.

'Well,' he says nonchalantly, shrugging his shoulders. 'Nobody's perfect!'

In a state of sheer disbelief and perplexment, Maria and I very slowly turn about face and begin to trudge downstairs. Captain Fletcher, the dirty bleeder, has disappeared down a hatch marked 'Private'. As he departed, he cried by way of a parting shot: 'I'm not a love walrus, but I know a man who is!'

Back at reception, it seems that everyone has gathered to see us off. I'm a bit weary of it all. The incident with Captain Fletcher has put me on guard. And there are too many wishes of good luck flying around. 'Good luck,' my mother once warned me, 'is an eel in the pond of fools.' Still, in this instance, I think they mean well.

Jolly Roger and Rosemary, the Ferret Fanciers, dash towards us. Rosemary's got one of those, 'I know something you don't know, but it's all right because I'm going to tell you anyway' looks. She's about to burst with excitement; it's written all over her face.

'Guess what,' she says, unable to keep it in any longer. 'We're going to name a baby ferret after you. We thought of it last night when we were having a last knock-up on the quoits deck. Just after we'd bumped into you waving those banana things around. Well, all of a sudden I had a turn. My mind flashed back to the Durex and I immediately thought – babies! I looked at Roger and screamed, "I'm going to give him one!" Just like that. I'm going to give you your own adopted ferret. We're calling it 'Malaria'. It's a mixture of your names: 'Mal' and 'Aria'. What about that then?'

Malaria. It's lovely. Having a baby ferret named after you is a truly great honour in anyone's eyes. We can't thank them enough. I'll visit Malaria the ferret on a regular basis. I'm quite touched. Roger and Rosemary say their final goodbyes, leaving behind only the faintest waft of stale ferret. I wonder if I'll ever see them again.

Kenneth arrives. 'Well, this is it then,' he says. 'I'll never forget this holiday as long as I live. It's been a real treat getting to know you. I knew on the first night we'd be great mates. It was the puppet on a string that swung it for me.'

It hasn't been the best of holidays for Kenneth. He lost his dignity on the Sunshine Deck, upended by a shove from the Lancashire Lassie who has now shagged the Captain on the quoits deck – we think. Come to think of it, she's probably had sex with half the boat by now. I reckon they've all been bonking each other. Except for poor Kenneth, who's finished up high and dry and minus his teeth. I'm the new, lucky owner of the now famous dancing dentures and I've got them on hand today, just in case he asks. The only thing he failed to lose was his glass slipper. But then, Linda the Stocky Boot Scooting Baby was one mountain too high for him to conquer. Still, he was my best man, so that's some consolation. We agree to meet again.

Before he goes, Maria asks the question I've been wanting to ask him all cruise. 'Do you really play the clarinet with your arse?' she tastefully enquires.

Kenneth's got a twinkle in his eye. 'You'll have to wait and see,' he replies. 'That's another treat for another time.'

As he leaves, I call out to him. 'Kenneth!' I wave his teeth in a sort of salute.

He salutes too, happy in the knowledge that his family heirloom is in good hands. 'Cheerio, Martin!' he shouts, then disappears into the crowd.

I've done well for mementos this holiday: Kenneth's teeth, a baby ferret, a pen from Gibraltar, a lifetime supply of oatmeal biscuits, two King Edwards, Al's shoe, and his daughter's glass slipper. Not a bad bag of booty by anyone's standards. Some passengers are content with a Lladro ballerina.

The time has come. Maria and I are first off the ship. Captain Fletcher, God bless him, has arranged it all. But there are more surprises still. There are passengers galore leaning over the glistening white rails, throwing streamers and waving us goodbye. The matching couple are done out in 'his and hers Pac-a-Macs'. Daphne and Claire are there too.

'Good luck Spud. We're off to the Canaries,' shouts Spiky Claire, the Punch and Judy Queen.

I think, in a way, she's happy for us and I'm happy for her and Daphne. I was never one to bear a grudge.

At the foot of the gangplank there's a line of staff. Arranged in a sort of guard of honour. Roger the Waiter's there with Donald the Downtrodden and Oh Danny Boy. There's a handshake from each one. And last of all...the Captain. How he's made it from quoits deck to gangplank in such a short space of time I shall never know; must have a secret route. He hands us two pieces of wedding cake. And the horseshoe draped in white lace.

' "You've only just begun to live," ' he says. ' "White lace and promises. A kiss for luck" ' – he bends to give Maria a peck – ' "and you're on your way." ' (The bloody Carpenters.)

Beyond the Captain, my car waits decked out in streamers. A 'Just Married' banner straddles the back window. Dicky Cox comes from out of nowhere. Well, of all things! Word has reached the British Potato Marketing Board. They've arranged for a heroes welcome. Dicky's come dressed up as a chauffeur and he's taking me – sorry, us – back home. (A hit for the England World Cup squad 1970!)

'Spud, you absolute bastard of a total twat,' he screams. It's a lovely welcome. I've missed him.

The band begins to play 'Yellow Bird, Up High in Banana Tree', as Alfred and Andy appear at the foot of the gangplank. They're trying to carry the rocking-chair from the ship to my car. They've nicked the bloody thing. Bickering and finger pointing like there's no tomorrow, the two of them clumsily try to lift it onto my roof-rack. How they can possibly think nobody's seen them is beyond me. It's like a scene from a black and white comedy film. Andy drops the one side of the chair on Alfred's toe.

'You dizzy fucking puff! Handle it like you handle my pantyhose you daft arsehole.' Alfred points to his flip-flop. 'Look I'm starting to stiffen up already. I'll be black and blue by this afternoon. My big toe will come up like a balloon.'

I turn to the Captain unsure of what he's going to make of the proceedings.

'They're hardly Bonnie and Clyde are they,' he says, thinking hard. He's probably going to have them arrested and banged up for the night in the Mermaid Suite. He thinks again. 'Keep it,' he says. 'It's your wedding present.'

Alfred and Andy are clearly hopeless thieves. In front of the whole ship, they're slagging each other off as the chair falls onto the tarmac for the umpteenth time. It's a disastrous undercover mission. But they've done it. They've pulled it off.

Soon Maria and I are setting off on the greatest adventure of them all, with a rocking-chair loosely strapped to the roof-rack of my old banger. (I'm certain Maria and I will make the long journey ahead – but I'm not so sure about the chair.)

'Malcolm,' says Maria. 'There's something I have to tell you.'

Oh shit. Here comes the bombshell. She's going to rip my world to shreds, I just know it. She's going to explain how she was once a boy – that's how she got tangled up with What's-his-name and his 'I Wantawilly Dot Com' nonsense. I always said she had a bit of tomboy inside her. She's going to tell me about her sex change operation. That's why she was a little reticent to have it off with me in the cabin. She had to build herself up for it. Mind you, I didn't notice anything strange when we finally got down to it. And I did give her a good going over. Maybe she's not a transsexual. Maybe she's already been married three times, or has five children by seven different blokes! She thought it might ruin the moment if she told me on the Sunshine Deck while Kenneth was playing 'Here Comes the Bride', down his nostril, on the recorder.

Just seconds after predicting a marriage made in heaven, I'm now bracing myself for the worst. But then, I can't complain. We had some good times while it lasted. And anyway, we're not legally married. I could just walk away from her now without so much as a two-fingered salute (although Dicky Cox would almost certainly give her one).

I might as well bite the bullet. 'What is it?' I ask rather sheepishly.

She looks at me straight in the eye. 'I love you.'

Thank heavens for that. The marriage is as solid as ever. I'll go back to planning our fiftieth wedding anniversary. Dicky Cox lets out one of his horrific snorting laughs. He sort of ruins the moment.

We settle into the back seat of my Vauxhall Vectra as the band plays and the crowd cheers us off in the background. Maria's soon holding court again. Firmly, she takes hold of my hand – it's a sure sign of love if ever I saw one.

'The thing is,' she says, determined to make a point. ' "Too many people, take second best. But I won't take anything less." '

All three of us burst into song. ' "It's got to be, yeah... Per-er-er-er-er-erfect!" '

'Katrina and the Waves,' I proudly announce.

Maria looks at me somewhat disgustedly. 'It's Fairground Attraction, you twat.'

Acknowledgements

Delilah
Words and Music by Barry Mason and Les Reed
© 1967
Reproduced by permission of Peter Maurice Music Co Ltd, London
WC2H 0QY

Food Glorious Food
By Lionel Bart
© 1959 Lakeview Music Publishing Co. Ltd
of Suite 2.07, Plaza 535 Kings Road, London, SW10 0SZ
International Copyright Secured
All Rights Reserved. Used by Permission.

Green, Green Grass of Home
Words and Music by Curly Putman
© 1963 Tree International, USA
Burlington Music Co Ltd, London W6 8BS
Reproduced by permission of International Music Publications Ltd
All Rights Reserved

I Got You Babe
Words and Music by Sonny Bono
© 1965 (renewed) Cotillion Music Inc and Chris Marc Music, USA
Warner/Chappell Music Ltd, London W6 8BS
Reproduced by permission of International Music Publications Ltd
All Rights Reserved.

Let's Twist Again
By Kal Mann and Dave Appell
© 1961 Kalman Music Inc. (Renewed) – all Rights for the world outside the United States administered by Chappell & co (ASCAP) – All Rights Reserved.
Lyrics reproduced by kind permission of Carlin Music Corp., London NW1 8BD

Perfect
Words & Music by Mark E Nevin
© Copyright 1988 MCA Music Limited. Universal/MCA Music Limited, (100%)
Used By Permission of Music Sales Limited
All Rights Reserved. International Copyright Secured.

Puppet On a String
Words and Music by Bill Martin and Phil Coulter
© 1967
Reproduced by permission of Peter Maurice Music Co. Ltd., London WC2H 0QY

The Old Rocking Chair
Words and Music by Michael Coleman and Brian Burke
© 1977
Reproduced by permission of EMI Music Pub. Ltd trading as Parrott Music, London WC2H 0QY

Wouldn't It Be Loverly (from *My Fair Lady*)
Words by Alan Jay Lerner
Music by Frederick Loewe
© 1956 Chappell & Co. Inc., USA
Chappell Music Ltd, London W6 8BS
Reproduced by permission of International Music Publications Ltd
All Rights Reserved